A Complete Course in
Home Economics for Beginners
2011 Edition

Deirdre Madden

All about Home Economics

Cover detail: Original image courtesy of MacDonnell's Good Food Kitchen, 1983.
Amended Design: DesignBOS.ie

Produced by DesignBOS.ie, 2011
Original edition edited by Mary Buggle and produced by Folens Publishers, 1983
Artist: Peter Haigh

ISBN: 978-0-9570626-0-3

Contents

Foreword

All About Home Economics was first published in 1983. It was the seminal text for intermediate certificate Home Economics for over 15 years. The author, Deirdre Madden, was a Home Economics teacher in Loreto Abbey Dalkey. Her energy and enthusiasm for teaching her students was boundless. Her frustration at the lack of a modern Irish Home Economics inter cert book resulted in her writing her own. She often quoted a much loved fairy tale - "I'll do it myself said the little red hen; and so she did." All About Home Economics is the result of passion for a subject that Deirdre felt was truly important to students - life skills.

All About Home Economics was studied by thousands of students in Ireland over the years. Not only was it studied in classrooms, it became the foundation for many students' cooking repertoire in college and later a much prized possession in the kitchens of those who were lucky enough to have kept their copy.

Over the years, we have often been asked about All About Home Economics - is it for sale anywhere; is it being republished? A decade after its last print, here is **All About Home Economics**, just as you remember it. The same recipes, the same sewing techniques and the same indispensable guide to running a home.

As this book is a reprint that is true to the original, we have kept the quirky typesetting and diagrams just as they were. However, things have changed since 1983. Nutritional, medical and technological advances have been made. Please bear this in mind while reading this book. Scientific and other information may have changed since then. If in doubt - ask a qualified professional! Also, where a recipe states a weight in margarine, you can substitute the same measurement with butter, if you prefer.

Deirdre died in 1999 at the age of 56. This publication of All About Home Economics is brought to you by Deirdre's daughters, Kate and Aisli Madden who hope that their Mum's guide to cooking, sewing and running a home will be enjoyed by those who remember Deirdre's books, and by a new generation.

10% of the profits of this book will be donated to the Irish Cancer Society, whose Daffodil Nurse, Carmel, helped support Deirdre and "her girls" in her final days.

Kate and Aisli Madden, October 2011

"To Non, the Little Red Hen that did it herself."

Kate and Aisli Madden wish to acknowledge and thank the following for original permissions to use photographic material in this text: McDonnell's Good Food Kitchen; Bord Iascaigh Mhara; Style Patterns, London.

We would also like to thank Ryan Tubridy and his team in RTE, without whom this project would not have been possible.

1

Cookery

1   *All About Food*

Why do we eat?

Is it because we feel hungry? Because we like the taste of food or because we think it is good for us? Perhaps it is because it is a social custom to eat meals with our families and friends?

All of these answers are true — but the most important reason of all is:

WE EAT TO LIVE

If we did not eat, we would die.

What is food?

Food is any substance, liquid or solid which is made up of **nutrients.** All food is made up of one or more of the following constituents:

Protein
Carbohydrate
Fat
Vitamins
Mineral elements
Water

A food which contains several nutrients would be called a nutritious food.
A nutritious or nourishing food is a food which is good for us and helps us stay healthy.

Why is food necessary for the body?

Some foods help the body **grow** and **repair** worn out cells. Food also gives **heat** — to keep our bodies warm, and **energy** for everyday activities. Certain nutrients help **protect** the body from disease — these include the vitamins and mineral elements.

All About Energy

Energy is a word we often use. We obviously need plenty of energy if we want to run in a marathon or dig the garden. But did you know that we even need energy when we are fast asleep? **Let's find out about energy.**

Summary		
Functions of food:		
1. *Growth and repair*	**Protein**	
2. *Heat and energy*	**Fats, Carbohydrates and Protein**	
3. *Protection from disease*	**Vitamins and Minerals**	

The dictionary tells us that energy is 'our ability to do work'. When we beat a cake, or walk to school, our muscles are using energy. The more active we are, the more energy we use.

But, we also need energy to power the 'machinery' inside our body — our heartbeat, digestive organs, and breathing. We even need energy to think!

Where does the body get energy?

Food is the fuel which powers our body 'motors'. Just like a car burns fuel to give it the energy to go, our body burns up the food we eat to give us all the energy we need.

The body needs oxygen to burn up this food. The lungs collect oxygen from the air when we breathe and the blood carries it around the body to the cells where it is oxidised (burned up).

This burning gives off heat as well as energy. It is this heat which keeps our bodies at a constant temperature of 37°C, which is the temperature required for our bodies to function properly.

Measuring Energy

The energy stored in food and the energy our body uses is measured in **Calories** (or more correctly **Kilocalories**). If we want to know how much energy we get from our food each day, we need to know the amount of kilocalories in each food we eat. Most food tables will tell you this. As a rough guide:

---

1 gram of pure protein gives about 4 kilocalories.

1 gram of pure carbohydrate gives about 4 kilocalories.

1 gram of pure fat gives about 9 kilocalories.

So we see that foods with a high fat content give more than twice as much energy as foods with a high carbohydrate content.

Food with a lot of water, such as green vegetables, and salad vegetables, like cucumber and tomatoes, have a very low energy value.

Watch your weight!

If we eat too many energy foods and don't use up all the energy they give us, the body stores this energy as fat, and we put on weight.

We must try to balance energy input (food) with energy output (activity).

How much do we need?

We all need a basic amount of energy just to keep alive — to keep our heart beating and to sustain body activity. This is called our **basal metabolism.** After that the more active we are, the more kilocalories we need from food. The list below will give you an idea how many kilocalories different people need, but remember — no two people are exactly alike and such figures are only a rough guide. Factors such as age, size and activity can alter this considerably.

Daily Kilocalorie requirements	*Kilocalories*
Child 2 – 3 years	1,400
Teenage girl	2,300
Teenage boy	2,800 – 3,000
Sedentary female	2,200
Active female	2,500
Pregnant/Nursing mother	2,400 – 2,700
Sedentary male	2,600
Active male	3,500

How much energy do you use?

Activity	Kc per hour
Walking upstairs	1000
Swimming	575
Squash	500
Dancing	450
Cycling	400
Scrubbing floor	315
Light housework	200
Strolling	185
Writing	115
Standing	90
Sitting/watching T.V.	85
Sleeping	70

You are what you Eat

In Ireland we are lucky to have a wide selection of good fresh food. Yet some people still suffer from malnutrition — that is, they lack one or more nutrients. Why? Because they are eating the **wrong foods,** perhaps too much of some (particularly carbohydrates), or too little of others (often the protective foods, for example iron or Vitamin C).

The important thing is we must learn to choose wisely.

What you eat influences your work and your ability to enjoy living. A good diet will keep you healthy and in peak condition.

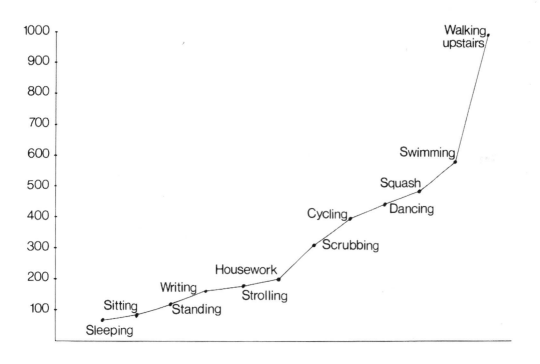

2   All About Nutrition

Protein

Protein is the most important nutrient. As it is a vital part of all body cells, we must have a regular supply or we would waste away and die. Proteins are like the building blocks of our body. As we grow, we need protein to make new cells. When we stop growing, we still need protein to replace and repair the body cells which get damaged and wear away.

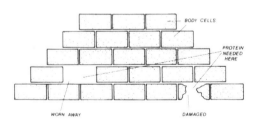

Proteins are divided into two classes:

    1. **Animal protein**
    2. **Vegetable protein**

Animal proteins are more important (*see Table 2.1*) so we sometimes call them **first class proteins.** Vegetable proteins come from plant foods and are also known as **second class proteins.**

Our daily diet should contain half animal and half vegetable protein. Each person needs one gram of protein daily for each kilo of body weight. (Find out how much *you* need every day). Children and expectant mothers need extra. As you cannot go into a shop and buy 50 g of protein, you must know the foods which are rich in protein. Many everyday foods are a good source.

The following foods contain approximately 50 g protein

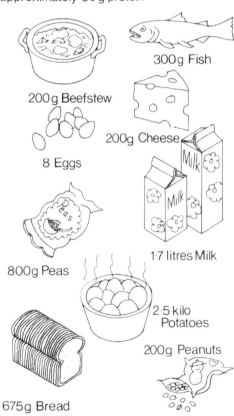

200g Beefstew

300g Fish

200g Cheese

8 Eggs

1·7 litres Milk

800g Peas

2·5 kilo Potatoes

200g Peanuts

675g Bread

Some people feel they haven't eaten a good meal if it doesn't have meat — look at the chart above to see the other foods which also provide plenty of protein.

Table 2.1

Class	Source	Function of Proteins
Animal	Meat, fish, eggs, milk, cheese	1. Growth and repair of body cells
Vegetable	Nuts, pulse vegetables whole cereals, bread, pasta; other vegetables, *e.g.* potatoes, contain a little.	2. Provide heat and energy

More About Protein

Proteins contain the elements **carbon, hydrogen, oxygen** *and* **nitrogen.** *Protein is the only nutrient which contains the element nitrogen and as nitrogen is essential for making body cells, we must make sure to have enough protein in our diet to carry out the essential work of growth and repair.*

Once the body has taken what it needs for growth and repair of our cells, the rest is used to supply heat and energy.

Protein structure

Amino acids

After digestion amino acids are set free

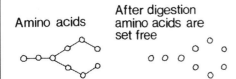

Each protein is made up of a chain of small units called **amino acids.** *When we eat a protein food, such as meat, it is broken down during digestion into single amino acids, which are then absorbed into the blood. This carries them around the body to where they are needed (for example, to repair cells or to add height to a growing child).*

Carbohydrates

CAR-BO-HYDRATE

As carbohydrate foods are usually cheap and plentiful they are used to fill out the diet after the more important nutrients, such as proteins and protective foods, have been allowed for. Foods which supply heat and energy, such as carbohydrates, can be fattening if we eat too much of them.

When you are choosing which carbohydrate foods to eat, pick those which also supply other nutrients, such as brown bread, fruit and vegetables, rather than those which are almost 100% carbohydrate, such as sugar.

Table 2.2

Class	Source	Functions
Sugars * Go easy on these – too many sugary foods are bad for the teeth	Fruit, fresh or dried Milk, honey, Ice cream, *Jam *Sugar, *soft drinks *Sweets, *cakes, *biscuits	1. Heat and energy 2. Excess carbohydrate is stored as fat which forms a layer under the skin and helps keep the body warm.
Starches	Cereals, flour, bread Potatoes, root and pulse vegetables, Rice and pasta	
Cellulose	Whole cereals, fruit and vegetables, especially the outer skins and husks *e.g.* bran	It forms bulk in the diet and helps move food through the intestine.

More about Carbohydrate

Carbohydrates contain the elements **carbon, hydrogen and oxygen.** *They are based on single sugar units such as glucose; some occur in pairs, others in long chains* (**starches**)*. When digested, all carbohydrates, both sugars and starches are broken down into glucose and in this form are absorbed into the bloodstream. Glucose is carried by the blood to all the cells of the body where it is converted to energy. Any glucose not required is stored as* **fat.**

Cellulose

The framework of all plant foods is a substance called cellulose which is most plentiful on the skins and outer layers of vegetables, fruit and cereals. Although the human body cannot digest cellulose, it plays an important part in our diet by helping to form bulk or **roughage** in the intestine, so that it stimulates the muscle walls to move the food more quickly through the bowel. In this way it prevents constipation and other bowel disorders.

Fibre

Because a lot of our modern food, such as white flour, sugar and instant convenience foods, lack cellulose (also called **fibre**) it is important to include high-fibre foods in our diet. Unlike other carbohydrate foods, **cellulose does not supply heat and energy.**

Fats or Lipids

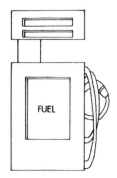

Fats are the most powerful fuel food, supplying more energy per gram than proteins and carbohydrates put together. If too much fat is eaten it will be stored by the body and will be likely to cause **obesity**. Ideally, about 10% of our diet should consist of fat — yet in many western countries, such as ours, over 35% fat is eaten, causing people to be greatly overweight.

'A little fat goes a long way'

> *Note:* Half our daily supply of fats should come from vegetable sources and fish, the rest from animal sources.

To avoid overweight

Grill rather than fry.
Watch out for 'invisible' fats — in cakes, pastry, milk, cheese, nuts, eggs, *etc.*
Avoid adding extra fat to cooking.
Be careful of 'snack' foods — crisps and peanuts contain large amounts of fats:-
Potato Crisps 36%; Roasted Peanuts 50%

More about Fats

Fats are made up of **carbon, hydrogen and oxygen.** *As they contain more carbon than protein or carbohydrates, they are a highly concentrated source of energy. They are ideal for those in energetic occupations, but as the body stores any extra fat, those who are unlikely to use up this energy will put on weight. During digestion, fats are broken down into their components —* **fatty acids** *and* **glycerol.**

Saturated fats come mainly from animal sources and are usually solid, e.g. suet, lard, dripping. **Unsaturated fats** *are found in marine and vegetable foods and are usually liquid at normal temperatures.*

Table 2.3

Class	Sources	Functions
Animal Fats (mainly 'saturated')	Butter, cheese, cream Fat meat, oily fish Egg yolk Suet, Lard, dripping	1. Provide heat and energy 2. Help protect delicate organs 3. Act as insulators 4. Source of fat soluble vitamins A, D, K
Vegetable Fats (mainly 'unsaturated')	Margarine, cooking oils and fats, *e.g. Cookeen* Nuts and cereals	

Percentage of fat in everyday foods

Food	%
VEGETABLE OIL	99·9
LARD/SUET	99
BUTTER	82
MARGARINE	82·5
LOW FAT SPREAD	40·7
CREAM	30
CREAM CHEESE	47
CHEDDAR CHEESE	33
COTTAGE CHEESE	4
MILK,FRESH	3·8
MILK,SKIMMED	0·1
CANNED SARDINES	28·3
COD	0·7
LAMB CHOP,GRILLED	29
MINCED BEEF	15·2
ROAST CHICKEN	5·4
PEANUTS	49
MAYONNAISE	78·9
FRENCH DRESSING	73
MILK CHOCOLATE	30·3
TOFFEES	17·2
EGGS	10·9

Approximate percentage of protein in everyday foods

ANIMAL PROTEIN

CHEDDAR CHEESE	27	

MEAT

BEEF	25	
LIVER	25	
LAMB	25	
CHICKEN	24	
MINCED BEEF	23	
BEEFBURGERS	18	

FISH

SARDINES	23·5	
HERRINGS	20	
WHITE FISH	19	
FISH FINGERS	13	
EGGS	12·3	
MILK	3·5	

VEGETABLE PROTEIN

PEANUTS	24·3	
BREAD	9	
BAKED BEANS	5·1	
PEAS	5	
POTATOES	2	

Percentage of carbohydrate in everyday foods

Food	%	
SUGAR	100	
CORNFLOUR	92	
RICE (raw)	86·8	
RICE (cooked)	29·6	
CORNFLAKES	85·1	
DRINKING CHOCOLATE	84·8	
PLAIN FLOUR	80·1	
SPAGHETTI	79·2	
JAM	69	
CRISPBREAD	69	
ICED CAKES	68·8	
CREAM CRACKERS	68·3	
WHOLEMEAL	65·8	
SCONES	55·9	
SHORT PASTRY	55·8	
FRUIT CAKE	55	
MILK CHOCOLATE	54·5	
POTATO CRISPS	49·3	
POTATOES	19·7	
BANANAS	19·2	
APPLES	11·9	
SAUSAGES	11·7	
BAKED BEANS	10·3	
ORANGES	8·5	
MILK	4·7	

NO CARBOHYDRATE: MEAT, FISH, EGGS, CHEESE

EGGS

CHEDDAR CHEESE

SUET PUDDING

BUTTER

CREAM CAKES

BROILED BREAST OF LAMB

Foods high in fats

Vitamins

The word vitamin means **'vital to life'**. In the past, and still today in developing countries, many serious diseases have been caused by lack of vitamins.

Vitamins are found in two groups:

Fat soluble —   A/D/E/K
Water soluble —   B/C

Fat Soluble Vitamins   *Table 2.4*

Vitamin	Source	Function	Deficiency
A	Fish liver oils Butter, margarine Milk, cheese, eggs	Necessary for: 1. Growth 2. Healthy eyes 3. Healthy skin and lining membranes, such as those of mouth and breathing organs	(a) Retarded growth (b) Night blindness
Carotene *(a substance which is converted into Vitamin A in the body).*	Carotene* Carrots, dark green vegetables (such as cabbage, watercress, spinach), peppers, peaches		
Special points: Very important in the diet of children and expectant mothers			
D	Sunshine Cod liver oil Oily fish Margarine, eggs Liver, cheese	Formation of bones and teeth	Rickets: a bone disease in children (in 1928 – 87% of all London 5 year olds had rickets, today it is very rare).
Special points: Very important for children, old people, invalids, pregnant and nursing mothers			
K	Made in human intestine Vegetables, cereals	Necessary for clotting blood	Delayed healing of wounds

Water Soluble Vitamins   *Table 2.5*

Vitamin	Source	Function	Deficiency
B group	Nuts, pulse vegetables Cereals, yeast Bread, especially wholemeal bread Meat and fish Milk, cheese, eggs	1. Controls release of energy from food 2. Affects nerves	(a) Beri-beri: (a nerve disease common in the East). (b) Pellagra: (a disease which causes the tongue and skin to become rough and sore).
C	Most *fresh* fruit and vegetables. Best sources: Rose hip syrup, black-currants, citrus fruits, peppers, green vegetables	1. Necessary for general health, particularly of skin and gums and of bloodvessels 2. Necessary for the absorption of iron	Scurvy

Vitamins are very easily destroyed, particularly by heat. Take care to:

1. Eat fresh raw food as much as possible.
2. Avoid steeping food.
3. Cook vegetables, if possible, with skins on.
4. Cook in very little liquid for the shortest possible time.
5. Use up any leftover cooking water for soups or sauces.
6. Avoid keeping food warm for long periods — this destroys vitamins.
7. Avoid too many processed foods and leftovers, as these usually have a low vitamin content.

Mineral Elements

These are essential substances which the body needs in very small amounts. They include:

1. Iron
2. Calcium
3. Iodine
4. Sodium
5. Phosphorous
6. Potassium
7. Flourine
8. Chlorine

Mineral elements — *The Protectors*

Table 2.6

Name	Sources	Functions	Deficiency
Iron	Meat, offal (especially liver) sardines, wholemeal bread	Necessary for formation of red blood corpuscles	Anaemia (too little haemoglobin in blood)
Calcium	Milk, cheese, yoghurt, white flour, eggs Green vegetables Bones of canned fish	Builds strong bones and teeth (assisted by phosphorus and *Vitamin D).*	Rickets Bone disease in adults Poor quality teeth
Phosphorus	Present in most foods	Helps calcium build strong bones and teeth	Unknown
Iodine	Sea fish, seaweed, cereals and some vegetables	Essential for the thyroid gland – which controls metabolism	Goitre: (enlargement of the throid gland)

More about Iron

Anaemia, caused by a shortage of iron, is the most common disease resulting from deficiency of a nutrient. A person suffering from anaemia is short of an important pigment of the blood called **haemoglobin**. *The function of haemoglobin is to carry oxygen from the lungs to every cell of the body. As so many body functions depend on oxygen, any shortage can damage and even destroy cells and will quickly become obvious, making the body less efficient.*

Symptoms *include tiredness, weakness, dizzyness, headache, poor appetite and a general feeling of lassitude – being 'run-down'.*

Absorption: *The body only absorbs as much iron from food as it needs; often as little as 10% of the iron present in a food is absorbed. Vitamin C plays an important part in this absorption.*

The main loss of iron from the body is due to bleeding, e.g. after injury or surgery. Women of childbearing age need extra iron in their diet to replace the monthly loss caused by menstruation. Pregnant and nursing mothers need to increase their iron intake to provide for the needs of the growing baby.

Babies are born with enough iron to last them six months, but after that, iron must be added to their diet, e.g. in the form of sieved green vegetables or liver. Growing children need iron both for repairing old blood cells and for making new ones.

Water

Next to oxygen, water is the most essential requirement for life. 70% of our body is made up of water, much of it forming cell fluid, as well as blood, digestive and other important body fluids. Although water supplies no heat or energy, it is a vital part of our diet.

The amount of water in the body is carefully controlled. Water is lost from the body mainly through the kidneys, as urine, and through the skin as perspiration. This water must be replaced daily or we would quickly become dehydrated.

Sources

Food and beverages: Water is present in almost all foods, particularly green vegetables and fruit. Milk is a very nourishing source of water, (87%). Foods which have little water are those with a high fat content *e.g.* cooking oil and butter, and dry foods such as sugar and flour.

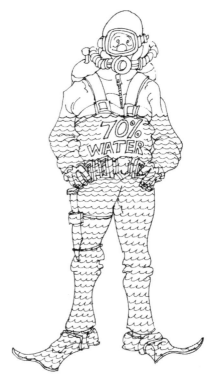

We are 70% water!

> ### More about Water
>
> * *Water contains the elements hydrogen and oxygen in the ratio 2:1. It is often written as H_2O.*
> * *It freezes at $0°C$ and boils at $100°C$.*
> * *It dissolves things easily.*
> * *It evaporates easily.*
> * *It is essential for our health to have a pure water supply. Pure water is colourless, odourless and contains no dangerous impurities.*

Functions of water in the body

1. Essential part of all body tissues	. . . .	Cells, muscle, *etc.*
2. Vital ingredient of body fluids	. . . .	Blood, digestive juices, *etc.*
3. Helps transport vital substances	. . . .	Such as oxygen, nutrients, hormones.
4. Aids digestion and absorption	. . . .	By dissolving food.
5. Assists removal of waste	. . . .	Kidneys filter urine from blood.
6. Helps control body temperature	. . . .	Through evaporation from skin.
7. Source of minerals	. . . .	Minerals such as calcium and flourine may be dissolved in the water we drink.

Balanced Eating

A Square Meal

Each meal should supply food from each of these **four** groups:

Table 2.7

1. **Milk Group**	2. **Protein Group**	
Milk Cheese Yoghurt	Meat Fish Eggs	Cheese Nuts Pulse vegetables
3. **Protective Group**	4. **Carbohydrate Group**	
All kinds of fruit and vegetables Eat one citrus fruit and 1 raw vegetable, daily.	Bread Breakfast Cereals Rice Choose whole grain, unrefined cereals rather than less nutritious refined foods.	Pasta Pastry Cake

A **well balanced meal** is one which has all the nutrients in the right proportions. Every meal, even a small snack or a picnic, should be a balanced one. A nutritious satisfying meal will reduce the chance of eating between-meal snacks.

A diet containing a **wide variety of fresh foods** will generally supply all the essential nutrients.

Healthy Eating

Scientific research is constantly discovering new facts about food and nutrition. While the modern diet is more varied than in the past, it is not necessarily more nutritious. Three changes which would improve our eating patterns and therefore our general health are:

1. **Reduce Sugar Intake.**
   Most of us eat far too much sugar. Sugar contains no nutrients except pure carbohydrate — it is very bad for the teeth and leads to overweight.

2. **Reduce Fats** (particularly animal fats). In this country, the average person eats far more fat than doctors and nutritionists consider safe — a high consumption of fat leads to obesity, heart disease and many other problems. Half our intake of fat should be from vegetable sources, *e.g.* margarine instead of butter, cooking oil instead of dripping or suet, fish instead of meat.

3. **Reduce intake of Refined Foods and increase the Fibre content of our diet.** Change from white to brown bread; use wholemeal and oatmeal, instead of white flour, to thicken and coat foods; eat lots of fruit and vegetables; try a vegetarian meal now and then — using lots of cereals, pulse vegetables and nuts.

Special Needs of Special People

Special needs of Adults

1. *Protein* — for repairing tissues (but too much is wasteful).
2. *Milk-type foods* — for protein, calcium and vitamins.
3. *Energy foods* — according to needs. Remember those leading an inactive, sedentary life need less and energetic manual workers need more.
4. *Protective foods* — most foods contain minerals and vitamins. Fruit and vegetables are a good source of Vitamin C + iron.
5. *Fibre* — in unrefined cereal foods, fruit and vegetables. It is needed to prevent constipation and bowel disorders.

Special needs of Babies and Toddlers

1. *Protein* — plenty needed for growth (more, in proportion to their size, than adults).
2. *Calcium* — for bones and teeth.
3. *Energy foods* — according to child's needs. Be careful, however. If a child shows a tendency to overweight, cut down on carbohydrates and fats.
4. *Protective foods* — important to introduce a wide variety of foods, especially fruit and vegetables, in order to supply the necessary minerals and vitamins.
5. Babies fed on cows milk must have their diet supplemented with iron and vitamins.
6. Discourage faddy eating and encourage savoury rather than sweet foods — give fruit for treats instead of sweets.
7. Do not encourage eating between meals — it spoils the appetite.
8. Serve food attractively in small portions.
9. Most family meals are suitable for a baby — they can be sieved or put through the blender. Cans of baby food should only be kept for emergencies.
10. Trim meat of fat, bone and gristle; mince or chop finely.
11. Avoid rich, spicy or greasy foods.

Special needs of Schoolchildren

Schoolchildren are very energetic and are growing rapidly. They should have plenty of *body building* and *energy foods* to allow for these needs. *Protective foods* are important for prevention of illness.

Packed lunches should be nourishing — encourage fresh fruit, milk and protein snacks, rather than biscuits, crisps, *etc.*

Special needs of Adolescents

Teenagers are also growing rapidly and many need even more *protein foods* than their parents. Their *energy food* needs are also high, as they are active and most are involved in sport, *etc.*

An inadequate diet at this stage can lead to tiredness and lack of concentration, causing problems at school.

Girls should be careful to include lots of *iron rich foods* in their diet to make good the iron lost due to menstruation. Other *protective foods* are also important — fresh fruit, green vegetables, salads, *etc.* should feature strongly in a teenage diet. These also help keep skin clear.

Avoid too many greasy foods, such as fries, pastry and cream cakes — these aggravate acne.

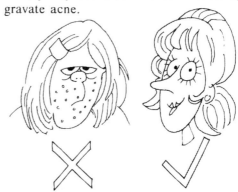

Special needs of Pregnant and Nursing Mothers

Although it is not necessary to 'eat for two', foods which are eaten should be a concentrated source of nutrients. Include lots of *protein foods* — for growth; *calcium* for bones and teeth formation and *Iron* and *Vitamin C* for healthy blood. Extra iron may be prescribed by the doctor at this time.

It is important not to put on too much weight at this time — avoid too many *high carbohydrate foods*, such as sugar and snack foods, which are fattening without being nutritious.

After the birth of the baby, a mother who is breastfeeding must keep up the nutritious diet she had during her pregnancy.

Special needs of Old People

Most old people continue to eat and enjoy a normal diet. They need just as much *body building* and *protective foods* as any adult. Their *energy food* needs may be lower, as they may not lead such active lives. As their appetites may be smaller, it is important to see that what they do eat is very nourishing.

Protein foods are very important for repair of ailing tissues. *Protective foods* help prevent disease — many old people suffer from vitamin deficiency diseases, such as scurvy and night blindness. *Iron* is important to prevent anaemia, which causes tiredness and *Vitamin C* to help its absorption. Unfortunately fruit, the best source of this vitamin, is quite expensive — a cheaper source is rosehip syrup. *Vitamin D* and *Calcium* are essential to prevent brittle bones — milk and cheese are good sources. *Fibre* is essential to prevent constipation.

Slimming

Overweight is almost always caused by eating more food than the body needs. Although many people are interested in losing weight in order to look more attractive, the main reason to watch your weight is because of the medical dangers caused by obesity. Fat people are more likely to suffer from heart disease, diabetes, high blood pressure, varicose veins and bronchial complaints. Remember 'well fed' does not mean overfed.

About Slimming Diets

1. Always check with your doctor before starting a diet — this particularly applies to children, teenagers and pregnant women.
2. The only way to lose weight is to cut down on kilocalories or take more exercise. Dieting is more effective, but exercise will help tone up muscles and make the body look slimmer.
3. All diets must be well balanced — all the essential nutrients must be provided. For this reason, avoid crash diets as many are dangerously unbalanced.
4. A person who is overweight has probably been eating too many of the **wrong** foods. A good diet will **re-train** the appetite to be satisfied with more suitable, and fewer, foods.
5. Do not wait until you are greatly overweight to begin a slimming diet — it is easier to cut down on food than to wait until a strict diet is necessary.
6. Do not measure your food intake by kilocalories alone — this could be dangerous. You must also consider whether the diet will supply all the essential nutrients. A good weight reducing diet has:
   (a) Reduced carbohydrate content.
   (b) Reduced fat content.
   (c) Average or increased protein content.
   (d) Plenty of fruit and vegetables.
   (e) Unrefined rather than refined cereals — they are more filling and rich in fibre.
   (f) No sugar.

Table 2.8

Avoid these foods	Restrict these	Eat plenty of these
Fried foods	Starchy vegetables	Lettuce/tomatoes
Cream	Pulse vegetables	Cucumber
Sugar/jam	Some fruit, especially	Green vegetables
Biscuits/sweets	grapes/bananas	Liver
Tinned fruit	Fat meats	Lean meat, esp. chicken
Cakes/pastry	Bread/toast	White fish
Mayonnaise	Breakfast cereals	Fresh fruit juice
Alcohol/soft drinks	Rice/pasta	Cottage cheese
Most convenience foods	Cocoa	Low-fat yoghurt
Nuts	Butter/margarine	
Dried fruit	Milk/cheese	

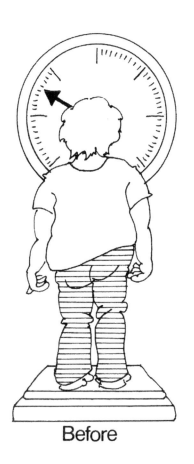

Before

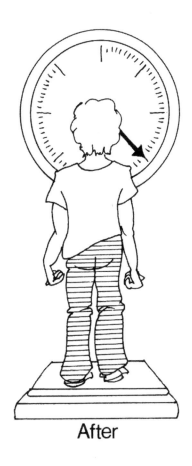

After

Table 2.9

Kilocalorie Content of Basic Foods

	HIGH			MEDIUM (contd.)	
200 - 250	Cooking Oil	225	10 - 50	Vanilla ice cream	48
	Lard	223.5		Fish fingers	40
	Cream Cheese	203		Boiled eggs	37
				Roast chicken	37
150 - 200	Margarine	183.5		Rice pudding	35.5
	Butter	183		Fried Cod	35
				Boiled rice	30.5
100 - 150	Bacon rashers (fried)	149		Cottage cheese	28.5
	Peanuts (roasted)	146.5		Fruit yoghurt	24
	Milk chocolate	144.5		Canned peaches	22.9
	Grilled lamb chop	133		Steamed fish	20.5
	Chocolate biscuits	124		Boiled potatoes	20
	Cream crackers	118		Bananas	19
	Roast pork	114		Milk	16
	Madeira Cake	106.5		Baked beans	16
	Cheddar Cheese	103		Grapes	15
				Tomato soup (canned)	14
50 - 100	Sugar, brown + white	98.5		Peas (boiled)	12
	Roast beef	96		Apples	11.5
	Fried sausage	92		Coca Cola	11.5
	Rich fruit cake	90			
	Cornflakes (dry)	88.5		LOW	
	Grilled pork chop	83			
	Cream	80	0 - 10	Fresh peaches	8.5
	Crispbread	79.5		Oranges	9
				Raspberries	6.5
	MEDIUM			Strawberries	6.5
	Grilled steak	76		Parsnips	6.5
	Roast lamb	73		Carrots, Onions	6
	Apple pie	70		Melon	5.75
	Cooked ham	67		Grapefruit	5.5
	Jam	65.5		Boiled green veg.	3.75
	White bread	63		Tomatoes	3
	Sultanas	62		Celery, cucumber	2
	Fried liver	61		Lettuce,	2
	Whole meal bread	60		Raw mushroom	2
	Brown bread	57.5		Lemon	1.75
	Spirits (whiskey)	55			

3 *All About Planning and Serving Meals*

Now that we have learned which foods are important for good health we must find out how to put them together in an interesting way in order to provide nourishing and appetising meals.

Styles of eating vary all over the world. In Ireland, family meals usually consist of breakfast, a main meal, and a smaller meal. Some people eat their main meal in the middle of the day, when it is usually called luncheon or lunch. The lighter evening meal in this case is called tea or supper. In other families, particularly when everyone is out all day, it is more convenient to have the main meal in the evening — this is called dinner.

A main meal usually has two or more courses. For everyday meals, we generally have two — perhaps soup and a main course, or a main course followed by a pudding. Tea or coffee is served after the meal, sometimes with cheese. If you are serving three or more courses, keep the portions smaller, to avoid making the meal too fattening.

A Menu

A menu is a written list of all the dishes in a meal. When eating out, a menu will give a choice of dishes for each course. An *à la carte* menu will have lots of choices for each course, each priced separately, so that you can pick one or two items from the menu and pay for what you get. A *table d'hôte* menu suggests a complete meal, usually with some choices in each course — the price of the whole meal is written on the menu and you pay that price, even if you leave out a course.

Writing Your Own Menu

When you are asked to plan a meal, it should be written out neatly. There is a special way to write a menu, just as there is a proper way to write an address on an envelope:

1. Write it down the centre of the page, using capital letters for each dish.
2. The main dish in each course is written first, with *accompaniments* such as sauces and vegetables underneath.
3. Leave a space between courses.
4. Describe the type and cut of meat or fish and the method of cooking it. For example, write 'Baked cutlet of cod' not 'baked fish' or 'cod cutlets'. If it is a well known recipe, write the name of the dish clearly, *e.g.* 'Queen of Puddings'.
5. *Do not* write

   2nd course — Roast Beef

   or

   Soup — Oxtail
6. Give one dish and its accompaniments for each course — a choice is not usually given.
7. For special occasions and cookery assignments, write your menu neatly on a card or notelet, or make your own menu card, choosing a picture to suit the menu or the occasion.

Sample Menus

The following are some suggestions for menus suitable for (a) Breakfast; (b) Lunch; (c) Dinner; (d) Tea or Supper.

Sample Menus

Breakfast

Orange juice
Grilled bacon and tomato
Brown bread, marmalade
Tea

or

Grapefruit
Muesli with sliced banana
Toast, tea

Lunch

Spaghetti Bolognese
Fruit Fool
Tea or coffee

Lunch/Dinner

Egg mayonnaise
Roast Pork
Apple sauce: Brown gravy
Roast potatoes, peas
Gooseberry Crumble
Custard

Dinner

Potato Soup
Grilled Chicken
New Potatoes
Cauliflower au Gratin
Fresh fruit Salad
Cream

Tea/Supper

Welsh Rarebit
Grilled mushrooms and tomato
Brown bread, honey
Jam sponge
Tea

Meal Planning

A good meal should be tasty, attractive and nourishing. The secret of successful meal planning is **organization** — plan your menus and do your shopping in plenty of time, then allow yourself enough time to prepare, cook and serve the meal. If cooking is done in a rush, without thinking or planning, the chances are that you will be short of a vital ingredient, that you will waste food and that mistakes will occur which would be less likely if you had allowed yourself more time.

Basic Rules for Planning Meals

1. The meal should be well balanced — consider the nutritional needs of those who will eat it.
2. Keep within your budget — the amount of money you have to spend will influence the food you can buy.
3. Consider the time available for cooking it — if time is short, you will have to choose dishes which are quick to prepare and cook, such as grills.
4. Consider the time of year:
   (a) So that you can choose fruit and vegetables in season.
   (b) Because light, cold dishes are more suitable for warm summer days, and hot, filling meals, for wintry weather.
5. Know the number of people eating — so that you can calculate the amount of food to buy.
6. Consider the type of meal — a simple everyday meal or an elaborate dinner party.
7. Take into account the likes and dislikes of the family or guests — within reason.

Use your imagination to make meals as interesting as possible. Do not serve the same meal on the same day every week. Try out new foods and new recipes. On the other hand, do not be too ambitious — a simple meal, well cooked and attractively served will be appreciated more than an elaborate flop!

Try to prevent food fads in the family, particularly among children. If they are used to eating a wide range of foods from the start, they will be unlikely to become faddy eaters. Many people take a strong dislike to certain foods, even though they have never even tasted them!

Economy

The average family spends 25–30% of its income on food. It is important not to skimp on the food budget — over economising in this area can lead to higher doctors and chemists bills.

Shortage of money is rarely an excuse for inferior meals. Many nutritious foods are quite cheap — potatoes, carrots, onions, cabbage and turnips are cheap but nourishing vegetables. Leg beef and streaky bacon are as nutritious as more expensive cuts. Liver is one of the cheapest and most nutritious meats. Two of the cheapest fish — herrings and mackerel — are also two of the most nourishing. Avoid convenience foods — most are expensive. Fresh food is usually better value for money.

Food Quantities Per Person

This varies according to age, climate and occupation. The following list is just an approximate guide. Remember, recipes in this, and in most cookery books, are for **4 people.**

Soup	200 ml.
Fish	150 g (boned) or 2 fillets.
Meat	100-150 g (boned); 200-250 g with bone.
Vegetables	100-200 g.
Rice/pasta	50 g (uncooked)
Puddings	One pudding — enough for 4.
Sauce	2 tablespoons.

Step by Step to Making a Menu

1. Decide on the main dish first. This is usually a protein food, such as meat, fish, eggs or cheese, but can be a vegetarian recipe, such as vegetable curry or risotto. Once you have decided on this, accompaniments should spring to mind.
2. Choose an appropriate sauce, if any, to go with the main dish.
3. Decide on the vegetables you will serve with the dish. These should provide a nice contrast of colour, texture and flavour. Include fresh vegetables or fruit (preferably raw) in every meal you make — a salad is ideal.

Economise by:
1. Careful planning and shopping.
2. Avoiding waste.
3. Clever use of leftovers.
4. Avoiding convenience foods.
5. Using cooker economically, *e.g.* if using the oven, cook the whole meal in the oven and do some baking at the same time.

Make full use of the oven

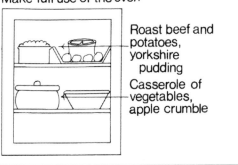

Roast beef and potatoes, yorkshire pudding

Casserole of vegetables, apple crumble

4. Decide on a carbohydrate food to fill out the meal, *e.g.* potatoes, pasta, bread, rice or other cereals. Go easy on these, however, if you are weight watching.

5. Now choose a first course and/or a pudding which will go well with your chosen main course. If the main course is filling, keep these light, *e.g.* don't serve soup followed by beef stew and then a suet pudding. A better choice would be fruit juice instead of soup and a lighter pudding, such as stewed fruit.

6. Each course should contrast in **colour, taste** and **texture** with the others — serve some soft foods, some chewy and some crisp.

7. Vary the cooking methods. Fish and chips, with fried onions, followed by apple fritters, would be a bad choice — why?

8. It is a good idea to serve one course cold — this provides contrast and saves fuel. Such a dish can be prepared in advance, covered and chilled in the refrigerator until needed, leaving more time for last minute dishing-up of food.

Examination Guidelines

Menus

Remember: A simple menu, using recipes you have learned in school, will gain just as many marks as a sophisticated meal.

On the other hand, avoid suggesting dishes such as jelly, ice cream or convenience foods — you must have learned more at Home Economics class than how to open a packet! Suggest wholesome, homemade dishes which require some skill in making them.

Costing

Exam questions often ask you to 'cost' a meal. This is a useful exercise if you want to calculate the cost of a recipe, or find out how it compares with a ready-made product.

To do this you must know the cost of basic food stuffs. It will be necessary to know the cost of each 25 g unit of food, *e.g.* sugar or flour. This involves dividing a 500 g pack of caster sugar by 20, or a 1 kg pack of sugar by 40.

List the main ingredients of the dish, with the price beside them. Smaller items such as seasonings, baking powder, *etc.*, can be lumped together and priced at one or two pence. Do not forget to allow for fuel if the dish is cooked.

Example:

Rice Pudding

500 ml milk	18p
50 g rice	2p
25 g sugar	3p
13 g margarine	$1\frac{1}{2}$p
1 egg	10p
Fuel	2p
Total cost (approx.)	$36\frac{1}{2}$p (for 4 people)

Reasons for Choosing a Menu

Sometimes, in an examination, you are asked the reasons for choosing the dishes on your menu. Many of the reasons have to do with the nutritive value of a dish, which is another reason to avoid dishes like jelly which have little or no nutritive value. Here is a menu and some reasons you might have for choosing it:

> *Grapefruit*
>
> *Baked, stuffed liver and bacon*
> *Gravy*
> *Baked potatoes; Green salad*
>
> *Apple Crumble*
> *Baked custard*

Reasons for choosing:

1. *Grapefruit:* Rich in Vitamin C. Sharp flavour stimulates appetite. Cool, light, first course contrasts with filling main course and pudding.

2. *Baked liver and bacon:* Liver is rich in protein, iron, Vitamin B. Bacon is also rich in protein, Vitamin B.
   Stuffing: Gives a more interesting flavour to the liver.
   Gravy: Helps prevent liver drying out; adds moisture to meal.
   Potatoes: Provide carbohydrate for energy. They are baked to make full use of the oven.
   Green salad: Provides a contrast in colour, flavour and texture, as well as providing minerals and vitamins.

3. *Apple crumble:* A tasty pudding, cheap if apples are in season. A baked pudding makes more use of oven space and saves fuel.
   Baked custard: Rich in protein, vitamins and minerals, due to presence of eggs and milk. Provides moisture and contrasts with apple pudding.

> *Note:* Custard must be put on lowest shelf of oven, and temperature reduced slightly, as it takes a lower temperature than the crumble.

General points: This is a reasonably cheap nutritious meal, providing lots of contrast in colour, texture and flavour. Full use is made of the oven — a considerable saving in fuel.

Making a Time Plan

Most beginner cooks find that it helps to make a time plan. This is essential if you are taking part in a practical test. Here's how to go about it:

Mixed vegetable soup

Boiled collar of bacon
Parsley sauce
Creamed potatoes; Curly Kale

Fresh fruit salad
Cream

1. Study the menu and work out the length of time each dish takes to prepare, *e.g. see Table 3.1 below.*
   As you get more practice, you can work it out in your head.

2. Note the serving time of the meal — say 1.00 p.m. Work back from that, beginning with the dish which takes longest, *i.e.* Bacon/Soup/Fruit salad/Potatoes/Kale/Sauce.

   As bacon takes 2 hours, start with that, at 11 a.m.

Table 3.1

Foodstuff	Preparing	Cooking	Dishing Up	Total
Soup	20 mins	40 mins	5 mins	1 hr 5 mins
Bacon (1½ kg)	5 mins	1 hr 40 mins	10 mins	1 hr 55 mins
Kale	10 mins	15 mins	5 mins	25 mins
Potatoes	10 mins	20 mins	5 mins	25 mins
Sauce	5 mins	10 mins	1 min	16 mins
Fruit salad	15 mins	5 mins (syrup)	1 min	26 mins
Cream	3 mins (whipping)	—	—	3 mins

3. Work out the plan roughly as first, as it usually takes a few attempts to get it right.
4. Allow time at the end for dishing-up and garnishing.
5. If there is a long space when there is nothing to do, you can prepare cold dishes at this time, set the table, or do some washing up.

Timeplan for Lunch

11.00	Prepare and put on bacon.
11.20	Set table.
11.30	Prepare fruit salad — cover and chill.
11.45	Prepare soup and put to cook.
12.05	Wash and tidy up.
12.15	Whip cream, place in bowl, cover and chill.
12.20	Prepare potatoes. } Put on water
12.25	Prepare Kale. } for cooking them.
12.30	Put potatoes to cook.
12.35	Put Kale to cook.
12.40	Make sauce, keep warm.
12.50	Take off bacon skin, cover with breadcrumbs and place under grill to brown.
12.55	Dish up soup, carve meat and dish up vegetables and sauce.
1.00	Serve the meal.

Don't forget!

A good cook will taste food as cooking progresses, and correct seasoning, etc. accordingly. Do not wait until the dish is finished. Use a clean teaspoon for tasting and rinse between tastes.

Presenting Meals

1. All food should be presented attractively on clean dishes or plates.
2. Wipe any spills with a clean damp cloth.
3. Hot foods should be served piping hot on hot dishes; cold foods, chilled on cold dishes.
4. Serve sweet foods on a fancy plate or a plain plate with a d'oyley; savoury foods on a dish with a dish paper under the food.

Simple Entertaining

It is nice to ask friends to your house; it may be just for a cup of coffee at eleven, or a more elaborate meal at lunch or dinner time. If you want to entertain a large number, then a buffet party is the easiest way to feed a crowd. When you entertain anyone in your home, do make them feel welcome. Remember you are the host/hostess — don't leave guests all alone while you potter about in the kitchen. Make sure you have organised your cooking so that everything is ready before the guests arrive.

Elevenses

If you want to meet your friends in the morning, serve them coffee with some scones, sandwiches and/or small cakes. Elevenses are usually served from a tray or trolley.

You will need:

1. A clean tray/trolley.
2. A freshly laundered traycloth, with matching table napkins.
3. Coffee perocolator or coffee pot.
4. Coffee cups and saucers.
5. Knives, spoons and pastry forks (small forks will do).
6. A small jug of cream and/or hot milk. Brown sugar.
7. Plate of fresh brown or white scones, buttered; savoury sandwiches, *e.g.* egg or cucumber. Sweet cakes or biscuits.

Afternoon Tea

This is a similar meal, except tea is served instead of coffee and teacups are used instead of coffee cups. White sugar and cold milk will also be needed. For afternoon tea you might also serve an apple tart or rich cake, *e.g.* fruit cake.

A Buffet Party

This is the simplest way to entertain a crowd:

1. The table should look colourful and attractive — use a fruit or floral centrepiece.
2. Provide lots of table napkins.
3. Arrange food, plates and cutlery so as to make it easy for guests to help themselves.
4. Food should be easy to eat with one hand; guests may be standing up, trying to balance a plate and glass together.
5. Serve a selection of savoury and sweet foods, both hot and cold.

Hot foods: Pizza; sausage rolls; cocktail sausages; savoury rice; lasagne; curry with rice; baked chicken joints; savoury flans.

Cold foods: Rice salad; green salad; cold meats; fish and poultry; coleslaw; potato salad; tomato salad. Serve some cheese attractively arranged on a cheeseboard.

Sweet foods: A fancy cake or gateau; sponge flans; mousses; cheesecake. A large bowl of fresh fruit or fruit salad will add colour to the tablesetting.

Rules for Serving a Formal Meal

1. Make sure all requirements are on the table at the beginning of the meal — butter, condiments, cold water, *etc.*
2. Dishes should be warming in the oven and the meal kept piping hot.
3. Serve food from dishes at the table (rather than filling up plates in the kitchen).
4. When serving a guest, serve from the left, take away from the right. Wine and water are served and removed from the right.
5. At the end of the main course, remove all condiments, serving dishes, *etc.*, so that table is cleared for the next course.
6. After the pudding is eaten, remove dishes, custard, *etc.* and leave table clear for coffee.

Table Manners

1. Don't lie over the table, sit up straight. Avoid putting elbows on the table.
2. Place napkin on your lap while eating (not tucked into your jacket or dress). At the end of the meal, lay it beside your plate — do not fold it up.
3. If in doubt about which cutlery to use, wait until someone else starts. The usual procedure is to work through the cutlery from the outside inwards.
4. Never dip bread or rolls in soup, or break bread into soup. Put roll on the side plate, break (do not cut) off a bite-sized piece at a time and butter each piece just before you eat it.
5. Do not stuff your mouth with food and never speak with your mouth full. Keep your mouth closed when eating — the person opposite you will hardly

want to see the contents of your mouth.

6. During the meal, lay your knife and fork down on your plate with prongs downwards — they should be at an angle. When you have finished, place them side by side with prongs of fork up — at right angles to table (the idea is to let the waiter know when you are finished).

7. Hold cutlery correctly — the handle of the knife and fork should be buried in the palm of your hand. They should not be held like a pencil.

8. Never smoke during a meal — it is extremely bad manners. If you *must* smoke, wait until everybody is finished before asking permission to smoke.

Tablesetting

1. Table should be clean — use heat resisting mats to protect table surface.

2. Collect all equipment on a tray and bring to the table.

3. China, glass, cutlery should complement each other and should be sparkling clean.

4. Arrange cutlery in order of use — the cutlery you use first is on the outside, the cutlery for the second course is next and so on. Main cutlery should be 2.5 cm from the edge of the table, each piece parallel to the next. Knives should have their cutting edge inwards, forks have their prongs facing upwards. Allow 60 cm per person.

5. The drinking glass is placed above the dinner knife. If there is more than one, the others are grouped behind it. Glasses should never be turned downwards.

6. Make sure condiments are filled, arrange sufficient for the numbers dining (1 for every 4).

7. Serve butter neatly in pats and iced water in a jug, filled just before the meal begins.

8. Bread should be cut in fingers; rolls arranged on side plates or in a basket.

9. Matching table napkins should be folded or rolled and placed on the side plate.

10. A low flower arrangement provides an attractive centrepiece.

Table setting for dinner

Tablesetting for dinner

Garnishing food

A garnish or decoration will improve a dish if it suits the food and/or provides a contrast. Do not allow hot food to cool, however, in order to arrange an elaborate garnish on the dish. A simple garnish, such as a fresh bunch of parsley, can be just as effective. Do not overdo a garnish — more than two garnishes, *e.g.* lemon and parsley, can look fussy on many dishes. Garnishes should be clean, and fresh looking — if parsley is to be chopped, it should be *finely* chopped. Here is a list of simple garnishes and decorations:

Garnish (Savoury)

Fish: parsley; lemon slices; chopped hard-
   boiled egg.
Meat: parsley; tomato; julienne strips.
Savouries: stuffed olives; capers; gerkins.
Soup: Whipped cream; chopped parsley;
   chives; croutons.
Salads: Cucumber slices/twists; tomato lilies
   lemon wedges or butterflies.

Decoration (Sweet)

Whipped cream
Cherries
Angelica
Chocolate flake
Chocolate leaves
Hundreds and thousands
Chopped or whole nuts.

Shopping and Storage

It's a good idea to plan the menus for the
family a week in advance. These will form
the basis of your weekly shopping list. A
weekly menu plan means that you use your
time more efficiently. You can double up
cooking sessions — cooking some of tomor-
row's meal today, making extra pastry for
the weekend and so on. By doing it this way,
there is less waste, as leftovers are catered
for and you are less likely to run out of a
vital ingredient or forget to defrost the
chicken.

A weekly menu plan ensures that the
family eats well all the year round — taking
advantage of seasonal foods and not relying
too much on convenience foods.

Remember, money spent on good food is
a wise investment — in the health of the
family. If you have to economise, do not cut
down on the nutritive value of food —
choose cheaper, but equally nourishing,
goods.

Planning your Shopping

1. The main shopping is best done once a
   week.
2. Make your weekly menu plan the day
   before you shop. Look through cupboards and list the items you need and
   those which are running low.
3. Add to this the foods needed for your
   menu plan — group foods according to
   kind, *e.g.* meat, fish, dry goods. Do not
   stick too rigidly to the list — if there is
   a good bargain, avail of it and adapt
   your menu.
4. Avoid shopping at rush hours or when
   you are hungry when you are inclined to
   buy more than you really need to.

A good shop is:

1. Hygienic and clean.
2. Good value — with cheaply priced
   goods.
3. Sells good quality food.
4. Convenient to home or work.
5. Has a friendly efficient staff.
6. Has a good turnover.

Hygiene

1. All food shops should be clean and
   hygienic.
2. Assistants should be clean, with fresh
   overalls and clean hands.
3. Perishible food should be displayed in
   chilled covered cabinets to protect
   against dust and flies.
4. Raw and cooked food should not be
   stored together.
5. **Food should not be handled unnecessarily — especially if money is also
   handled.**
6. No animals should be allowed.
7. Frozen food cabinets should keep food
   properly frozen. Food should not be
   stored above the load line.

At the Shop

1. Buy essentials first.

2. Keep to your list as far as possible — do not be tempted to spend on non-essentials.

3. Be aware of prices — so that you notice any price increases or reductions.

4. Shop for good quality; shop around for better value.

5. Buy foods in season — out of season foods are expensive. Shop early for freshest produce.

6. Buy perishibles (meat, fish vegetables, *etc.*) in fairly small amounts, as they go off quickly.

7. Dry goods can be bought in bulk — bulk buying can be cheaper (but this is not always so). Large sizes are usually better value than small.

8. Avail of special offers — they are good value if items you need are at a reduced price.

9. Get to know the cheaper cuts of meat and fish and learn to cook them in interesting ways.

10. Pay in cash — avoid running up bills.

Storing Food

All food eventually decays — milk goes sour, fruit and vegetables rot, flour goes bad. Many changes are caused by tiny microorganisms, which are present in the air and can contaminate our food by lack of hygiene. Growth of these organisms can be slowed down by storing the food properly. Keep it:

COVERED/CLEAN/COOL

Perishible foods should be used up as soon as possible — so they should be bought in small amounts. Fruit and vegetables will lose their vitamins if stored for any length of time. Green vegetables should be washed and stored in a plastic bag in the drawer of a refrigerator. Other vegetables should be stored in a cool place. Storage cupboards should be clean, dry and safe from vermin. The modern kitchen unit, lined with laminated plastic, is easy to clean and ideal for storage.

Rules for Storing Food

1. Remove wrappers and store food in covered containers. Do not store foods in paper bags.
2. Store perishible foods in a refrigerator or a cool place. Fruit and vegetables should be stored in a cool dry dark place — a warm kitchen is not suitable.
3. Non perishible foods should be stored in air-tight containers — glass, plastic or metal. Never put fresh stores over old ones.
4. Check over and clean storage cupboards regularly.

For storage of individual foods, see relevant chapters.

4   *All About Cooking Methods*

Although we eat lots of food **raw** — *e.g.* fruit and vegetables, most of the food we eat is cooked in some way.

The Reasons We Cook Food

1. Cooking kills harmful bacteria, making food **safer to eat.**
2. Cooking makes many foods **more attractive** to look at.
3. It **improves the flavour** of food.
4. It makes some foods **easier to digest** *e.g.* flour, rice.
5. By mixing different foods together it **adds variety** and **develops new flavours.**

There are many ways of cooking food — all methods use **heat.**
The method you choose depends on the type of food you are cooking and the kind of result you want.

Boiling

Basic Methods of Cooking

1. **Boiling — Cooking food in rapidly bubbling liquid (100°C — boiling point).**

Boiling

2. **Simmering** — cooking food at a slightly lower temperature, with the water barely bubbling.

Simmering   Poaching

3. **Poaching** — the water should be moving slightly but no bubbling — used for delicate foods which break up easily *e.g.* eggs, fish.

When food is cooked in liquid, the heat travels from the heat source, *e.g.* electric ring, to the cooking utensil, *e.g.* pot, then through the liquid to the food. This process is known as **conduction.**

In all cases the food is just covered with liquid.

Foods Suitable for Boiling

1. Salt meat, *e.g.* bacon, corned beef.
2. Fresh meat (less common), *e.g.* leg of mutton, chicken.
3. Vegetables.
4. Rice and pasta, *e.g.* spaghetti.
5. Fish — thick pieces or whole fish may be **poached.**
6. Eggs.

Rules for Boiling

1. Use a pan which just fits the food. It should be covered with a tight fitting lid (in order to reduce vitamin loss).
2. Water should only just cover the food; in some cases, *e.g.* boiled cabbage, it comes less than half way up. The less water used, the less is the loss of nutrients.
3. To improve the flavour of boiled food, use stock instead of water; a knob of butter or margarine when boiling vegetables; salt (except for salted foods), herbs and other seasonings.
4. **Fresh meat** is immersed in **boiling salted water** to seal the surface protein, then reduced to simmering point.
   Salted meat is started in **cold water** to draw out the salt and make the meat tender.
5. Vegetables should be cooked for the minimum time until they are just tender, not soft and soggy.
6. Drain all boiled food well, keeping the cooking water for sauces and soups.

Drain into a jug or through a colander into a bowl

Advantages

1. Easy, quick and clean.
2. Needs little attention.
3. Food remains moist and juicy.
4. Not too wasteful on fuel — once liquid comes to the boil reduce heat and simmer until cooked.
5. Vegetables can be cooked with the meat, *e.g.* root vegetables with mutton.
6. Cooking liquid provides a ready made stock.

Disadvantages

1. Boiling adds little flavour to food *(see Rules — No. 3)*.
2. Flavour, vitamins and minerals are lost into the cooking liquid.
3. Appearance of food, *e.g.* meat and fish, is not improved. (Use a sauce to make food look and taste more attractive.)
4. Not suitable for tough cuts of meat.

Stewing

Stewing is slow, gentle cooking in a little liquid in a covered cooking pot. The liquid is always served with the food.

Food can be stewed:

(i)   On top of the cooker — in a heavy saucepan with a close fitting lid.
(ii) In the oven — in a covered casserole (this takes about 30 mins longer).

Because the cooking temperature is low, stewing takes a long time, but the gentle, moist cooking makes even the toughest cuts of meat tender and allows time for the different ingredients to mingle and develop appetising flavours.

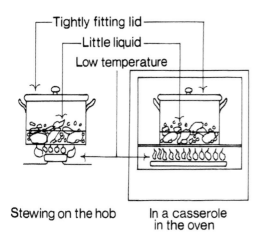

Stewing on the hob   In a casserole
in the oven

Foods suitable for stewing

1. Tough cuts of meat; poultry.
2. Vegetables, particularly roots and pulses.
3. Fish.
4. Fruit, whole or sliced.

Advantages

1. Stewing is one of the most economical methods of cooking because:
   (a) Cheaper tougher cuts of meat can be used.
   (b) Cheap root vegetables and pulses can be used to make meat go further.
   (c) A whole meal is cooked in one pot — saving fuel, space and washing up. If oven-to-tableware is used, the stew can be cooked and served in the same casserole.
   (d) Little fuel is needed to keep stew at simmering point.
2. Stews need little attention, once they start cooking.
3. A nourishing method, as juices are served with the stewed food.

Disadvantages

1. Takes time to prepare.
2. Very slow method of cooking.
3. Lacks texture.

Rules for Stewing

A stew boiled is a stew spoiled

1. The cooking temperature must be low (80°–90°C). Rapid cooking will toughen meat or break up fruit, vegetables and fish.
2. Cover cooking pot to prevent moisture evaporating as this would cause the stew to dry up and burn.
3. Most stews taste better if stock is used instead of water. Season well with pepper, salt and herbs.
4. Trim gristle, skin and extra fat from meat, cut up very tough meat into small pieces.
5. Stews can be made in advance and reheated or frozen for future use.

Aids to Stewing

A. **Slow cookers** — electric stewing pots which cook stews gently at a very low temperature. These need no attention during cooking.

B. **Pressure cookers** — these speed up the cooking of stews, by cooking them at a higher temperature.

Braising is a combination of stewing and steaming. It is suitable for not-so-tender cuts of meat. Vegetables and fish may also be braised.

Meat for braising is not cut up but left in one piece. It is browned, then cooked on a bed of diced vegetables, surrounded by a well flavoured liquid which is used to baste the meat. Food can be braised in a saucepan or in a casserole in the oven. In both cases the cooking pot must be tightly covered and the temperature should be low.

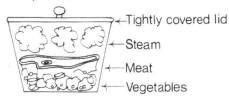

Tightly covered lid
Steam
Meat
Vegetables

Steaming

Steaming is cooking food in the steam rising from boiling water. The food is never in contact with the liquid.

There are 4 ways of steaming:

1. In a steamer.*
2. Between two greased plates, over a saucepan of boiling water — suitable for thin food such as fish.

3. In a covered bowl, standing in a saucepan of boiling water — suitable for steamed puddings, *e.g.* plum pudding.

4. In a pressure cooker, *see p. 39.*

*Steamers

A steamer is a straight-sided vessel made to fit over most sizes of saucepan. It has holes on the base which allow steam to pass up from the boiling water beneath, in order to cook the food.

A tiered steamer (3 or 4 saucepans with a connecting tube which allows steam into each section) may also be used. In both cases, the steamer must fit well and have a tightly fitting lid to prevent steam escaping.

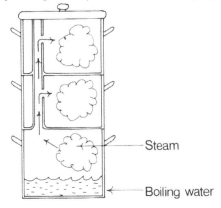

Steam

Boiling water

Foods suitable for Steaming

1. Thin pieces of meat *e.g.* breast of chicken.
2. Thin pieces of fish.
3. Most vegetables.
4. Puddings *e.g.* suet puddings.

Rules for Steaming

1. Season or flavour well; steamed dishes tend to be insipid.
2. Cover saucepan tightly with a lid to keep in steam and prevent evaporation.
3. Water must remain 'on the boil'. If it is necessary to replace water lost by evaporation, use **boiling water** or the timing of the dish will be affected.

Advantages

1. Steaming is a digestible method of cooking, ideal for invalids.
2. Little loss of nutrients (none are lost into the cooking liquid).
3. A complete meal can be cooked on one ring, using a tiered steamer or pressure cooker. This saves fuel.
4. Ideal for cooking vegetables, they are less likely to be overdone and lose nutrients.

Disadvantages

1. Steamed foods lack flavour (only foods which have a good flavour should be steamed).
2. Food does not look very appetising.
3. Very slow method of cooking.

Pressure Cooking

A **pressure cooker** is a heavy saucepan with a special locking lid, which seals the steam into the saucepan. An adjustable weight fits over the escape valve. This controls the temperature in the pressure cooker and can

be set to High, Medium or Low. Here is how it works:

Steam cannot escape . . .

pressure builds up . . . .

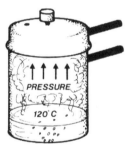

raising temperature in the pressure cooker so that food cooks more quickly.

A modern pressure cooker

Rules for Pressure Cooking

1. Follow manufacturers instructions exactly.
2. Use correct amount of water. Do not overfill or underfill.
3. Allow steam to build up and escape freely before adding weight.
4. Time cooking carefully.
5. **Never** try to open lid while any steam remains in cooker. Allow steam to reduce, by cooling under running water or standing at room temperature for about 10 mins (during this time the food continues to cook).

Advantages

1. Very quick — food cooks in ¼ to ⅓ of the time.
2. Suitable for steaming, stewing, braising and pot roasting.
3. Saves time and fuel.

Disadvantages

1. Danger of overcooking, as food cannot be tested without reducing steam.
2. Food less tasty than other methods.
3. High temperature causes some loss of Vitamins B and C.

Grilling

Grilling is cooking food at a high temperature by radiant heat. This may be done under a gas or electric grill or over a charcoal or wood fire, *e.g.* a barbeque. The food is placed on a grid, which should be greased to prevent food sticking.

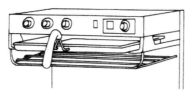

Foods suitable for Grilling

1. Meat: Only thin cuts of top quality meat can be grilled — steaks, loin chops, liver, kidney, chicken joints, rashers, sausages and hamburgers are all suitable. Meat should be 3 cm thick, or less.
2. Fish: Whole fish, fillets, cutlets, fish-fingers, fishcakes.
3. Vegetables: Mushrooms and tomatoes.
4. Toast and toasted sandwiches.
5. 'Au gratin' dishes are often browned under the grill.

Rules for Grilling

1. Use only best quality meat — all but the most tender meat becomes tough under the strong heat.
2. Preheat grill for at least 5 mins.
3. Brush grid and food lightly with cooking oil or melted fat.
4. Season lightly with pepper. Salt draws out the meat juices.
5. Grill meat quickly on both sides to seal juices — otherwise juices escape and food value and flavour is lost.
6. Cooking time depends on the thickness of the food, how close it is to the heat source and how 'well done' the food is required to be.
7. Use a tongs to turn food. Never prod with a knife or fork, this will release juices.
8. Serve savoury butter with grilled meat or fish.

Advantages

1. Very quick.
2. Little preparation required.
3. Food has an attractive appearance and taste.
4. Little loss of nutrients (due to quick cooking).

5. Fat melts and drips off, making grilled food less greasy and fattening, and more digestible, than fried food.

Disadvantages

1. Constant care is necessary due to high temperature.
2. Can be dirty due to spattering of fat.
3. Expensive; only best quality meat can be used.

Frying

Frying is cooking food in hot fat or oil. It is a quick tasty method of cooking but is inclined to be greasy. Too much fried food should be avoided as it is indigestible and fattening. There are two basic methods of frying:

1. **Shallow frying**
2. **Deep fat frying**

Shallow frying

This is frying food in a shallow frying pan.

The amount of fat used depends on the food:
  (a) 1–2 cm fat: for reheats, *e.g.* fish cakes.
  (b) Just covering base of pan: for beef-burgers, steak, eggs.
  (c) No fat (dry frying): for fatty foods, *e.g.* rashers, chops.

Only thin pieces of food are suitable for shallow frying. They must be turned during cooking.

Sautéing

This is tossing food in a little melted fat, either at the beginning of cooking, *e.g.* soup, or at the end, *e.g.* sautéed vegetables. This adds food value and flavour.

Deep Frying

This is cooking food in a deep pan using enough oil or fat to cover the food. The pan must be heavy enough to withstand the strong heat. A wire basket makes it easier to lift food in and out of the hot fat.

Coating food

Many foods are coated before frying:
  1. To protect them from the hot fat.
  2. To prevent the food getting soggy and breaking up.
  3. To prevent the outside of meat, *etc.*, becoming hard.
  4. To prevent the strong flavour of certain foods, *e.g.* fish or onions, getting into the fat.

Suitable coatings:

Shallow frying: Flour, oatmeal, egg & bread-crumbs.

Deep frying: Egg and breadcrumbs or batter.

Frying Temperatures

The temperature and type of fat you use for frying is very important. If the temperature is **too hot** the food will begin to burn on the outside before the inside is cooked. If it is **too cool** the food will absorb too much fat making it greasy.

Solid fats show a bluish haze when they reach frying temperature, but a haze rising from cooking oil indicates that it is burning. A cooking thermometer is the only true guide to the correct temperature for frying (between 175–195°C). As a rough guide, drop a cube of bread into the hot fat. If it turns golden brown in about 35-40 seconds, the fat is ready for frying.

Suitable frying fats

Vegetable oil, lard, dripping, cooking fat, *e.g. Frytex.*

Foods suitable for Frying

1. **Meat:** Only thin cuts of best quality meat are suitable, *e.g.* steak, chops, rashers, sausages, hamburgers, chicken joints, liver, kidney.
2. **Fish:** Whole fish, fillets, cutlets, fish fingers.
3. **Vegetables:** Onions, mushrooms, tomatoes, potatoes.
4. **Reheats:** Rissoles, potato croquettes, *etc.*
5. **Eggs:** Fried, omelettes, pancakes.

Care of Oil or Fat

1. Never allow fat to overheat — this gives food a burnt taste.
2. After use, allow to cool, then strain through a fine strainer.
3. Keep in a covered light-proof container — fat in a refrigerator, oil in a cupboard.
4. Throw away burned fat.

Rules for Frying

1. Fat must be really hot before food is added.
2. Dry food before frying and lower gently into fat to prevent splashing.

'Dry before you fry.'

3. Do not overcrowd pan — this lowers the temperature, delays browning, and may cause fragile foods to break up.
4. Do not cover frying pan — this will prevent food getting crisp.
5. Never fill a chip-pan more than half full, to allow for bubbling when food is immersed.
6. Reheat oil between batches; never add cold fat while food is cooking.
7. Drain fried food well in basket or draining spoon and then in kitchen paper to remove excess fat. Serve very hot.

Advantages

1. Quick and tasty.
2. Little preparation.
3. Food looks attractive.
4. Little loss of food value.

Disadvantages

1. Only expensive cuts of meat can be used.
2. Not suitable for large or thick pieces of food.
3. Fried food can be greasy and indigestible.
4. It is high in kilocalories — therefore fattening.
5. Unsuitable method for large numbers.
6. Dangerous — needs constant attention.

Danger: Fryer at work!

Frying is the most dangerous of all forms of cooking. If the fat is overheated it can burst into flames and cause a major fire.

Never!

... overheat fat
... overfill chip pan
... move pan when cooking
... allow flames to lick up sides of pan
... leave fat unattended — lift out food and turn off heat if the phone or doorbell rings.

Have a lid nearby which fits the frying pan in case of fire.

If fat goes on Fire . . .

1. Turn off heat.
2. Do not attempt to move pan.
3. **Never** throw water over burning fat.
4. Quickly place the lid or a damp cloth over the flames — without oxygen they will go out. If there is time, first wrap your hand in a damp cloth to protect it.

5. Keep a fire extinguisher or fire blanket near the cooker — a fire blanket is the best way of putting out such a fire.

Fire blanket

Oven Cooking

Food may be cooked in an oven by **roasting, baking** or in a **casserole.**

Roasting

Baking

In a casserole

The oven may be heated by gas jets, electric elements or by solid fuel. These give out (radiate) heat which then circulates around the oven (convection) heating the food. As hot air rises and falls when it cools — the hottest part of the oven is the top shelf and the coolest part is the lowest shelf.

Baking

Baking is cooking food in dry heat in an oven. When cooked, baked food is crisp and golden brown on the outside, *e.g.* bread, pies, *etc.*

Foods suitable for Baking

1. Bread and cakes.
2. Puddings.
3. Pastry dishes.
4. Fish.

Rules for Ovencooking

1. Oven should be preheated to correct temperature.
2. Place food in correct position in oven — never place dishes on the floor of the oven.
3. Allow room for heat to circulate — don't pack dishes too closely.
4. Avoid opening the door — the cold air may affect the dish being cooked.
5. Always use oven gloves or a dry cloth when removing hot dishes.
6. Keep oven clean — a dirty oven will smoke and smell. Dishes which are likely to spill over should be placed on tins. Wipe out oven after use.

Economy tips

1. **Make full use of the oven.** It is extravagant to switch on an oven for one dish. Arrange to cook, at one time, several dishes which require similar cooking temperatures.
2. Most fuel is used heating up the oven, it takes little extra to retain the heat. Do a large batch of baking or cooking on the same day.
3. Turn off **electric** ovens 10 minutes before the end of cooking as they retain heat well.
4. Casseroles can be put into a cold oven and the **rising heat** used to start the cooking.

Advantages

1. Dishes look and taste very appetising.
2. Little attention is needed.
3. Auto-timer cooking allows great freedom to the cook.

Disadvantages

1. Extravagant, unless full use is made of oven.
2. Oven needs regular cleaning.

Roasting

Roasting is cooking food in an oven using hot fat. The food is usually basted with fat to prevent it drying out.

True roasting is done on a rotating spit over an open fire. A rotisserie (electric revolving spit) on a modern cooker or grill gives the same effect; as the meat rotates, it bastes itself. You may have seen a rotisserie in your local supermarket or 'take-away' shop.

True roasting is done on a spit over an open fire

Foods suitable for Roasting

1. **Tender joints of meat**: (cheap cuts would toughen with the high temperatures).
2. **Poultry and game.**
3. **Potatoes** and other **root vegetables.**

Meat can be:
1. **Quick roasted** — at a very high temperature.
2. **Slow roasted** — at a lower temperature for a longer time.

Quick roasting

This is used for best quality tender cuts of meat. The food is cooked for the first 20-30 minutes in a **hot oven** — 230°C (450°F) Gas 7 — to seal the surface protein and keep the juices in. The heat is then reduced to 205°C (400°F), Gas 5, to finish the cooking.

Slow roasting

This is used for very lean and less tender cuts, *e.g.* housekeepers cut, which would toughen at higher temperatures. The meat is cooked at 175°C (350°F), Gas 4, for the full time.

With this method the meat shrinks less and becomes tender but is not as crisp and brown as when cooked at higher temperatures.

Covering the Joint

Open roasting: is done in an uncovered tin; the meat gets nicely browned but it shrinks a lot and the oven gets very dirty.

Closed roasting: is done by placing the meat in a covered roasting tin or casserole. The meat is not as crisp and tasty by this method, but it shrinks less, and the oven stays clean. The lid should be removed for the last half hour to help brown the meat.

Foil and Roasting bags: The meat can be wrapped in foil or placed in transparent plastic roasting bags. The effect is the same as closed roasting. The foil or bag should be removed for the last 30 minutes..

Note: Closed roasts generally take about 20 mins longer than open roasts.

Rules for Roasting

(Follow basic rules for Baking)

1. Remove meat from refrigerator one hour before cooking.
2. Set shelves correctly and preheat oven to correct temperature.
3. Wipe meat with moistened kitchen paper and skewer into shape (replace wooden butchers skewers with metal ones).
4. Weigh meat to calculate cooking time, *see p. 84.*
5. Place roasting tin, containing 50 g dripping, into the oven to heat.
6. When hot, place meat in the roasting tin (or on a grid over the tin) and baste with hot fat.
7. Roast for required time, reducing heat if necessary.
8. Lean meat should be basted 2-3 times during cooking.
9. Drain well and allow to stand in a warm place for 10 minutes to make carving easier. Gravy can be made during this time.

Advantages

1. Good flavour.
2. Attractive crisp appearance.
3. A whole meal can be cooked in the oven at one time, *e.g.*

Roast Beef
Yorkshire Pudding
Roast potatoes; Casserole of vegetables

Apple Crumble

Disadvantages

1. Expensive — only suitable for tender cuts of meat.
2. Extravagant, unless full use is made of oven.
3. Meat shrinks considerably (by up to one third).
4. Open roasting leaves the oven very dirty.

Basting: Spooning hot fat over food to prevent it drying out.

Pot Roasting

Pot roasting is a method of cooking small roasts in a tightly covered heavy saucepan on top of the cooker. The meat is cooked in a little fat over a very moderate heat.

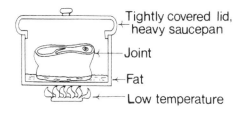

Tightly covered lid, heavy saucepan
Joint
Fat
Low temperature

Foods suitable for Pot Roasting

1. Small joints of meat.
2. Small chickens.
3. Stuffed sheeps heart.

Rules for Pot Roasting

1. Use a very heavy saucepan or stewpan with a tightly fitting lid (a cast iron pan is ideal). A thin saucepan will burn the roast.
2. Prepare meat as for roasting.
3. Heat fat, brown meat quickly on all sides.
4. Cover and cook over a very moderate heat.
5. Cooking time — same as for oven roasting.
6. Turn joint now and then to prevent meat getting tough and hard on the side nearest the heat. Shake the pan occasionally to prevent sticking.
7. Drain and serve as for roasting.

Advantages

1. Economical on fuel — as it is done on one hot plate.
2. Those without an oven, *e.g.* in a small bedsitters and caravans, can still enjoy a roast.
3. Less shrinkage of meat.
4. Cleaner.

Disadvantages

1. Great care and attention is needed as it is very easy to burn the outside of the meat.
2. Not as crisp and tasty as oven roasts.
3. Large joints are unsuitable.

Over to You . . .

Nutrition

1. Underline the energy foods in this list: Oranges; Cauliflower; Butter; Bread; Cheese; Macaroni; Salt; Herrings; Sugar; Cod; Apple Tart.

2. Vegetarians are people who eat no animal protein food. Plan a nourishing days menu for a family of vegetarians — make sure you include plenty of protein.

3. In the case of each of the nutrients listed below, list four foods which contain a high percentage of the nutrient: (a) fat; (b) starch; (c) animal protein.

4. Name three 'protective' nutrients. What are their functions. List three foods rich in each named nutrient.

5. List the nutrients which are particularly important in the diet of a pregnant or nursing mother. Give reasons for your choice.

Menu Planning

7. Write a nourishing menu for (a) a summer lunch; (b) a dinner in winter; (c) a teenage party.
   Write a time plan for one of the menus above, and make a shopping list for the perishable items on your menu.

8. Compare shopping in a supermarket with shopping in a small family store. List your answer in points.

Cooking methods:

9. Compare boiling and grilling as methods of cooking (a) meat; (b) vegetables.

10. What do you think is the best way of cooking each of the following foods: (a) an invalid dish; (b) green vegetables; (c) a chicken; (d) sirloin steak; (e) a fish fillet. Give two reasons why you picked each one.

5   *All About Starting to Cook*

Before you decide to make a dish . . . .

> **Check:** Have you got the right ingredients?
>
> Have you got all equipment needed?
>
> Have you enough time to make and bake the dish?
>
> If you say no to any of these — do not start.

Before you start . . . . .

1. Put an apron on and tie long hair back.

2. Wash your hands — NEVER lick your fingers.
3. Wipe cooking surface over with a clean damp cloth.
4. Read the recipe right through.
5. Collect all utensils and set them out neatly (*see below*).
6. Collect ingredients — weigh and measure carefully (*p. 51/52*).

Then . . .

7. Follow recipe, step by step.
8. Never waste food.
10. Clean up after you — leave work place clean and tidy.

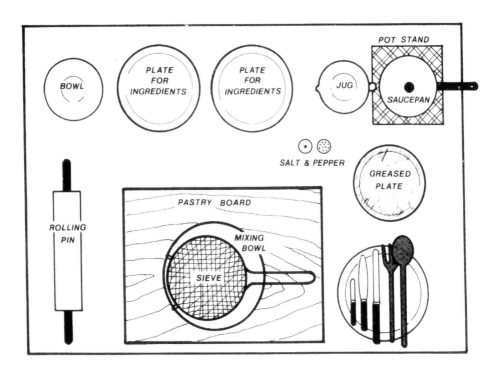

Setting a table for cookery class

Don't forget!

If you are cooking more than one dish, check which makes the longest and make that first.

Safety first

When cooking, you are working with many dangerous things — electricity, gas, hot objects and liquids, sharp knives and gadgets.

RESPECT DANGER

1. Use oven gloves when handling hot casseroles or tins.
2. Turn saucepan handles away from edge of cooker.
3. Take care when using kinves — never point a knife at anyone, even in play. Cut away from yourself in case the knife slips. Use a wooden board for chopping — it's less slippy.
4. Never touch electric plugs or equipment with wet hands. Turn off electric items before cleaning.
5. Wipe up spills at once, especially on the floor.
6. Keep a fire blanket near at hand, in case of fire.

If you see this sign ⚠ on a recipe — be careful! — it may be a dangerous stage, or something may go wrong.

Using the Cooker

If you hope to get good results when cooking, you must learn how to use the oven correctly. Too hot or cold an oven can have disastrous results.

Preheating

This means bringing the oven to the right temperature *before* you put food in. The oven is preheated for most baking — breads, cakes, pastry and roasts. Casseroles and moist puddings, *e.g.* rice pudding, can be started in a cold oven.

It takes about 15 minutes to heat up an electric oven — a gas oven will heat in 10 minutes — so turn them on in plenty of time. Electric ovens have a little light, which switches off when the temperature is reached.

Lighting a gas oven

Many gas ovens must be lit with a match or a gaslighter.
1. Never turn an oven switch until you are ready to light it.
2. Turn on switch, put a match or lighter to burners or lighting point. Make sure it is lighting, then close oven.

Temperature differences

Two ovens will often give a different temperature, even though the temperature dial is set at the same number. One oven may be hotter than normal. If you find that this is the case, at home or in school, remember to set the temperature dial a little lower or else you dish will be overcooked.

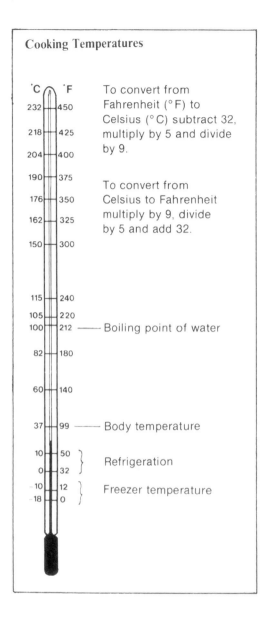

Cooking Temperatures

°C	°F	
232	450	To convert from Fahrenheit (°F) to Celsius (°C) subtract 32, multiply by 5 and divide by 9.
218	425	
204	400	
190	375	
176	350	To convert from Celsius to Fahrenheit multiply by 9, divide by 5 and add 32.
162	325	
150	300	
115	240	
105	220	
100	212	Boiling point of water
82	180	
60	140	
37	99	Body temperature
10	50	} Refrigeration
0	32	
-10	12	} Freezer temperature
-18	0	

Liquid temperatures

Stage	°C	°F
Boiling	100	212
Simmering	90	195
Tepid (lukewarm)	37	98
Freezing	0	32

Shelf position

Place the shelf in the correct position *before* you turn on the oven — it is easier and safer to move a cold shelf. Most ovens are **hottest** near the top and **coolest** near the bottom. In general, most cooking is done in the **centre of the oven** where the temperature corresponds to that shown on the temperature dial (fan ovens are an exception as they have an even temperature throughout).

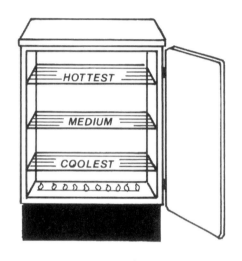

When using an oven to cook several items, *e.g.* a dinner, it is useful to have this slight variation in temperature. Dishes requiring the hottest temperature, *e.g.* pastry, can be placed on the top shelf, a roast can be placed in the middle, and boiled vegetables on the lowest shelf. If all dishes require the same temperature, *e.g.* if they are all pastry, they must be changed around during cooking to allow each to brown evenly.

Baking tins should never touch each other or the walls of the oven — this would prevent heat circulating. Place them in the centre of each shelf. Never place anything on the floor. In a gas oven, the dish will not cook; in some electric ovens, the element is under the floor and the food would burn.

Oven temperatures

Table 5.1

Description	°C	°F	Gas	Uses
Very cool	110 120	225 250	¼ ½	Meringues/bottling/ slow stewing
Cool	140 150	275 300	1 2	Casseroles milk puddings/custards
Very moderate	160	325	3	Slow roasting/casseroles
Moderate	180 190	350 375	4 5	Fruit cake/biscuits small cakes
Moderately or fairly hot	200	400	6	Sponges/scones
Hot	220 230	425 450	7 8	Fast roasting/bread Pastry
Very hot	240	475	9	Sealing roast meat

Weighing and Measuring

When you start cooking it is important to follow every recipe **exactly.** As you get more experienced you will discover that you can adapt recipes to suit the ingredients you have. For example, one carrot more or less in a casserole, or one extra apple in a tart, will not spoil the dish.

But when it comes to baking — cakes, pastry and buns for example — the ingredients have been very carefully worked out to give a certain result. If you alter these, even slightly, the dish could be ruined.

In this book, **only** metric measures have been used, as the only way to get used to the metric system is to start using it and forget about ounces and pounds. If you try to compare and convert, you will never get the hang of it. If you are using a recipe which has both imperial and metric measurements, **use one or the other.** When cooking by the metric system, it is essential to have metric scales and measuring jug. The scales can be spring type with a dial, or a balancing scales, for which you will need a set of metric weights.

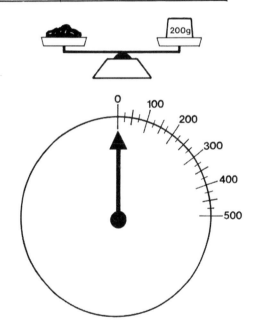

In this, as in most metric recipe books, the unit of weight is **25 grammes** and this is shown as one mark on the spring scale. 25 g is quite a small amount, about one tablespoonful of flour, sugar or rice.

When very small amounts are needed, *e.g.* half the 25 g unit, it is shown as 13 g and the indicator should point **between** the two lines.

The kilogram is the large unit — 40 times greater than the 25 g unit. It contains 1000 grams.

We buy many groceries by the kilo — meat, fruit, vegetables, flour and sugar. Sugar comes in 1 kilo bags, flour in 2 kilos.

Margarine and Cooking Fat

This is at present sold in 8 oz (227 g) packs. As fat would make the scales sticky, use the following method to measure it.

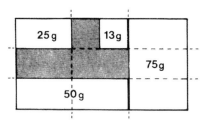

Divide margarine in 9 . . .

Measuring liquids

The metric units of liquid measurement are the litre (l) and millilitre (ml). One litre contains 1000 ml.

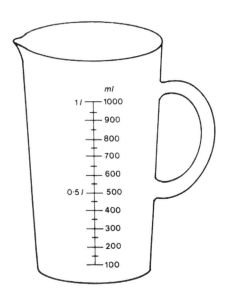

Spoon measurements

Metric measuring spoons come in 5 sizes. These correspond to spoon measures as follows:

> 1.25 = ¼ teaspoon.
> 2.5 ml = ½ teaspoon.
> 5 ml = 1 teaspoon.
> 10 ml = 1 dessertspoon.
> 15 ml = 1 tablespoon.

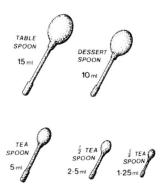

Medicine spoons, from the chemist measure 5 ml.

A spoonful of an ingredient means a rounded spoonful (as much above the spoon as below it). Half a spoon means a level spoonful. A quarter of a spoon means half a level spoonful.

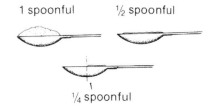

The Metric Unit of Length

This may be required to measure the depth of pastry or the width of a tin. It is based on 1 metre (m):

> **1 metre** = 100 centimetres (cm)
> **1 centimetre** = 10 millimetres.

Cookery Terms

Au gratin: Food which has been covered with sauce, sprinkled with cheese and/or bread-crumbs and browned under the grill or in the oven.

Bainmarie: A large flat pan or tin, containing simmering water, in which saucepans of food, *e.g.* sauces, can be kept warm. A double saucepan is based on the same idea.

Baking blind: To bake a pastry case without a filling.

Basting: Spooning hot fat over roast meat to prevent drying out.

Beating: Mixing briskly to introduce air.

Blanch: To put food in cold water and bring to the boil — this is done to whiten, cleanse, remove skins or strong flavours.

Blend: To mix smoothly, usually a starchy powder with cold liquid so that it does not lump.

Boil: To cook food in rapidly bubbling liquid.

Bouillon: Stock.

Bouquet garni: A bunch of herbs tied with string or wrapped in muslin for easy removal. It is used to add flavour to soups and stews.

Brine: Salted water.

Broil: An American term for grilling food.

Chill: To refrigerate.

Coating: Covering food with a protective layer, *e.g.* for frying, or with a sauce.

Consistency: The thickness of a mixture.

Court bouillon: Vegetable stock used for poaching fish.

Creaming: To mix fat and sugar together until it is white and fluffy.

Croûtons: Small dice of fried bread served with soup.

Dough: A fairly stiff mixture of flour and liquid used in bread and scones.

Dredge: To sprinkle with sugar or flour.

Flan: A shallow case of pastry or sponge, which may be filled with a savoury or sweet filling.

Fold: To lightly add a dry ingredient, *e.g.* flour, to a moist mixture, usually with a metal spoon.

Force Meat: Stuffing.

Fricassé: A white stew.

Garnish: To decorate a savoury dish.

Glaze: To brush over baked dishes with beaten egg or milk, to improve the finish and give a shine.

Infuse: To heat to a very low temperature in liquid, in order to draw out the flavour.

Knead: To work dough with the hands, in order to develop elasticity and make the mixture smooth.

Liason: A thickening ingredient for soups, stews and sauces, *e.g.* roux, cornflour.

Marinade: A mixture of oil, acid and seasoning, used to flavour and tenderise meat.

Menu: A list of foods available for a meal.

Panard (panada): A thick sauce used to bind ingredients together.

Parboil: To half cook by boiling.

Poach: To cook very gently in water, well below boiling point.

Purée: A soft mixture of fruit or vegetables which have been sieved, or a thick soup.

Quiche: An open pastry case with a savoury custard filling.

Raising agent: Added to baked dishes in order to make them light and well risen, *e.g.* baking powder.

Rechauffé: A reheated dish, *e.g.* Fish Pie.

Roux: A mixture of flour and fat used to thicken soups and sauces.

Rub in: To crumble fat into flour using the fingertips.

Sauté: To toss quickly in hot fat.

Seasoning: Adding flavour to savoury dishes, by using salt, pepper, herbs or spices.

Shortening: Any fat used in baking (particularly pastry making) which produces a brittle texture, *e.g.* lard, margarine, butter.

Simmer: To cook in liquid just below boiling point.

Skim: To remove a substance from the top of a liquid (*e.g.* scum from jam) using a flat spoon.

Syrup: A solution of sugar and water.

Whisk: To beat air into ingredients with a whisk.

6   *All About Breakfast*

Do you hate getting up?

The reason many people are tired and irritable in the mornings is because blood sugar is low after the long overnight fast and the body needs refuelling. A nourishing breakfast will provide this fuel — which is why breakfast is probably the most important meal of the day. If we skip breakfast, we deprive the body of food when it most needs it.

Remember, most of our day's work is done in the morning. Research has shown that those who miss a proper breakfast find it is hard to concentrate, work less efficiently and are more accident prone. Those who skip breakfast will be tempted to fill up at mid morning with sugary snacks. It is particularly important to have a good breakfast if you are only having a packed lunch at midday.

If you find you can't face food first thing in the morning, start with grapefruit or orange juice — its sharp fresh taste will sharpen your appetite and wake you up.

Planning your breakfast

1. Food from each nutrient group should be included.
2. Breakfast should be substantial, but not heavy or indigestible.
3. It should be quick and easy to prepare.
4. Set the table the night before to avoid a last minute rush.
5. Some dishes can be prepared or partly cooked the night before *e.g.* muesli, porridge.
6. Introduce variety from day to day.
7. Set the table attractively — it helps create the right atmosphere for the day.

Start the day the nutritious way

Protein and fat (bacon, egg, kippers) will provide building material and energy and delay the feeling of hunger.
Include Vitamins A and D (dairy produce, eggs); Vitamin C (fruit); and Vitamin B (cereals) — many breakfast cereals have added B vitamins.
Roughage and carbohydrate are plentiful in cereals and brown bread.
Make sure to get some iron and calcium by including meat, eggs and milk.

Choose from these:

> *Fruit*
>
> *Tomato, orange, grapefruit juice*
> *Grapefruit segments*
> *Grilled grapefruit*
> *Stewed fruit, e.g. rhubarb, prunes*
> *Melon*

> *Cereal*
>
> *Porridge*
> *Muesli*
> *Breakfast cereals, e.g. Wheatflakes*

Main Course

Grilled fish e.g. kippers, plaice
Eggs – boiled, poached, fried,
scrambled, omelettes
Bacon — fried, grilled,
Liver, kidney — fried, grilled
Grilled tomato, mushrooms
Welsh rarebit
French toast

Finish off with a carbohydrate food — toast; brown or white bread or scones; waffles; croissants — and a hot drink, such as tea or coffee. Children should have a milky drink.

Fresh Grapefruit

Ingredients

1 grapefruit (2 persons)
Honey, sugar or sweetener
Cherry (optional)

Method

1. Wash grapefruit and cut in half around the 'equator' of the fruit.
2. Using a grapefruit or serrated knife, cut flesh of fruit away from pith. Separate segments so that each piece can be lifted out easily.
3. Remove white core and pips.
4. Sweeten with sugar or honey. Weightwatchers should use artificial sweetener.
5. Place in sundae glass and decorate with a cherry.
6. Place glass on small plate with teaspoon alongside.

Grilled Grapefruit

1. Prepare grapefruit as above.
2. Sprinkle with brown sugar, leave to stand for 15 minutes.
3. Place under preheated grill for 2-3 mins. until sugar starts to darken.
4. Serve as above.

Porridge

Ingredients

500 ml boiling water
100 g flakemeal
½ tsp. salt

To serve:

Milk or cream
Brown/white sugar or honey

Method

1. Put water, flakemeal and salt into a saucepan.
2. Bring to the boil, stirring frequently. Reduce heat.
3. Cover and simmer gently for 5 – 20 mins., depending on flakemeal used and consistency required.
4. Stir now and then to prevent sticking.
5. Serve hot in warm cereal dishes, with milk or cream and sugar or honey to sweeten.

Note: Steep flakemeal overnight to shorten cooking time.

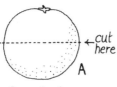

Grapefruit

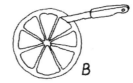

Cut flesh from pith

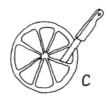

Separate segments

Muesli

(A nourishing Swiss breakfast dish which is almost a complete meal in itself.)

Ingredients

100 g flakemeal
75 g sultanas
25 g brown sugar or
* honey (optional)*
2 tablespoons chopped nuts
* (e.g. walnuts, hazelnuts)*
1 grated apple or sliced banana
200 ml milk.

Method

1. Soak flakemeal and sultanas in milk, overnight.
2. In the morning, grate apple or slice banana.
3. Add to flakemeal; stir in nuts and sugar.

Breakfast Eggs

Boiled Egg

1. Remove egg from refrigerator at least 30 minutes before cooking.
2. Place egg in cold water, bring to the boil. Cover.
3. Simmer gently for 3 minutes (soft); 4 mins. (medium); 5 mins. (hard).
4. Place in egg cup and serve with fingers of buttered toast.

Hardboiled egg (for salads, *etc.*)
As above, but simmer for 8–10 mins. Cool quickly in cold water.

Poached egg on Toast

Ingredients

1 fresh egg $\frac{1}{2}$ *teaspoon salt*
Boiling water   *Slice buttered toast*

Method

1. Bring 5 cm water to the boil in saucepan, add salt.
2. Break egg into cup.
3. Make a 'whirlpool' in the boiling water and slide egg into centre.
4. Poach gently until set (3 minutes).
5. Meanwhile make toast.
6. Lift out egg with draining spoon.
7. Serve egg on buttered toast. Garnish with parsley and grilled tomato if wished.
8. If poacher is used, grease 'cups' before use and cook as above.

Scrambled Egg on toast

Ingredients per person

1 fresh egg   *Pepper and salt*
Small knob butter   *1 slice buttered toast.*
1 tablespoon milk

Method

1. Break egg into bowl, beat well with fork.
2. Heat grill, toast bread, butter and keep warm under grill.
3. Melt butter in saucepan, add milk and seasoning.
4. Add egg, stir over a moderate heat, until thick and creamy. Be careful not to cook too long or it will curdle and separate.
5. Pile onto toast; garnish with parsley.

Variations

1. Add 25 g grated cheese at end of cooking.
2. Add chopped cooked ham or bacon during cooking.
3. Add 1 skinned, chopped tomato during cooking.

Fried Bacon and Egg

Ingredients per person

2 back or streaky rashers
1 egg
Parsley

Method

1. Brush pan with melted fat.
2. Remove rind and bone from rashers with scissors. Place rinds and rashers on warm pan.
3. Cook at medium heat until just beginning to crisp.
4. Lift out with fish slice. Drain and keep warm on a plate.
5. Break egg into a cup, then slide into warm bacon fat.
6. Cook gently until set, basting now and then with bacon fat.
7. Lift out with fish slice. Drain well.
8. Place rashers on heated breakfast plate with egg on top.
9. Garnish with parsley.

Fried bread:

If you have some bacon fat left in the pan, fry some sliced bread on each side until golden. Drain well.

Breakfast Grill

(Ideal for a late breakfast at the weekend)

Ingredients per person

1–2 sausages
1 slice liver or 1 kidney
1 slice black pudding
1 slice white pudding
1 tomato or 3 mushrooms
Melted fat

Method

1. Preheat grill.
2. Remove skin from kidney and cut in two, using kitchen scissors; remove core. Cut any blood vessels from liver with scissors.
3. Wash liver or kidney in tepid water. Dry in kitchen paper.
4. Halve tomato; wipe mushrooms and trim off base.
5. Brush ingredients with melted fat, season and place on grill.
6. Cook in the following order:
   (a) Liver — 10 mins (5 mins each side).
   (b) Sausage and kidney — 8 mins (4 mins each side).
   (c) Black and white pudding — 6 mins.
   (d) Tomato, mushroom — 5 mins.
   In this way everything will be cooked at the same time.
7. Drain and serve on a warm breakfast plate; garnish with parsley.

Toast

1. Use thickly sliced, day-old bread, or thick sliced toasting pan.
2. If wished, remove crusts, but be sure to keep them for crumbs.
3. Preheat grill, place slices on grill rack and toast each side until golden brown.
4. Cut in triangles and place in toast rack. Cover with a clean napkin to keep warm.

It is more convenient and economical to use an electric toaster.

French Toast

Ingredients

4 slices bread   *Pepper and salt*
1 egg   *Oil or dripping*
3 tablespoons milk   *Parsley*

Method

1. Beat egg in shallow bowl, mix in milk and seasoning.

2. Remove crusts from bread and dip slices in egg mixture.
3. Fry in hot fat until golden brown. Drain on kitchen paper.
4. Serve on warm plate with grilled/fried sausages and tomatoes. Garnish with parsley.

Variations

Cinnamon toast: Omit seasoning and sprinkle cooked toast with caster sugar flavoured with cinnamon.

Tea

1. Put enough fresh water in kettle to cover the element. Bring to boil.
2. Scald teapot with a little boiling water and pour out. (This heats teapot which helps draw out the flavour of the tea).
3. Put in one teaspoon of tea per person or according to taste.
4. Pour on **boiling** water, place lid on teapot.
5. Cover with tea cosy and leave to draw for 3–4 mins.
6. Serve with milk and sugar. For lemon tea, serve in a glass with a slice of lemon on top — great for slimmers!

Coffee

1. Put 1 rounded tablespoon ground coffee in a warmed jug or saucepan and warm slightly.
2. Pour over 250 ml boiling water, stir, cover and leave in a warm place for 5–6 mins. **Do not boil.**
3. Strain through fine strainer or filter paper into heated coffee pot.
4. Serve at once — (a) black, (b) with cold milk, (c) with hot (not boiled) milk or (d) with cream.

If using a percolater, follow instruction book exactly.

Cocoa

(A good drink for children as it can be made on milk and is rich in iron)

Ingredients

1 teaspoon cocoa
1 cupful milk or milk and water
Sugar to taste

Method

1. Blend cocoa to a smooth paste with a little of the milk.
2. Bring rest of milk to boil, and stir into blended cocoa.
3. Sweeten to taste.

Setting a Breakfast Tray

It is nice to give someone a special treat by bringing them breakfast in bed. A member of your family may be ill, you may want to spoil a guest or give your Mum or Dad a well earned rest. Whatever the occasion — do make an effort to have the tray looking as attractive as possible.

— Naturally, everything should be spotless — cloth, cutlery, china.
— Try to have matching china and coordinating colours.
— Use the smallest dishes, teapot, *etc.,* so that they will fit easily on the tray.
— Place items on the tray in logical order: put the dishes one eats from to the front of the tray, sugar and milk near cup and teapot; butter and marmalade near the side plate for buttering bread.
— Do not clutter the tray with unnecessary items, although a single flower or small posy in a tiny container, and perhaps a copy of the morning paper, will show that you have gone to extra trouble.
— Cover hot dishes with a dish cover, or an upturned plate to keep them warm.
— Make sure to include a napkin, to wipe sticky fingers.

Step by step to setting the tray

1. Clean tray and polish with a dry cloth.
2. Cover with a clean traycloth if you wish. (Many trays have attractive designs and need no cloth).
3. Collect cutlery, glasses, china and make sure they are sparkling clean.
4. Collect and fill cruets, sugar bowl, milk jug, butter and marmalade dish.
5. Fold table napkin and place on side plate.
6. Arrange tray as in diagram.
7. If you are preparing the tray the night before, leave butter and milk covered in the fridge, and cover tray with a clean tea towel.

Breakfast tray:

A Toast rack   C Marmalade   E Milk jug
B Butter   D Orange juice F Main course

Breakfast Menu for Winter

To be served at 8.00 a.m.

Fresh Orange Juice

Porridge
Milk

Grilled Bacon, Sausage, Tomato
Wholemeal Bread
Marmalade
Tea

Timeplan
(breakfast to be served at 8.00 am)

7.30	Squeeze oranges. Place glasses of juice in fridge.
7.35	Put on porridge — leave simmering.
7.40	Turn on grill. Set table.
7.45	Put bacon, sausage, tomato, to cook.
7.50	Put on kettle, slice bread.
7.55	Make tea, leave to draw.
7.58	Dish up bacon, *etc.* Keep warm.
8.00	Serve up juice and porridge.

Over to you . . .

1. Plan 2 breakfast menus — one for a warm summer's morning, the other for a cold winter's morning. Give reasons for your choice of dishes in each menu.

2. Draw a diagram of a breakfast table setting for 4 (use breakfast tray diagram as a guide).

3. Here's a breakfast many people eat when they have to rush out to work in the morning. Make a list of the 'faults' in this menu and re-write it to make a more nourishing breakfast.

    Toast and butter
    A cup of tea

4. Plan a well balanced breakfast menu for a young man or woman who wishes to lose weight.

7   *All About Soups and Starters*

Stock

Most soups and sauces are based on a good **stock.** Stock is a liquid which contains the juices, flavour and nourishment of bones, lean mean or fish and vegetables. These are drawn out by simmering the ingredients in water for a long time.

Food value of Stock

Stock has little food value — it is mainly gelatine and water — but it makes a great difference to homemade soups and sauces by adding extra **flavour.** Soups made without stock are often insipid.

Basic Stock

Ingredients

500 g beef bones	2 sticks celery
2 litres cold water	½ teaspoon salt
1 onion	3–4 peppercorns
1 carrot	

Bouquet garni (optional):
2–3 parsley stalks/sprig of thyme/bay leaf

Method

1. Have butcher chop beef bones.
2. Trim all fat and wipe well.
3. Wash and peel vegetables, cut in large pieces.
4. Cover with water, add salt and flavourings.
5. Bring slowly to the boil, remove scum after five minutes.
6. Reduce heat and simmer gently for 2 hours.
7. Strain into bowl, cool quickly.
8. Store in refrigerator and use up within 2-3 days.
9. Remove fat just before use.

Variations

Brown Stock: Brown bones first in oven. Fry onion to brown.
Chicken Stock: Use chicken carcase and giblets (except liver).
Fish Stock: Use fish bones and skin, cover with water. Add bayleaf, onion, seasoning and slice of lemon. Cook for 20 minutes only.
Vegetable Stock: Simmer a mixture of vegetables in a litre of water for about 40 mins. Strain, or use the water in which the vegetables have been cooked.

Rules for Stockmaking

1. Only use fresh ingredients, preferably raw.
2. **Do not use** green or starchy vegetables, turnip, or milky or fatty foods, Mutton bones are unsuitable for stock — unless it is used for Mutton Broth.
3. **Season lightly.** The stock will become more concentrated with the long cooking, making the seasoning too strong.
4. **Simmer stock gently;** boiling causes cloudiness.
5. Use a large **heavy saucepan** with a well fitting lid. A pressure cooker is useful, reducing cooking time to one third.

Stock Cubes

These are made from concentrated, dried stock. They are handy in emergencies, but not as good as real stock. They contain additives and preservatives and may be too heavily seasoned for certain dishes.

Soups

Soups are useful in the diet.

1. They add variety.
2. They provide warmth.
3. When used as a first course, they are a useful aid to digestion as they stimulate the digestive juices.
4. They are ideal for snacks, light lunches and as a nourishing beverage for invalids.

Food value

As soups contain a large amount of water, their food value is not very high. Yet as a beverage they are much more nourishing than tea or coffee, providing small amounts of nourishment in an easily digested form. Thick soups, containing vegetables and meat, are quite substantial and are useful for snacks and light lunches. Broths are useful in invalid cookery.

Soups may be grouped as follows:

Thin soups — clear soups and broths.
Thick soups — purées and thickened soups.

1. **Clear soups** — are based on a rich stock. They are transparent and take their name from the type of garnish used, *e.g. Consommé à la Julienne* — garnished with thin strips of vegetable.

2. **Broths** consist of a clear soup containing finely chopped meat and/or vegetables. Broths are made more filling by adding starchy ingredients such as barley, rice or pasta, which also help to thicken them, *e.g.* Chicken broth; Scotch broth.

3. **Purées** — a soup thickened by sieving its own ingredients. These are kept in suspension by starchy thickeners such as blended flour or cornflour, *e.g.* Potato Soup.

4. **Thickened soups:** finely chopped meat and/or vegetable cooked in liquid, with blended flour or cornflour added to thicken, *e.g.* Mixed Vegetable Soup.

Thickening soups

A substance used to thicken soup is called a **liaison.** This binds the ingredients together and makes the soup more substantial.

1. **Starch:** flour, cornflour, arrowroot, blended with cold liquid before adding to the soup.

2. **Roux:** equal amounts of flour and fat, cooked at the beginning of the soup.

3. **Whole cereals:** barley, sago, rice, added to broths and some thick soups.

4. **Egg yolk:** used to thicken rich soups.

Proportions: 25 g – 30 g thickener to each litre of liquid used.

Rules for Soupmaking

1. Use a heavy saucepan with a well fitting lid.
2. Use correct proportions of fresh ingredients — the main ingredient should predominate.
3. Use a good stock.
4. Ingredients should be thinly sliced or finely chopped, to extract maximum flavour.
5. Sauté ingredients in fat to improve flavour and food value.
6. Bring slowly to boil and simmer gently to draw out flavour and nutrients.
7. Blend thickeners carefully to avoid lumping.
8. Use of a pressure cooker and liquidiser helps to speed up soup making.

Characteristics of a well made soup

A good soup should be:
1. **Well flavoured** — tasting of the main ingredient.
2. **Correct consistency** — thin, clear or thick.
3. **Smooth**, with no lumps.
4. **A good colour.**
5. **Free from grease.**
6. **Piping hot** — unless it is a cold soup.

Accompaniments

Fingers of brown or white bread.
Bread rolls or dinner buns
Melba toast — very thin slices of toast (baked in the oven or under a grill)
Croûtons — diced fried bread

Garnishes

Chopped chives or parsley
Blob of cream
Grated cheese

Quick Soups

Tinned and packet soups are a good stand-by when you are in a hurry:

1. They are quick and easy to use.
2. They can be stored for a long time.
3. They are useful in emergencies.
4. They save time and fuel.
5. They can be used in stews and savoury dishes.

Instructions should be followed exactly
These soups take only 5–10 minutes to cook.

Convenience Soups	Vs	Homemade Soups
Quick — saves fuel		Pure, wholesome
Easy to make		ingredients
but		Interesting varia-
Not good value for		tions possible
money		*but*
Taste can be		Expensive unless
monotonous		home grown vege
Too many additives,		tables are used
e.g. colouring		More troublesome
		Take longer to cook

Vegetable Purée (Potato Soup)
Basic Recipe for most Vegetable Purées

Ingredients

Basic Ingredients

1 medium onion	*1 litre stock or water*
2 sticks celery	*Pepper/salt*
25 g butter	*Bouquet garni*
or margarine	*250 ml milk*
25 g flour	

For Potato Soup
(see variations below)

500 g potatoes	*Finely chopped chives*
1-2 leeks	

Method

1. Prepare vegetables — wash, peel (if necessary) and slice.
2. Melt fat; add vegetables.
3. Sauté gently for about 5 mins. Do not brown.
4. Add stock, seasoning and bouquet garni.
5. Bring to the boil, cover and simmer gently for about 40 minutes — until vegetables are soft.
6. Remove bouquet garni; sieve or blend in liquidiser.
7. Blend flour with a little milk or water.
8. Return with soup to rinsed saucepan; bring to boil and simmer for 5 minutes.
9. Add enough milk to give correct colour and consistency. Reheat, but do not boil.
10. Serve in a warmed soup tureen or in individual soup bowls. Sprinkle with chopped chives or parsley.

Variations

Celery soup: 1 small head of celery, washed and chopped.
Mushroom soup: 250 g mushrooms, squeeze of lemon, 1 teasp. mushroom ketchup.
Tomato soup: 400 g fresh tomatoes or 1 can tinned tomatoes, 1 dessertsp. tomatoe purée, 1 sliced carrot, Basil.
Lentil soup: 100 g washed lentils, 1 medium carrot, sliced.
Cauliflower soup: 1 small head cauliflower

Meat Purée

(basic recipe)

Ingredients

250 g lean stewing meat (see variations below)	25 g dripping
1 litre stock or water	25 g flour
1 medium onion	Pepper, salt
1 medium carrot	Bouquet garni
2 sticks celery	1 dessertspoon
3 or 4 mushrooms (optional)	ketchup or savoury sauce, e.g. H.P.

Method

1. Remove skin, fat and bone from meat. Mince or chop finely. Steep in cold stock for an hour.
2. Prepare vegetables according to kind, and slice or chop.
3. Melt dripping in saucepan, fry vegetables until browned (5 minutes).
4. Add stock, meat, seasoning, bouquet garni and ketchup. Bring to boil. Simmer gently for $1\frac{1}{2}$ – 2 hours.
5. Remove bouquet garni and sieve or blend in liquidiser.
6. Blend flour with a little cold water, return to rinsed saucepan with soup. Add browning, if necessary.
7. Bring to the boil, stirring all the time. Cook for 5 minutes.
8. Serve in a hot soup tureen, or soup bowls. Sprinkle with finely chopped parsley.

Variations (instead of 250 g stewing meat)

Liver soup: Use 250 g liver, brown stock.
Kidney soup: Use 150 g Kidney, 100 g minced beef, brown stock.
Oxtail soup: Use 1 oxtail, fat removed, brown stock.
Cream of Chicken soup: Use 150 g chicken flesh, chicken stock. Omit carrot, ketchup. Serve with cream on top.

Broths

(basic recipe)

Ingredients

200 g stewing meat	2 sticks celery
1 litre stock or water	Pepper, salt
25 g pearl barley or rice	1 tablespoon peas
1 small carrot	Finely chopped
1 medium onion	parsley

Method

1. Wipe meat, remove fat and spinal cord. Cut meat into small pieces.

2. Prepare and dice vegetables. Wash barley or rice in sieve.
3. Put meat, bones (if any), stock or water, barley and seasoning into a saucepan. Bring to the boil.
4. Simmer for 1 hour, skimming now and then.
5. Add vegetables (except peas) and cook for 1 hour, adding peas for final 10 minutes.
6. Remove meat and bones, chop leanest meat into small pieces.
7. Remove grease by drawing kitchen paper over surface of broth. Correct seasoning.
8. Serve in a hot soup tureen, or soup bowls. Sprinkle with chopped parsley.

Variations

Beef Broth: Use leg beef, brown stock.
Mutton (Scotch) broth: Use neck of mutton, water.
Chicken broth: Use chicken stock, a little left over chicken meat and 30–40 g rice. Cook for 45 minutes altogether, adding the vegetables at the start.

Thickened Soup (Mixed Vegetable)
(basic recipe)

Ingredients

A mixture of vegetables (c. 400–500 g) e.g.

  1 medium onion
  1 medium carrot
  1 medium potato
  1 medium parsnip
  2 sticks celery
  1 leek
  1 tablespoon frozen peas
  25 g butter or margarine
  25 g flour or cornflour
  1 litre stock
  Pepper, salt
  Bouquet garni
  Chopped parsley
  125 ml milk (optional)

Method

1. Wash and peel vegetables (if necessary).
2. Melt margarine, sauté vegetables for 5 minutes. Do not brown.
3. Add stock, seasonings and bouquet garni; bring to boil, simmer until vegetables are soft — about 40 minutes.
5. Blend flour with a little cold milk, and add to soup.
6. Remove bouquet garni, bring to the boil, boil for 5 minutes.
7. Stir in remaining milk if required and heat without boiling.
8. Serve in warm soup tureen, or in individual soup bowls, with a blob of cream on top. Sprinkle with chopped parsley.

French Onion Soup
(An easy thickened soup from France)

Ingredients

25 g butter/margarine
$\frac{1}{2}$ *kg. large onions*
50 g flour
1 litre brown stock
Salt, pepper

To serve:

4 slices French/Vienna bread
50 g Cheddar cheese (grated)

For special occasions:

1 tablespoon sherry or brandy

Method

1. Peel and slice onions thinly. Slice bread, grate cheese.
2. Melt fat and fry onions until soft and golden.
3. Stir in flour and cook gently for one minute, stirring all the time.

4. Gradually stir in stock and bring to the boil. Season.
5. Lower heat and simmer for about 25 minutes, until onions are soft.
6. Toast bread.
7. Pour soup into individual soup bowls, float a slice of toast on each, sprinkle with grated cheese and place under a preheated grill, until cheese is soft and starts to bubble.

Fish Chowder

(A filling fish soup/stew from the United States)

Ingredients

400 g smoked cod or haddock	1 medium potato
1 medium onion	25 g margarine
1 medium carrot	25 g flour
2 sticks celery	1 pt. fish stock
	Pepper and salt

To serve: **For special occasions:**
25 g grated cheddar   *A few shrimps*
or blob of cream

Method

1. Wipe fish, skin if necessary, remove bones and cut in 2 cm chunks.
2. Scrub, peel and dice potatoes and carrot; wash and dice celery; peel and chop onion.
3. Melt margarine, sauté vegetables, without browning, for about five minutes.
4. Add flour and seasoning, cook over a low heat for 2–3 minutes.
5. Add stock very slowly, stirring all the time, reduce heat and simmer for 20 minutes — until vegetables are cooked.
6. Add fish and prawns (if used) and simmer for 5–10 minutes, until fish is cooked.
7. Serve in a warm soup tureen (or individual bowls) garnished with a blob of cream and/or grated cheese.

Simple Starters

The reason for serving an appetiser at the beginning of a meal is to stimulate the appetite. The first course of a meal should be served attractively, in small amounts. The most usual first course is soup — but here are some alternative suggestions, which are suitable for warm days when soup would be too hot and filling.

Hors d'oeuvre

(This is a selection of tasty mouthfuls of food which can be served on individual plates or arranged attractively on a large dish.)

Suitable foods are:
Fresh raw or cooked vegetables tossed in dressing: *e.g.* tomatoes, lettuce, fresh beans, beetroot.
Fish: *e.g.* sardines, smoked salmon.
Meat: cold cooked meats, *e.g.* ham, salami, chicken.
Fruit: *e.g.* melon, grapefruit or mixed fruits.

Smoked Mackerel Paté

Ingredients

300 g smoked mackerel	2 teaspoons lemon juice
Pepper, salt	75 g cream cheese
75 g butter	1 teaspoon tomato purée

Method

1. Place fish in bowl, pour boiling water over and stand for 1 minute. Drain well. Remove skin and bones.
2. Flake with two forks, then mix in butter, cheese, seasoning, juice and purée, until a smooth paste, or blend in liquidiser.
3. Place in a small dish, garnish with cucumber or lemon slices and parsley.
4. Serve with triangles of toast.

Seafood Cocktail

Ingredients

300 g white fish, e.g. cod
A few lettuce leaves

Dressing:

3 tablespoons mayonnaise
1 teaspoon tomato purée
Worcester sauce or lemon juice
Paprika pepper

Method

1. Poach fish gently for about 5 minutes. Drain well and cool.
2. Shred lettuce leaves and arrange in a sundae glass.
3. Add flaked fish. Blend dressing ingredients and pour over.
4. Garnish with lemon slices and parsley.
5. Sprinkle with paprika.

Liver Paté

Ingredients

350 g chicken livers	*1 teaspoon sherry*
1 clove garlic	*1 small onion*
25 g margarine	*Salt/pepper*

Method

1. Trim chicken livers, wash in warm water and dry in kitchen paper.

2. Melt margarine, sauté livers gently until they begin to brown.
3. Peel and chop onion, add to liver with garlic. Cook for 5 minutes.
4. Cool slightly and stir in sherry and seasoning.
5. Rub mixture through sieve, or liquidise.
6. Put into small dish. Chill. Garnish with lettuce, tomato and parsley. Serve with melba toast or fingers of hot or cold toast.

Cheese and Ham Rolls

Ingredients

4 slices cooked ham
Small tin of pineapple slices
1 small carton cream or cottage cheese
Lettuce leaves

Method

1. Chop 2 slices of pineapple into small pieces and mix with cheese.
2. Spread cheese over ham slices and roll up.
3. Wash lettuce leaves well, shake dry and arrange on a small serving dish.
4. Place ham rolls on lettuce and decorate with 4 slices of pineapple.

Over to you . . .

1. Compare homemade stock with stock cubes. List your answer in points.

2. In your vegetable rack, at home, you have 2 onions, some celery and 300 g french beans. There is some fresh chicken stock in the fridge. Using basic store cupboard ingredients, write a recipe for soup modal from these ingredients.

3. Make up a simple recipe for a hors d'oeuvre
   (a) using fish;
   (b) using mixed vegetables;
   (c) using fruit.

8 All About Meat

Because meat is the most expensive food in our diet it is important to know all about it if we are to get best value for money. Meat comes from:

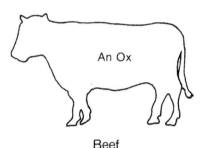

An Ox

Beef

A Sheep

Mutton, Lamb

A Pig

Pork, Bacon

We also eat:

Poultry — chicken, turkey, duck.
Game — wild birds and animals, *e.g.* deer.

Food Value of Meat

Meat is a very nourishing food. It contains:

Protein: in the lean parts — it is one of our main body building foods.
Fat: visible fat around the edges of meat and invisible fat between fibres.
B group Vitamins
Iron, phosphorus and **Calcium:** Large amounts of iron are present in beef, corned beef, liver and kidneys.
About 60% water: but there is less in fatty cuts of meat.

Because meat has **no carbohydrate** we usually serve it with a starchy food *e.g.* potatoes, spaghetti or rice.

Structure of Meat

Look at a piece of meat — it is made up of long fibres filled with meat juices. These are held together with a tough, indigestible tissue called **connective tissue.** If we ate meat raw, we would find it difficult to chew and digest this tissue, as it makes the meat tough. Cooking dissolves it and makes it easy to digest.

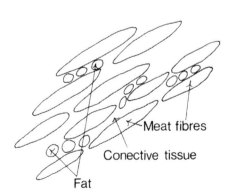

Meat fibres

Conective tissue

Fat

Some meat has short fibres with little connective tissue. This comes from parts of the animal which are not very active — the back, for example. Other cuts, from the more active parts of the animal, *e.g.* neck and legs, have long sinewy fibres and more connective tissue.

Hanging Meat

Soon after animals are killed their muscles stiffen and become tough. In order to make meat nice and tender, the butcher hangs it in a cold store for a few days. During this time acids within the meat break down the fibres and make them tender.

Value for Money

Most meat is expensive, but some cuts are much dearer than others. Why?

The **most expensive cuts** are usually very lean and tender; they have a fine grain, little connective tissue and can be cooked by the quickest methods, such as grilling, frying or roasting.

The **cheaper cuts** are tougher or have more fat and must be cooked by moist gentle cooking, such as stewing, in order to make them tender. Cheaper cuts are sometimes minced by the butcher; as this breaks down the fibres, they can then be cooked at higher temperatures *e.g.* grilled hamburgers. Cheap cuts have a good flavour and are every bit as nourishing as expensive cuts. Liver and kidney are very good value, as they are cheap and they have little waste.

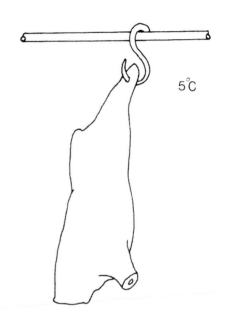

If meat is not hung for long enough, it will be tough, and no amount of cooking will make it tender. A good butcher will hang meat for the correct time before he sells it.

You can help to tenderise meat before cooking it by beating it with a wooden spoon or steak hammer.

Composition of Cooked Meat   *Table 8.1*

Water	Protein	Fat	Carbohydrate	Vitamins	Minerals
50–60%*	20–25%	20%	0%	B group	Iron/Phosphorus/Calcium

Raw meat contains more water than cooked.

Beef

Beef — from an ox (cow)	Veal — from a calf
Colour: *Lean* — bright red with specks of fat. *Fat* — cream	**Colour:** *Lean* — pale pink *Fat* — white

Grilling/Frying: Sirloin
T-bone
Fillet steaks
Mince

Boiling: Tailend
Silverside (corned beef)
Brisket

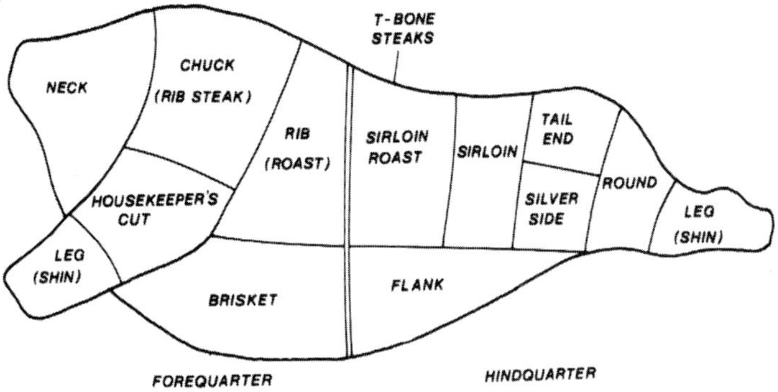

Stewing: Neck
Leg
Flank
Ribsteak
Round

Soups/Stock: Leg
Neck

Roasting: Sirloin
Rib
Silverside
Housekeepers cut

Mince: Quality varies. It is safest to buy lean stewing beef and ask the butcher to mince it for you.

Mutton/Lamb

Mutton — from a sheep over 1 year Lamb — from a sheep under 1 year	**Colour:** *Lean* — dark red *Fat* — hard, waxy, pearly white

Soup: Neck

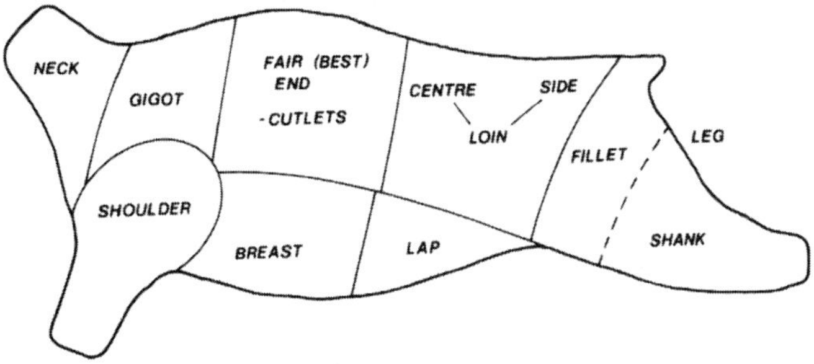

Roasting: Leg – fillet or shank
Rolled stuffed breast
Fair-end – in piece
Loin – in piece
Shoulder – boned
and stuffed

Boiling: Leg
Shoulder

Stewing: Neck
Gigot
Breast

Grilling/Frying: Fair-end cutlets
Centre Loin chops
Side loin chops

Pork

Pork — fresh meat from a pig	Colour: *Lean* — pale pink, fine grain *Fat* — pearly white — no dis-coloured spots *Rind* — smooth and thin. Ask the butcher to score it.

Boiling: Leg
Shoulder
(pork is not usually boiled)

Stewing: Gigot
Belly

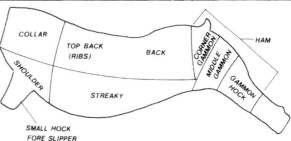

Grilling/Frying: Loin chops
Rib chops

Roasting: Leg
Fillet
Loin
Shoulder
Belly
Porksteak (tender loin)

Also from pork: sausages, brawn, black and white pudding, tongue.

Note: Pork must *always* be thoroughly cooked.

Bacon

Bacon — salted (cured) meat from a pig. It is sometimes smoked.	Colour: *Lean* — bright pink *Fat* — pinkish white *Rind* — thin, smooth (smoked bacon has a darker rind).

Stewing: Streaky
Shank
(Not usually stewed although a little bacon is often added to other meat stews for extra flavour.)

Boiling: Head
Feet
Collar
Shoulder
Streaky
Flank
Gammon

Baking: Ham
Grilling/Frying: Back rashers
Streaky rashers
Loin
Gammon steaks

Meat Matters

Buying Meat

1. Buy from a butcher who keeps a **clean shop** and sells **good quality meat.** A Butcher should not handle money, nor sell cooked meat with raw meat — this could cause food poisoning.
2. Choose a cut of meat **suitable for the dish** you are cooking.
3. Remember to **allow for bone and fat** when working out how much you need.
4. Ask to see both sides of a joint — **there should not be too much bone and gristle.**
5. Remember **cheaper cuts are just as nutritious** as expensive cuts.
6. **Flesh should be firm, elastic and slightly moist,** with no beads of moisture on the surface.
7. Meat should be **well hung** — it should **look clean** with **no smell.**

Storing meat

Much of the meat we buy contains bacteria. If we are careless about buying and storing meat we can get **food poisoning.**

1. **Use meat quickly** — ideally within 1–2 days.
2. **Offal** (liver, kidneys, *etc.*) and minced meat should be **used on the day** you buy them, as they don't keep well.
3. Bacon will keep for a few days, sausages and cooked meat for 2–3 days.
4. **Store meat in a cool place** (a refrigerator is ideal).
5. Remove from butcher's wrappings, place on a plate and **cover loosely with polythene or foil** to prevent it drying out.
6. If you buy meat and cannot use it up quickly, either freeze it or cook it at once. **Do not half cook it** and finish the cooking another day. This is very dangerous.
7. **Cooked meat should be cooled quickly,** placed on a clean dish, **covered with cling film or foil** and stored in the refrigerator.

Accompaniments

Over the years, people have discovered that certain sauces and flavourings go very well with particular meats. These are called **accompaniments.**

For example:

Roast Beef:	*Yorkshire Pudding; Horseradish sauce*
Roast Lamb:	*Mint sauce*
Roast Mutton:	*Red currant jelly or Onion sauce*
Roast Pork:	*Apple sauce*
Roast Chicken:	*Bread sauce; Bacon rolls*
Roast Duck:	*Sage and onion stuffing; Orange sauce*
Roast Turkey:	*Sausage or Chestnut stuffing; Bread or Cranberry sauce*
Boiled Bacon:	*Cabbage; White or Parsley sauce.*

These accompaniments are traditional — but you do not have to serve them. You may not like horseradish sauce, or your family may like to eat Yorkshire pudding with all roast meat. It's really a matter of personal taste.

A **green salad** is a good accompaniment to most meats. It is nourishing and provides a nice contrast in colour, flavour and texture.

Why do we cook meat?

1. To make it tender and more digestible.
2. To make it look and taste more attractive.
3. To make it safer, killing bacteria.

Effects of Cooking

1. Surface protein coagulates and seals in juices.
2. Connective tissue softens and meat becomes more digestible.
3. Colour changes, usually red to brown.
4. Meat develops an attractive appearance, odour and flavour.
5. Fat melts.
6. Some juices are lost, and meat shrinks.
7. Overcooking toughens and dries out meat, making it indigestible.
8. Bacteria are destroyed, and so meat keeps longer.

Preparation of Meat for Cooking

1. Defrost frozen meat in plenty of time. Most poultry and joints will take several hours to defrost.
2. Remove meat from refrigerator 1 hour before cooking.
3. Trim gristle and extra fat, wipe with damp kitchen paper.
4. Weigh, if necessary, to calculate cooking time.

Offal

Most of the meat we eat comes from the carcase or flesh of the animal. Many of the internal organs can also be eaten — together these are called **offal**. Many of these cuts have a higher food value than meat. They are cheaper than carcase meat and, as there is little waste (no bone or fat for example); most are very good value for money.

Offal includes heart, liver, kidney, sweetbreads, tripe, head, feet, brains, tongue and oxtail.

The most frequently eaten are liver and kidney, and these are also the most nourishing.

Liver: is very rich in protein, iron and Vitamins A and B. Lamb's and calf's liver have the best flavour and can be grilled or fried. Ox liver is very strongly flavoured, coarse in texture and only used in stews.

Kidneys: also rich in protein, iron and Vitamins A and B. Sheep's or lamb's kidneys are best for grilling and frying. Ox kidney, much larger and strongly flavoured, is used in stews and pies, such as *Steak and Kidney Pie.*

Heart: rich in protein, iron and Vitamin B, sheep's heart is usually stuffed and braised, stewed or pot roasted.

Sweetbreads: are glands, usually from a lamb or calf. They are tender and very digestible.

Tripe: is the lining of the stomach of an ox, which is prepared and partly cooked by the butcher. It is then gently stewed, with onions, to make a very digestible meal.

Rules for using Offal

1. Offal must be eaten very fresh — it goes off quickly.
2. Wash well in tepid salted water. Strongly flavoured offal, such as ox liver or kidney, can be soaked for an hour or two before cooking. Dry in kitchen paper, before cooking.
3. Remove any fat, blood vessels and membranes — a kitchen scissors is best for this job.
4. Cook gently to prevent toughening.

Meat Products

Sausages are made from minced pork or beef, fat, cereal and seasoning. Although they contain preservatives, they must be eaten quickly (within three days).
N.B. Cook sausages thoroughly — to avoid danger of food poisoning.
Black pudding is made from pig's blood, fat and seasonings.
White pudding is made from minced pork and internal organs, cereal and seasoning.

Fats from Meat

Suet: the inside fat of an ox or sheep. Can be melted down to make dripping.
Dripping: melted down suet, or drippings of fat from roasting meat.
Lard: the inside fat of a pig, melted down and cooled. Used for roasting meat and pastry making.

Boiled Meat

Boiled Bacon and Cabbage

Ingredients

1 kg collar or streaky bacon
1 head cabbage
Cold water
Browned crumbs
Knob of butter
Seasoning

To serve:
Onion Sauce, p. 111.

Method

1. Wipe meat and tie into shape.
2. Steep bacon for 1–2 hours, or overnight.
3. Put into a saucepan and barely cover with cold water.
4. Bring slowly to the boil, boil for 5 mins, skim, reduce heat and simmer for 1 hour and 15 mins (25 mins per $\frac{1}{2}$ kilo + 25 mins over).
5. Lift out, drain, remove skin, cover fat with breadcrumbs and place under a medium grill to brown and crisp surface.
6. Trim and wash the cabbage well under running water. Add to boiling bacon water, cook until tender but not too soft.
7. Drain in colander, chop well with knife.
8. Melt a knob of butter in saucepan, add seasoning, sauté cabbage in butter for a few seconds, then empty into a hot vegetable dish.
9. Serve bacon on hot dish. Serve onion sauce separately in a hot sauceboat.

> *Note:* Follow the same recipe for cooking ham or corned beef.

Boiled Mutton and Root Vegetables

Ingredients

1$\frac{1}{2}$ kg. leg mutton
4 carrots
Saucepan of water
1 swede turnip

To serve:

Parsley sauce

Times for Boiling Meat   *Table 8.2*

Fresh Meat	Salt Meat	Chicken
20 mins per ½ kilo + 20 mins over	25 mins per ½ kilo + 25 mins over	15 mins per ½ kilo + 15 mins over

Method

1. Put water on to boil.
2. Wipe, trim, weigh and calculate cooking time.
3. Tie meat in shape, if necessary.
4. Lower carefully into water, return to boil and start timing.
5. Simmer gently for 1 hour 20 mins (20 mins per $\frac{1}{2}$ kilo + 20 mins over).
6. Wash, peel and slice vegetables. Dice turnip. Add to meat about 25 mins before serving time. Cook until tender.
7. Drain meat and vegetables in colander.
8. Place meat on a hot dish surrounded by vegetables, or carve meat and serve on individual plates. Serve vegetables separately in a hot vegetable dish. Garnish with parsley.
9. Serve parsley sauce in a hot sauceboat.

Irish Stew

Ingredients

500 g breast of mutton
  or 4 medium gigot chops
2 large onions
2 sticks celery
1 kg potatoes
Salt/pepper
375 ml cold water
1 tablespoon parsley (chopped)

To garnish:

Parsley

Method

1. Wipe and trim meat and remove bones.
2. Cut breast of mutton into thin slices, gigot chops may be cut up or left whole.
3. Wash, trim and slice celery. Peel and slice onions.
4. Wash and peel potatoes. Cut one potato in thin slices and use these to cover the base of the stewpan.
5. Arrange meat and onions in layers; adding seasoning and a little parsley between each layer.
6. Add water, bring to boil; skim, reduce heat, simmer for 1 hour.
7. Arrange potatoes on top, halving any large ones and simmer for 30–40 mins more.
8. Place meat and onions in the centre of a hot dish, arrange potatoes around the dish.
9. Pour a little sauce over. Serve extra sauce in a hot sauceboat.
10. Garnish with parsley.

Hot Pot

(a regional dish from Lancashire)

Ingredients

As for Irish Stew, with the addition of 2-3 carrots

Method

Prepare as for Irish stew, arrange ingredients in layers in a casserole, cover and cook in a moderate oven for 2 hours. Remove lid for last half hour, if wished, to brown potatoes.

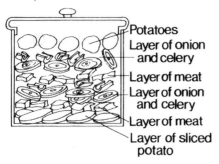

Potatoes
Layer of onion and celery
Layer of meat
Layer of onion and celery
Layer of meat
Layer of sliced potato

Brown or Beef Stew

Ingredients

400 g round, rib or neck beef
2 medium onions
2–3 medium carrots
2 medium parsnips
25 g dripping
25 g flour
375 ml brown stock
Pepper/salt
1 dessertspoon savoury sauce
  e.g. Tomato ketchup, H.P.

To garnish:

Parsley

Method

1. Wipe meat, trim away bone, gristle and extra fat. Cut in 3 cm pieces.
2. Scrub carrots and parsnip. Peel vegetables thinly and slice.
3. Melt dripping in a heavy stew pan. Fry meat until lightly browned.
4. Add onion and fry until beginning to brown.
5. Reduce heat, stir in flour and cook gently for 1-2 minutes, stirring all the time.

6. Slowly stir in stock, and continue stirring until it boils.
7. Add carrots, parsnip, seasoning and sauce.
8. Cover and simmer gently for 1½-2 hours, Stir now and then.
9. Serve on a hot oval dish, with the meat in the centre and vegetables around it. Garnish with parsley.
10. Extra sauce can be strained and served in a hot sauce boat.

Beef Casserole

Made as for Beef Stew, but at *Stage 8* transfer to a casserole. Cover and cook in a very moderate oven, 175°C (350°F), Gas 4, for 2 hours. Serve in the casserole on a large dish.

Variation

Beef and Kidney Stew — add 100 g beef kidney, washed and dried.

Beef Goulash

(This is a Hungarian recipe using tomatoes and
paprika — a tasty red pepper)

Ingredients

400 g stewing beef or mutton
2 medium onions
1 red or green pepper
2 large tomatoes + 1 tsp. tomato purée
25 g dripping
25 g flour
1 dessertspoon paprika
375 ml stock
Pepper/salt
2 tablespoons soured cream
  or plain yoghurt (optional)

To serve:

Creamed potato or noodles

Method

1. Wipe, trim and cut meat into 3 cm pieces.
2. Peel and chop onion.
3. Remove seeds from pepper and chop.
4. Skin and slice tomatoes.
5. Melt dripping, add meat and fry until browned.
6. Add onion and fry for 1-2 minutes, stirring all the time.
7. Reduce heat, add flour and paprika and cook gently for 1-2 minutes, stirring all the time.
8. Slowly add stock and continue to stir until it comes to the boil.
9. Add pepper, tomatoes and seasoning. Cover and simmer gently for 1½-2 hours until meat is tender — on top of stove or in oven at 175°C (350°F), Gas 4.
10. Stir in soured cream or yoghurt and serve on an oval dish, surrounded by cooked noodles or piped mashed potato.

Goulash

Meat Curry

Ingredients

500 g stewing beef or mutton
2 onions
25 g cooking fat
25 g flour
1 tablespoon curry powder
  (or to taste)
250–375 ml stock
1 small cooking apple
1–2 tsp. chutney
1–2 tsp. lemon juice
1 tsp. tomato purée
25 g sultanas (optional)
Salt

To serve:

200 g rice

Method

1. Wipe, trim and cut meat into 3 cm pieces.
2. Peel and chop onion.
3. Melt fat, add meat and fry until browned.
4. Add onion and fry for 1-2 minutes. Reduce heat.
5. Add curry powder and flour, cook gently for 1-2 minutes, stirring all the time.
6. Slowly add stock and continue to stir until it comes to the boil.
7. Peel, core and chop apple, add to stew, together with chutney, lemon juice, tomato purée, sultanas (if using) and salt.
8. Simmer gently for 1½-2 hours, stirring now and then. Curry can be cooked on top of the stove or in the oven at 175°C (350°F), Gas 4.

Beef curry

To serve: Curry may be served on an oval dish surrounded by rice. Garnish with lemon and paprika.

In India — curry is served in a separate dish from the rice with lots of accompaniments (sambals) such as:–

chutney
stewed lentils
sliced bananas
    (dipped in lemon juice)
sliced hard boiled egg
sliced green and red peppers
thinly sliced onion
mixed nuts or coconut

Rabbit Stew

Ingredients

*1 rabbit**	*25 g flour*
100 g streaky bacon	*375 ml brown stock*
2 onions	*Salt/pepper*
2 tomatoes	*Pinch mixed herbs*
25 g dripping	

Method

1. *Cut prepared rabbit into joints and steep overnight in cold salted water.
2. Rinse joints and dry well in kitchen paper. Coat with seasoned flour.
3. Remove rind and bone from bacon and cut into small pieces.
4. Skin and slice onions. Skin and slice tomatoes.
5. Melt dripping and fry rashers in a heavy saucepan until beginning to brown.
6. Add rabbit pieces and fry until browned. Remove.
7. Add onions, fry for 1-2 mins, then flour for 1-2 mins, stirring all the time.
8. Slowly add stock, and continue to stir until it comes to the boil.
9. Return rabbit pieces, add tomatoes, seasoning and herbs and simmer gently until tender — 1½ hours.
10. Serve on a hot dish — garnish with parsley.

Steamed Meat

Steaming is rarely used to cook meat, except for invalids, as the meat tastes insipid and does not look very attractive.

Steamed Breast of Chicken

Ingredients

1 breast of chicken
Lemon juice
2 tablespoons cold water
Pepper and salt (if allowed)

Method

1. Remove breast from bone of chicken. .Skin.
2. Brush over with lemon juice and sprinkle with seasoning, if allowed.
3. Place on a lightly buttered plate and add water — to prevent chicken becoming dry.
4. Cover with another plate and steam over gently boiling water for about 40-45 minutes, until cooked.
5. Serve on a clean warmed plate, pouring cooking liquid over.
6. Serve with boiled potatoes and carrots. Garnish with parsley.

Grilled Meat

(Grilling is a quick, tasty way of cooking meat)

Don't forget! — preheat grill
Don't delay! — serve at once

Length of cooking times depends on type and thickness of meat and how well done you like it.

This chart will guide you: *Table 8.3*

Meat	Time	Temperature	Suggested Accompaniments
Steak (25 mm) (serve pink and juicy inside)	7-12 mins	High	Maître d'hotel butter; grilled tomatoes; French fried potatoes; green salad.
Lamb chops	8-12 mins	High	As above
Pork chops	15-20 mins	High then reduce to mod.	Apple sauce; grilled tomatoes
Gammon steak	7-10 mins	Mod. to high	Apple sauce or pineapple slice
Liver	5-6 mins	Mod. to high	Grilled bacon; tomatoes
Kidney	5-6 mins	Mod. to high	Maître d'hotel butter
Sausage	8-10 mins	Moderate	Bacon; mashed potato
Rasher	4-5 mins	Moderate	Sausage and tomato

Mixed Grill

Ingredients

1 lamb chop or cutlet
1 lamb's kidney
1 bacon rasher
1 slice liver
1 sausage

1 tomato, or a few
  mushrooms
Melted fat
Pepper

To serve:

Maître d'hotel butter

Method

1. Preheat grill.
2. Wipe chop, remove skin, excess fat and spinal cord.
3. Skin, core, wash and dry kidney. Skewer in flat shape.
4. Wash and dry liver, trim away blood vessels.
5. Remove rind and bone from rasher.
6. Cut tomato in half and remove stems. Wash and dry mushrooms.
7. Brush grid and food with melted fat. Season meat with pepper only (salt makes juices run).
8. Cook in this order under a hot grill:— cutlet; then liver and kidney; then sausage, rasher; and finally tomato and/or mushrooms, so that all cooking will be finished at the same time.
9. Serve at once, on a hot dish, garnish with parsley and maître d'hotel butter.
10. Serve with chipped potatoes and a green salad.

Kidney skewered for grilling

Grilled Steak

Ingredients per person

150 g sirloin or fillet steak
(25 mm thick)
Black pepper, freshly ground
Melted fat

To serve:

Mâitre d'hotel butter

Method

1. Preheat grill and brush with melted fat.
2. Wipe meat and trim away extra fat.
3. Brush with melted fat. Season with pepper.
4. Grill at 'high' for 3 minutes on each side, reduce heat to moderate and continue cooking until done, turning now and then with a tongs. Do not prick with a fork.
5. Serve on a hot dish, with mâitre d'hotel butter. Serve green salad and chipped, boiled, or baked potatoes as an accompaniment.

Kebabs

(A kebab is a Turkish dish made up of small pieces of meat and vegetables threaded on skewers and cooked under a hot grill. They are usually served on a bed of rice.)

Ingredients

400 g lamb fillet, rump steak or pork steak
1 large onion   *Melted fat*
A few bayleaves   *4 small tomatoes*

Marinade:

Pepper and salt   *2 tablespoons lemon juice*
1 tablespoon oil   *Pinch mixed herbs*

Method

1. Wipe meat, trim off fat and cut into 4 cm cubes.
2. Peel and slice onion into sections.
3. Place meat in a bowl with onion, herbs, seasoning, oil and lemon juice. Cover and leave in a cold place for 2 hours, or overnight.
4. Wash tomatoes and bayleaves.
5. Thread pieces of meat, onion and bayleaf alternatively, on 4 long kebab skewers.
6. Preheat grill, brush grid and kebabs with melted fat.
7. Grill for about 15 minutes. Turning once. Add one tomato to the end of each skewer for about 5 minutes before the end of cooking time.
8. Serve on a bed of freshly boiled brown or white rice, with a side salad as an accompaniment.
9. Barbeque sauce goes well with this dish.

Variations

1. Add chunks of pineapple to pork kebabs.
2. Thread rolls of steaky rashers and cocktail sausages on skewers for children's kebabs.
3. Make 'mixed grill' kebabs, using cubes of liver, mushroom and kidney.

> *Note:* Tomatoes are best added at the end — as they get too soft and fall off skewers if cooked from the beginning.

Fried Meat

Only best quality meat should be fried.

Remember!
Dry — before you fry
Drain — after frying

Use this chart as a guide   *Table 8.4*

Meat (not more than 25 mm thick)	Time	Accompaniments
Lamb chops or cutlets	10-15 mins	Fried tomatoes, boiled potatoes, green salad
Pork chops	12-15 mins	Apple sauce, green salad
Steak	7-10 mins	Fried onions or mushrooms, green salad
Bacon rashers	3-5 mins	Fried eggs, sauté potatoes
Gammon steaks	7-10 mins	Fried apple or tinned pineapple, green salad
Kidneys	4-5 mins	Fried bacon, green salad
Liver	5-7 mins	Fried bacon, green salad
Sausages	10-12 mins	Mashed potato, gravy

Fried foods tend to be greasy. Avoid eating them too often. Avoid serving other greasy foods, such as fried potatoes, with fried meat or fish. Instead, serve boiled or creamed potatoes, a boiled vegetable, *e.g.* sprouts or carrots, and a crisp green side salad. Gravy can be made from meat juices remaining in the pan.

Bangers and Mash

(A well known British national dish, ideal for young children, made up of sausages and mashed potato.)

Ingredients

2–3 sausages per person
25 g dripping
1 kg potatoes
Pepper and salt
2 tablespoons milk, knob of butter

Method

1. Scrub, peel and halve large potatoes.
2. Put to cook in a saucepan of boiling salted water.
3. Melt dripping in frying pan, fry sausages over a moderate heat until nicely browned (about 15 mins.). It is important to cook sausages thoroughly.
4. When potatoes are soft, drain well, return to saucepan and cover with a clean dry teatowel — to dry them out.
5. Mash well, using potato masher; add pepper, salt, butter and milk, and cream with a wooden spoon.

6. Pile onto the centre of a warmed dish. Score with a fork and stand sausages all around.
7. Garnish with sliced tomato and parsley.
8. Serve thick brown gravy, or homemade tomato sauce, separately, in a hot sauce boat.

Tasty Recipes Using Mince

Hamburgers

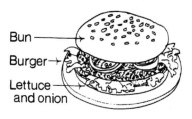

Bun —
Burger →
Lettuce —
and onion

Fried Steak and Onions

Ingredients

150–200 g steak per person
  (sirloin or fillet)
2 large onions
Freshly ground black pepper
A little fat

Garnish:

Parsley or watercress

Method

1. Wipe steak, sprinkle with pepper. Peel and slice onions into rings.
2. Melt fat in heavy frying pan, add steak, and fry quickly on both sides until well browned.
3. Reduce heat and continue frying for 7-10 minutes in all. Turn 3 or 4 times using a tongs.
4. Lift onto a hot plate.
5. Fry onions in remaining fat until soft and golden brown (about 3-4 minutes). Drain well.
6. Pour remaining fat from pan. Stir in stock and season. Bring to boil. Strain into a hot sauce boat.
7. Serve steak on a hot dish, with onions to one side. Garnish with lettuce leaves and tomato.

Ingredients

400 g minced beef
1 small onion
Pepper/salt
1 small egg, beaten
Lettuce leaves ⎫
Onion rings ⎭ *to serve*

To fry:

Dripping or cooking fat

Method

1. Peel and grate onion (or chop very finely).
2. Put beef, onion and seasoning into a bowl, moisten with beaten egg. Mix well.
3. Turn onto floured board, shape into 4 'cakes' and press well together.
4. Melt fat, add hamburgers and fry until brown (5 minutes on each side). Reduce heat and continue cooking for 10 more minutes, until cooked through.
5. Drain well on kitchen paper and serve (a) in a toasted hamburger bun, including a lettuce leaf, slice of raw onion and some relish, *e.g.* tomato sauce, H.P. sauce or chutney, or, (b) on a hot plate with chipped or mashed potatoes. Garnish with lettuce and tomato.

Note: Hamburgers may also be grilled.

Meat Balls in Spicy Sauce

Ingredients

400 g minced beef
50 g breadcrumbs
1 small onion, finely grated
1 clove of garlic, crushed (optional)
1 dessertsp. finely chopped parsley
25 g grated cheese
1 egg, beaten
½ teaspoon salt
Pepper

Sauce:

Brown stewing sauce
*   or 1 packet or can of oxtail soup*

To fry:

A little dripping

Method

1. Mix beef, breadcrumbs, onion, garlic, parsley, cheese and seasoning together in a bowl.
2. Moisten with beaten egg.
3. Shape into about 16 balls (the size of a walnut) on a floured board.
4. Melt dripping, fry meat balls gently on all sides until brown (for about 10 minutes). Drain well.
5. Make sauce or make up soup according to directions on packet or tin.
6. Place meat balls into casserole, pour sauce over and place in a moderate oven — 175°C (350°F), Gas 4 — for about 45 minutes.
7. Serve in a casserole with baked potatoes (bake them with the meatballs in the oven) and peas or French beans.

Variations

1. Make up a curry sauce (*see p. 112*) and cook meatballs in this. Serve with boiled rice.
2. Cook in a tomato sauce.

Meat Loaf

Ingredients

400 g minced lean beef
100 g sausage meat
1 level teaspoon salt
Pepper
1 medium onion
Good pinch nutmeg
1 beaten egg
⅛ teaspoon mixed herbs
1 teaspoon finely chopped parsley
1 clove garlic (optional)
1 teaspoon savoury sauce, e.g. H.P.
1–2 tablespoons stock
Browned crumbs

To serve:

Tomato sauce

Method

1. Peel and grate onion.
2. Place meat and all other ingredients in a bowl and mix well, moistening with beaten egg.
3. Grease a loaf tin and dust with browned crumbs.
4. Pack mixture into tin, pressing well down.

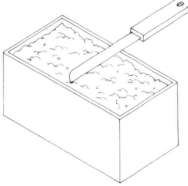

5. Cover with foil and bake for ¾–1 hour in a moderate oven 180°C (350°F), Gas 4, until firm to touch.
6. Make tomato sauce (*see p. 113*).
7. Turn meat loaf onto a hot dish and pour sauce around it. Garnish with parsley and tomato lilies.

Spaghetti alla Bolognese

Ingredients

200 g spaghetti
1 tablespoon olive oil

Sauce:

1 tablespoon cooking oil
1 medium onion
1 clove garlic, crushed
200 g minced beef
5 large ripe tomatoes
  or 1 can tomatoes (drained)
150 ml stock or liquid from tomatoes
Pepper and salt
Oregano, majoram, or mixed herbs

To serve:

Parmesan cheese
  or grated Cheddar cheese

> *Note:* Oregano and marjoram are two
> quite similar herbs, often used in
> Italian dishes to give them an
> authentic Italian taste. If you
> have neither, mixed herbs are
> fine.

Method

1. Peel and chop onion finely. Skin tomatoes and chop.
2. Heat oil in medium-sized saucepan; fry mince until beginning to brown (about 7 minutes).
3. Add onion and garlic and fry until golden.
4. Add tomatoes, seasoning and stock, bring to boil, then simmer gently for about 30 minutes.
5. Meanwhile cook spaghetti in boiling salted water until soft (about 12 mins.). Drain and toss in oil.
6. Serve spaghetti in a hot dish with the sauce poured into a hollow in the centre.
7. Sprinkle with grated cheese.

Roast Meat

Follow rules on p. 46.

Roast Beef

Ingredients
1½ kg ribs or sirloin
50 g dripping
4 medium potatoes

Gravy:
250 ml brown stock
Pepper/salt

To serve:
Horseradish sauce
Thin brown gravy
Yorkshire pudding
Roast potatoes

Method

1. Wipe, trim and weigh meat, calculate cooking time.
2. Tie or skewer in shape, with metal skewers.
3. Melt dripping in oven. When hot, place meat on grid over roasting tin, baste with hot fat, and cook at 230°C (450°F), Gas 8, for 20 mins. Reduce and cook for 1 hour (20 mins per 500 kg and 20 mins over). Cover with foil if wished, but, if so, allow an extra 20 mins.
4. Scrub and peel potatoes. Par-boil for 5 minutes. Drain and place in hot fat 1 hour before meat is cooked.
5. Place cooked meat on hot carving dish, with roast potatoes around it. Keep hot while making gravy.

Thin Brown Gravy

1. Pour off extra fat, keeping back about 1-2 tablespoons of sediment from meat.
2. Add stock and seasoning, stir well and bring to boil.
3. Simmer for 2 minutes, then strain into hot sauceboat.

Roasting Chart

Use this chart as a guide: *Table 8.5*

Meat:	Slow Roasting: 175°C (350°F), Gas 4	Quick Roasting: 230°C (450°F) Gas 7 (reduce to 190°C (375°F) Gas 5 after 20 mins)
Beef — ribs, sirloin	35 mins per 500 g	20 mins per 500 g + 20 mins over (15 mins per 500 g + 15 for rare beef)
Mutton/Lamb — loin, leg, shoulder, breast	35 mins per 500 g	25 mins per 500 g + 25 mins over
Pork — leg, loin	50 mins per 500 g	30-35 mins per 500 g + 30 mins over

Roast Stuffed Shoulder or Breast of Mutton

Ingredients

1½ kg shoulder or breast of lamb or mutton
50 g fat

Stuffing:

100 g breadcrumbs
1 dessertspoon chopped parsley
¼ teaspoon dried sage or herbs
1 small onion
Pepper and salt
25 g margarine
A little stock to moisten

To serve:

Thickened Brown Gravy, p. 112

Method

1. Chop onion finely. Put breadcrumbs into bowl, add parsley, herbs, onion, seasoning and mix well.
2. Moisten with melted margarine, and a little stock if necessary. Stuffing should cling together without being too moist.
3. Wipe, trim and remove bones from meat if necessary.
4. Press stuffing into boned side of meat and roll or fold up tightly. Secure with twine or skewers.

5. Weigh and calculate cooking time.
6. Roast by slow method — for 2 hours 20 minutes at 175°C (350°F) Gas 4.
7. Drain and remove twine or skewers. Place on a warm dish while making gravy.
8. Serve with roast or baked potatoes, and red currant jelly. Thickened gravy is served in a hot sauce boat.

Roast Stuffed Porksteak

Ingredients

2 porksteaks weighing a total of 1 kg
50 g dripping

Stuffing:

As for Roast Mutton

To serve:

Thick brown gravy, p. 112
Apple sauce, p. 113
Roast potatoes

Method

1. Preheat oven, melt dripping in roasting tin.
2. Trim meat, wipe, weigh. Make stuffing.

3. Lay one porksteak on chopping board, press stuffing onto it and cover with a second porksteak. Tie securely with twine, or stitch with needle and strong thread.
4. Roast at 230°C (450°F), Gas 8, for 20 minutes, reduce heat and cook at moderate heat for a further hour. Potatoes are added at this stage.
5. Half an hour before meat is ready, make apple sauce.
6. Drain meat, remove twine and keep warm while making gravy.
7. Carve meat neatly and arrange on a heated dish.
8. Serve apple sauce and gravy in warmed sauce boats.

Pot Roasted Heart
(see rules, p. 47)

Ingredients

4 sheeps' hearts
50 g dripping

Stuffing:

As for *Baked Liver and Bacon (see next recipe).*

To serve:

Thick brown gravy, p. 112

Method

1. Make stuffing and moisten with stock. *(see Roast Mutton, p. 84).*
2. Cut away bloodvessels and fat, using a scissors, and cutting the central dividing wall of hearts.
3. Wash well in several changes of warm water, making sure all blood is removed. Wipe dry with kitchen paper.
4. Press stuffing into hearts and stitch opening securely, or tie doubled tin foil securely over opening with twine.
5. Melt fat in heavy stewpan and brown meat on all sides.
6. Cover and cook over a **very moderate** heat for about 45 minutes to 1 hour,

depending on size. Turn and shake gently now and then, to prevent sticking.
7. Drain, remove thread or foil and keep warm while making gravy.
8. Arrange hearts on a warmed dish, pour a little gravy around them and serve the remainder in a warmed sauceboat. Garnish with parsley.

Baked Liver and Bacon

Ingredients

250 g lamb's liver
2-3 streaky rashers

Stuffing:

50 g breadcrumbs
1 teaspoon chopped parsley
1 slice finely chopped onion
Pepper/salt
13 g melted margarine
A little stock to bind

Gravy:

125 ml brown stock
½ teaspoon savoury sauce
Salt/pepper

Method

1. Wash and dry liver. Cut into slices 1 cm thick. Place on greased tin.
2. Make stuffing and press a little on each slice of liver.
3. Remove rind and bone from rashers and cut in two.
4. Arrange rasher slices on stuffing.
5. Pour a little stock into tin, cover with foil and bake in a moderate oven 190°C (375°F), Gas 5, for 30 minutes.
6. Lift onto warmed dish. Add remaining stock, seasoning and savoury sauce to tin, stir and bring to boil.
7. Strain and pour around liver on dish. Garnish with parsley.
8. Serve with baked potatoes and baked tomatoes.

Beefsteak and Kidney Pie

Ingredients

200 g rough puff pastry
  or small packet of frozen pastry

Filling:

400 g round steak
100 g beef kidney
1 onion
1 carrot
1-2 sticks celery (optional)
1-2 tomatoes
1 tablespoon flour
Pepper/salt
Chopped parsley
Stock or water

Method

1. Make pastry and place in refrigerator. Defrost frozen pastry.
2. Trim and wipe meat, cut in 2 cm pieces.
3. Skin and core kidney, wash in warm water, cut in 1 cm pieces.
4. Toss meat in seasoned flour.
5. Wash, scrape and slice carrot; wash and chop celery. Peel and slice onion. Skin and slice tomatoes.
6. Arrange meat, vegetables and parsley in layers in a pie dish. Add enough stock to come a little over half way up.
7. Roll out pastry a little larger than pie dish. Trim off strip, dampen, and use to line edge of dish. Damp and cover with pastry lid, pressing well in.
8. Flake and decorate, leaving a hole in centre for steam to escape. Glaze with beaten egg.
9. Bake in a hot oven 230°C (450°F), Gas 8, for 20 minutes. Reduce heat to 175°C (350°F), Gas 4, and cook for 1 hour 15 minutes.
10. Garnish with parsley. Serve with baked potatoes and a green salad.

Over to you . . .

1. In your Home Economics copy, make a list of the main cuts of (a) beef; (b) mutton.

   Pay a visit to your local butcher or supermarket during the next week and find out the cost of each of these meats per 500 g.

2. Name two stewing cuts of (a) beef; (b) mutton. State why these cuts should be stewed, rather than roasted or fried. Look through some cookery books and magazines and find a recipe for a beef stew or a mutton stew which differs from those in this book. Write it into your copybook.

3. Draw two diagrams of a pig and show where the main cuts of (a) pork and (b) bacon lie.

   Find out the cost of each cut per 500 g from your local butcher.

4. Name the main nutrients in meat.

   How does cooking affect these nutrients. What do you consider is the most nourishing way of cooking meat? Why?

5. Choose an accompaniment from column X to go with a meat in column Y.

X	Y
1. Maître d'hotel butter	A. Roast pork
2. Mint sauce	B. Boiled Bacon
3. Bread sauce	C. Grilled steak
4. Apple sauce	D. Roast chicken
5. Cabbage; white sauce	E. Roast lamb

   How would you calculate the cooking time for A, B, D and E?

9 All About Poultry

Poultry includes chicken, turkey, duck and goose. The main type of poultry we eat is chicken.

Food value

Chicken is a very nutritious food — it contains just as much protein as most meats. It has a little iron and B group vitamins, but is not as good a source of these as are red meats. Chicken has little fat — this makes it a good protein food for slimmers, invalids and those on low-fat diets. Another reason that chicken is useful in these diets is because it is easy to digest.

Value for money

Chicken can seem cheap when you work out its cost per kilogram, but don't forget you are paying for lots of bones, and possibly giblets which will not be eaten (although they can be used to make a well flavoured stock).

Buying

Poultry is a common cause of food poisoning, so make sure you buy from a clean reliable source and , if wrapped, choose a reliable brand name. If there is any suspicion when you bring it home that the fowl has gone off, bring it straight back to the shop or supermarket, which should replace it with a fresh one, or return your money.

Chickens today come prepared for cooking — plucked, drawn and trussed. Weight and expiry date will be printed on the label of wrapped birds. Look for the following signs of freshness:

1. Skin should be white and unwrinkled with no sign of discolouration.
2. Legs and breast should be plump and firm.
3. There should be no unpleasant smell.
4. Breast bone should be pliable.
5. Never buy a bird past its expiry date.
6. Roasting fowl — birds for roasting and grilling are usually between 6 and 9 months old — are usually 1½-2 kg in weight.

Boiling fowl are older, and cheaper. These are used for stewing, pies, *etc.*

Frozen poultry

1. Make sure it is frozen solid.
2. There should be no discolouration.
3. Wrapping should not be torn.

At home

1. Store at once in freezer (for up to six months).
2. Before use, remove giblets and thaw overnight for 12–18 hours in a refrigerator.
3. Poultry must **never** be cooked until it is completely thawed out, as this would be highly dangerous.

Storing chicken

1. Remove wrapper and giblets. Cover loosely with foil and place on a plate in the refrigerator.
2. Use within 2–3 days.
3. Wash giblets and use for stock; liver is used for paté or stuffing.

Preparing for cooking

1. Wash well, inside and out, making sure all internal organs have been removed. Drain well.
2. Dry thoroughly with kitchen paper.
3. Season inside carcase with a knob of butter, pepper, salt and a pinch of mixed herbs.
4. Loosen skin around neck end of breast and fill cavity with stuffing . Draw skin back and hold in place with the wing tips.
5. With neck towards you, lift wings out and under to keep neckflap in position.
6. Push legs up towards wings, pressing them against the body of the bird to give a neat shape.
7. Insert a skewer through the joint of one wing, then the thigh joint beside it, through the body and out through the thigh and wing joint on the other side.
8. Tie legbones together with twine, bring it around tail, across the back and tie securely onto the skewer at each side.

Boiled Chicken

Ingredients

1½ – 2 kg chicken
Boiling water
1 piece of cut lemon
1 onion
1 stick celery

To serve:

Boiled rice
Béchamel sauce
(Hot) — Boiled bacon or ham
(Cold) — Lettuce and salad ingredients/ Mayonnaise

Method

1. Wash, prepare and truss bird. Rub skin with lemon.

2. Place with vegetables in boiling salted water, breast side down. Return to the boil.
3. Cover, reduce heat and simmer gently for 15 minutes per ½ kg and 15 minutes over *i.e.* 1 hour – 1 hour 15 minutes.
4. Lift out and drain well. Remove skewer, twine and knee bones. Strain liquid and keep for stock.
5. **Serving hot:** Divide into 4 large portions, remove skin and pour sauce over. Garnish with parsley. Serve with boiled rice or potatoes, and ham.
6. **Serving cold:** Cool quickly, remove skin, carve and arrange attractively on a large dish. Garnish with lettuce, tomatoes, cucumber and other salad vegetables. Coat with mayonnaise, if wished.

Roast Chicken

Ingredients

1½-2 kg chicken   *2-3 slices fat bacon*
50 g fat

Stuffing:

100 g breadcrumbs
½ teaspoon mixed herbs
1 dessertspoon chopped parsley
1 small onion
Salt/pepper
25 g margarine
A little stock

To serve:

Bread sauce/bacon rolls/thin brown gravy

Method

1. Prepare bird — draw, wash, dry. Turn on oven to 200°C (400°F), Gas 6, and melt fat in roasting tin.
2. **Make stuffing:** Peel and grate onion. Mix dry ingredients in a bowl. Moisten with melted margarine and a little stock, if necessary.

3. Press stuffing into neck-end of bird, fold back neckflap and secure with wing tips.
4. Truss bird with skewer and twine. Cover breast with two or three slices of fat bacon.
5. Place chicken in hot dripping, breast side up. Baste well.
6. Cook for 50–75 minutes depending on temperature and size of bird. Baste 2 or 3 times during cooking.
7. Add bacon rolls 30 minutes before chicken is cooked and remove slices from breast.
8. Lift out chicken, drain well. Remove kneebones, skewer and twine. Keep warm while making gravy.
9. Serve on a hot dish garnished with parsley and bacon rolls.
10. Serve with roast potatoes, a green vegetable, such as Brussels sprouts, and/or a green salad.

Grilled Chicken

Ingredients

4 chicken joints   *1 tablespoon lemon juice*
Salt/pepper   *1 tablespoon oil*

Method

1. Mix oil, seasoning and lemon juice and marinate (steep) chicken in this mixture for at least 2 hours, or better still, overnight.
2. Preheat grill to moderate — remove grid.
   Place joints in grill pan, (wrong side up); pour marinade over them.
4. Grill for 10 mins, turn, baste and grill right side up for ten minutes. If very large, cook on each side for 5 minutes more.
5. Serve on hot plate with chipped or boiled potatoes and a green salad. For spicy flavoured chicken use a barbeque sauce for marinading and grilling.

Chicken Casserole

Ingredients

1 chicken
2 streaky rashers
2 medium onions
25 g dripping/oil
100 g mushrooms
25 g flour
2 tomatoes
Salt/pepper
1 stick celery (optional)
375 ml stock (or stock and a little wine)

Method

1. Wash and dry chicken. Joint chicken using a sharp knife. First cut away legs at the hip joints. Divide leg in two. Remove wings. Pare away breasts and cut each in two. Trim any other pieces of flesh from carcase. Remove skin from joints and wing tips (these can be used for stock). Alternatively, buy ready jointed chicken pieces.
2. Toss joints in seasoned flour.
3. Peel and slice onion, wash and slice celery. Wash, dry and slice mushrooms. Skin and slice tomatoes.
4. Remove rind and bone from rashers, cut in small pieces.
5. Fry rashers, add dripping and fry chicken joints in a frying pan until brown. Place in a casserole.
6. Sauté onions and celery lightly.
7. Add to chicken, with mushrooms and tomato.
8. Add remaining flour to fat in pan, cook for one minute. Slowly add stock and bring to the boil. Add seasoning and pour over chicken.
9. Cover casserole and cook in a moderate oven for 1 hour 30 minutes.
10. Serve casserole with baked potatoes; garnish with parsley.

10   *All About Left-Overs*

No matter how carefully we plan our cooking, there are always times when there are 'left-overs' to be used up — meat and vegetables from an earlier meal, or small amounts of food, such as egg yolk, left behind after cooking. At little extra cost, a good cook can transform such leftovers into tasty, nourishing dishes.

Waste not — want not!

With the cost of food today, no one can afford to throw away the smallest scrap of food. Even the trimmings of vegetables and meat can add flavour to soups and stock. Pea pods, tomato and onion skins, leek and celery trimmings, can all be used in soups.

Get into the habit of checking the refrigerator each morning to see what can be used up. Do not wait until food becomes stale, use it up as quickly as possible.

Planned left overs

Busy cooks can save time and trouble by planning their cooking, so that they cook double on one day and serve it up, in a different guise, the following day. This also saves fuel.

Food Value

Reheated foods are less nutritious than freshly cooked foods, particularly fruit and vegetables. Because they lack minerals and vitamins, reheated dishes should always be served with nutritious foods, such as salads or freshly cooked vegetables.

When the main course is to be a reheated dish, take care to plan an extra-nourishing first or last course *e.g.*

Mixed salad hors d'oeuvre
Fish Pie
Carrots. Baked Potatoes
Lemon Meringue Pie

Making the most of leftovers

Twice-cooked foods lack colour, flavour and moisture. The skill in cooking leftovers is to know how to put these qualities back into the food:

1. **Colour:** Use colourful sauces, vegetables (*e.g.* tomatoes) and garnishes.
2. **Moisture:** Reheat in a sauce, first dicing or mincing the food to enable the sauce to penetrate and flavour the food. Cold meat and vegetables can be tossed in mayonnaise or French Dressing.
3. **Flavour:** To improve flavour, use:
   Lots of seasoning — pepper, salt, mustard.
   Herbs and spices — thyme, parsley, mixed herbs, *etc.*
   Grated cheese — in sauces, or sprinkled over dishes.
   Savoury sauces — Worcester, tomato and mushroom ketchup, chutney.
   Stock or meat extract — instead of water.
   Cream and egg yolk — where suitable, to add richness and nourishment.
   Onions and celery — but make sure they are fully cooked before adding the leftovers, as reheating is not sufficient to cook raw ingredients.

Uses for left over foods

Left overs can be used up cold or reheated (*rechauffé*).

Table 10.1

Food	Cold Dishes	Reheated Dishes
Meat	Sandwiches, rolls, salads, savouries	Shepherds pie, meat cakes, rissoles, curry, Spaghetti Bolognese, soup, savoury flans
Fish	Salads, sandwiches, savouries, Fish Cocktail	Fish pie, fish cakes, fish au gratin, quiches and savoury flans, pancake fillings
Potatoes	Potato salad	Sauté potatoes, potato cakes, potato croquettes, cheese & potato pie, toppings for pies, *e.g.* Fish pie
Vegetables	Salads *e.g.* Russian salad	Vegetables in cheese sauce, omelettes, casseroles, curries, vegetable casserole
Fruit (stewed) or tinned	Flan fillings, fools, apple snow, cold sweets	Puddings, *e.g.* charlottes, pies, crumbles
Bread	Fresh breadcrumbs	Bread and Butter pudding, Queen of Puddings, crumble toppings stuffing, meat loaf, breadsauce, toasted or fried, croûtons
Cake	Trifle, cold sweets	Crumble toppings, Queen of Puddings
Egg yolk	Mayonnaise, cold sweets	Scrambled eggs, cakes, scones, pastry, puddings, Duchess Potatoes
Egg white	Cold sweets, *e.g.* apple snow; makes cream go further	Meringues, Angel cake, meringue toppings, frosting
Hardboiled eggs	Salads, sandwiches	Curried eggs, Scotch eggs.
Cheese	Grated — use for salads	Au gratin dishes, cheese sauce
Sauces		Reheated meat and fish dishes
Milk		Baking

The Dangers of Food Poisoning

Reheated food is a likely source of food poisoning. To avoid this danger follow these rules:

1. Cooked food should be placed on a **clean plate, covered with foil or cling film, cooled quickly,** then **stored in the refrigerator.**
2. Use within **2 days.**
3. If there is a chance that the food has 'gone off', it is safer to throw it out.
4. When reheating protein foods, **bring quickly to a high temperature,** then simmer or cook gently to heat the food through. This is essential, to destroy food poisoning germs.
5. Do not leave food in a warm place for any length of time — **bacteria breed rapidly at warm temperatures.**
6. **Never reheat a second time.**
7. **Avoid overhandling.**

Reheating Meat and Fish

1. Remove bone, gristle and excess fat from meat.
2. Mince or chop finely to enable sauce to penetrate the meat.
3. Remove the skin and bone from fish; flake, or leave in pieces.
4. Use a well seasoned sauce, to add moisture and flavour, cool slightly, before adding meat or fish.
5. All raw ingredients and sauce must be fully cooked before meat or fish is added.
6. Bring to boiling point but *do not* overcook.
7. Serve and garnish attractively.

> *Note:* Brown meat is usually cooked in brown or dark coloured sauces, *e.g.* brown stewing sauce. White meat may be served in white sauce, or in sauces such as curry or tomato sauce.

Tasty recipes such as Spaghetti Bolognese or Curried Meat, can be adapted to suit leftover meat. Make sauce in the usual way, and add prepared meat/fish for final 10-15 minutes, bringing it to boiling point for at least 3 minutes.

Quiches, pancakes and omelettes are ideal for using up leftovers such as chopped ham, grated cheese and left over vegetables.

Minced beef or diced chicken can be added to a savoury coating sauce and used to fill savoury pancakes (*see p. 95*).

Using Left-overs

Advantages
1. Avoids waste
2. Very economical
3. Handy in emergencies
4. Adds variety to menu.

Disadvantages
1. Loss of food value
2. Lack flavour
3. They require time to prepare
4. Extra ingredients must be added to make them tasty and attractive.

Recipes for Leftovers

Shepherd's Pie

Ingredients	Sauce:
300 g cooked meat	*25 g dripping*
	25 g flour
Creamed potatoes:	*1 medium onion*
500 g potatoes	*300 ml stock*
2 tablesp. milk	*Salt/pepper*
knob margarine	*1 tsp. chopped parsley*
	1 teasp. savoury sauce,
	e.g. ketchup

Method

1. Peel potatoes and put to cook, or use ready mashed potatoes.
2. Trim and mince meat.
3. Peel and mince, or chop onion.
4. Melt dripping, fry onion until beginning to brown.
5. Add flour, cook for 1 minute on low heat.
6. Gradually add stock, stirring all the time. Add seasoning, parsley and sauce.
7. Bring to boil, then simmer for 5-10 mins, stirring regularly.
8. Meanwhile drain and mash potatoes, beat in milk and margarine and season with pepper and salt.
9. Cool sauce slightly, stir in meat, then pour into a greased pie dish.
10. Spread potato carefully over top, scoring with a knife or fork to decorate. Brush with a little milk or melted fat.
11. Bake at the top of a fairly hot oven 200°C (400°F), Gas 6, for about ½ hour until lightly browned.
12. Serve on a large dish; garnish with sliced tomato and parsley.

Variation

Cottage pie — made with beef.
Shepherds Pie — made with lamb or mutton.

For a really quick pie, use a packet of brown sauce mix and instant mashed potato.

Meat Cakes

Ingredients

200 g cooked meat   *1 teasp. chopped parsley*
200 g mashed potato   *Pepper/salt*
A small onion   *1 teasp. savoury sauce*
Pinch of mixed herbs   *Beaten egg*

To coat: *Beaten egg and breadcrumbs*
To fry: *50 g dripping or cooking fat*
To serve: *Brown gravy, mashed potato*
To garnish: *Parsley, tomato slices*

Method

1. Trim and mince meat. Peel and mince onion.
2. Put all ingredients except egg into a bowl, and mix well together. Bind with beaten egg.
3. Shape into a long 'sausage' on a floured board.
4. Cut into eight pieces. Shape each into a flat cake about 1 cm thick.
5. Coat with egg and breadcrumbs, pressing well in.
6. Fry in hot fat until golden brown, turn and fry other side. Drain on kitchen paper. Keep warm.
7. Make gravy from sediment on pan, arrange meat cakes overlapping on a warmed oval dish, pipe potato around the edge of the dish and pour gravy around meat cakes.

Meat Croquettes

Ingredients

250 g cooked minced meat
Salt and pepper
1 teasp. ketchup
1 teasp. chopped parsley

Binding sauce:
25 g dripping/cooking fat
1 teasp. finely chopped onion
25 g flour
125-150 ml stock

To coat: *Beaten egg and breadcrumbs*
To fry: *Bath of cooking oil*
To garnish: *Parsley*

Method

1. Melt dripping, fry onion until beginning to brown. Stir in flour, cook for one minute.
2. Gradually stir in stock and bring to boil. Boil for 3 minutes.

3. Add seasoning, ketchup, parsley and finally stir in meat.
4. Bring to boil then turn onto a wet plate, smooth out and allow to cool. (It is easier to handle and shape mixture if it is cold).
5. Divide mixture into 8, shape into croquettes, on a floured board.
6. Coat with egg and breadcrumbs, pressing crumbs well in.
7. Heat fat and fry croquettes until golden brown. Drain on kitchen paper.
8. Serve on a hot dish. Garnish with parsley.

Variation

For economy, add 100 g mashed potato or 50 g breadcrumbs to mixture — this will make it go further.

Rissoles: Same mixture shaped into flat cakes.

Chicken Pie

Ingredients

250 g cooked chicken (or turkey)	1 medium onion
	100 g mushrooms
2 streaky rashers	1 tomato

Sauce:

25 g fat	Pepper, salt
25 g flour	1 dessertsp. sauce or
200 ml chicken stock	ketchup

Pastry:

200 g shortcrust pastry

Method

1. Peel and slice onion, wash and slice mushrooms and tomato.
2. Remove bone and rind from rashers and cut into 3 or 4 pieces.
3. Fry in a saucepan, until brown. Add fat and onions and fry these until beginning to brown.
4. Add flour, cook for one minute, then gradually add stock, stirring all the time. Add seasoning and ketchup.

5. Add sliced mushrooms, chicken meat and tomato and bring to the boil. Empty into greased pie dish. Cool.
6. Roll out pastry a little larger than pie dish. Cut and damp strips and use around edge of dish.
7. Place pastry on pie dish, damping edges. Cut a hole in the centre, flake and decorate.
8. Bake in hot oven 220°C (425°F) Gas 7 for 15 minutes, reduce to 180°C (350°F) Gas 4 and continue to cook for 20-30 minutes, until pastry is crisp and golden brown.

Chicken Mayonnaise

Ingredients

200-250 g cooked chicken or turkey
1 red eating apple
1 green eating apple
4 sticks celery
50 g chopped walnuts
2 tablesp. lemon juice
Pepper/salt
Mayonnaise
100 ml whipped cream (optional)

To garnish: *Lettuce, Tomatoes*

Method

1. Wash and chop celery. Wash, quarter and core apples. Do not peel. Chop and toss in lemon juice to prevent browning.
2. Wipe walnuts with clean cloth or kitchen paper and chop roughly.
3. Cut chicken meat into 1 cm cubes, put into bowl with apple (drained), celery, walnuts and seasoning.
4. Mix well together with mayonnaise and cream.
5. Pile roughly into a dish or salad bowl.
6. Arrange lettuce leaves around, garnish with tomato lilies.

Savoury Pancakes

Ingredients
250 ml pancake batter (see p. 150)
25 g butter or margarine

Fillings — Choose one of these:

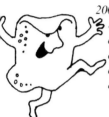

200 g cooked meat or fish	*250 ml coating sauce*
e.g. chicken/turkey	*Béchamel sauce*
or minced/chopped beef	*Brown stewing or curry sauce*
or ham	*Bechamel or tomato sauce*
or white/smoked fish	*Parsley or cheese sauce*
or tinned salmon	*Béchamel sauce*

Method

1. Fry pancakes and keep warm over saucepan of boiling water.
2. Make sauce, season and keep warm.
3. Trim meat or fish, removing bone, skin, fat, gristle, *etc.* Dice or mince meat; flake or break fish into pieces.
4. Stir into sauce and bring to boil.
5. Spoon filling onto centre of each pancake, roll up and arrange in a flameproof dish.
6. Rinse out saucepan with 1-2 tablesp. stock/milk and strain this liquid over pancakes.
7. Dot with butter and place under preheated hot grill for a few minutes until golden brown, or cover with foil in a fairly hot oven 200°C (400°F), Gas 6, until piping hot. Remove foil for last 10 minutes.
8. Serve in cooking dish, garnish with parsley.

Variation

Filled vol-au-vents: Use 1 packet frozen vol-au-vents, cooked meat and sauce as above. Bake pastry according to directions on packet. Fill with hot meat/fish sauce and serve at once.

Potato Cakes

Ingredients

250 g mashed potatoes
50 g flour
¼ teasp. salt
¼ teasp. baking powder
Pepper
2 teasp. melted margarine

To fry:
Cooking fat or butter.

Method

1. Sieve flour, salt and baking powder into a mixing bowl.
2. Mix in potatoes and season with pepper.
3. Add margarine and blend well in.
4. Turn onto floured board. Knead slightly and divide in two.
5. Roll each piece into a round about ½ cm thick. Cut into 6 or 8 triangles.
6. Fry in hot fat until golden brown on each side. Drain.
7. Serve with butter and garnish with chopped parsley.

Duchesse Potatoes

Ingredients

250 g mashed potatoes
13 g melted margarine
Salt, pepper, nutmeg
1 egg yolk

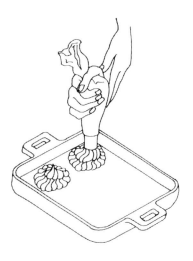

Method

1. Mix hot potatoes and seasoning in a bowl. Mix in margarine.
2. Add enough egg yolk to bind. Beat well.
3. Put into a forcing bag, fitted with a large rose pipe.
4. Form into large roses on a greased tin. Cool for 10 mins.
5. Brush with beaten egg and bake at 200°C (400°F), Gas 6, until crisp and beginning to brown at the edges.

Variation

Pipe into larger hollow cases and use as containers for vegetables such as peas.

Other Recipes for Leftovers

Fish Pie, see p. 108.
Fish Cakes, see p. 107.
Potato Croquettes, see p. 123.

Over to you . . .

1. Look up a recipe book which explains how to clean out a chicken. Write it down in your copybook. using a chicken as the main meat dish, write a menu for a celebration dinner you would plan for your parents' wedding anniversary.
2. You have the following leftovers in your kitchen. Write a recipe for a dish you could make from them:
   stale swiss roll; half a tin of fruit salad; half a carton of cream; left-over cold custard.
3. Two unexpected guests are arriving in an hour — plan a dinner menu combining the following fresh and left-over foods:

   1 head lettuce   *400 g cooked meat*
   ½ dozen eggs   *500 g cooked*
   2 onions   *potatoes*
   4 tomatoes   *200 g cheddar cheese*
   Stewed apple
   ½ loaf stale bread

4. Look at the recipe for chicken pie. Write a recipe for a similar dish based on left-over pork. What extra ingredients would you include to add flavour to your recipe?
5. What nourishing accompaniments would you serve with the following left-over dishes to increase their food value? (a) Shepherd's pie; (b) fish cakes; (c) vegetable curry.

   Write a recipe for a nourishing dish to serve either before or after the main courses listed above.

11   All About Fish

Most of the fish we eat comes from the sea, but freshwater fish (from rivers and lakes) is also available.

Many people do not like fish — often this is because they have only tasted one kind of fish or because they have only tried it cooked in one way. Remember there are many varieties of fish and lots of different delicious ways of cooking it. Try some of the recipes at the end of this chapter and learn how to make the most of this nutritious food.

Food value of Fish

All fish is a good source of **protein,** almost as good as meat. It contains a large amount of water, as well as Vitamin B and the minerals iodine, iron and potassium. If you can eat the bones, *e.g.* canned fish, they are a good source of calcium and phosphorus and therefore good for *our* bones also!

Classification

Fish can be placed in three groups, according to their structure and food value, see *Table 11.1.*

White Fish

Because it has most of its fat in the liver, which is removed when cleaning, white fish is very digestible, making it ideal for invalids, and old people. Because it is low in calories, it is good for slimmers.

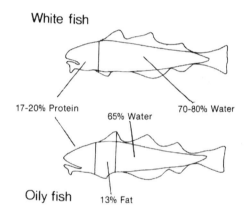

White fish

17-20% Protein   65% Water   70-80% Water

Oily fish   13% Fat

Oily Fish

Its name tells us that oily fish has some oil or fat in the flesh. This gives it a stronger flavour and makes it 'go off' more quickly. On the other hand, it is more satisfying and nourishing than white fish. It contains less water, more fat, Vitamins A and D, as well as B, and several minerals, including iodine, sodium and potassium.

Table 11.1

White Fish	Oily Fish	Shell Fish
Cod/Haddock Plaice/Sole Whiting/Sole	Herrings/Mackerel Salmon/Trout Sardines/Eels	Mussels/Crab Lobster/Shrimps Scallops/Periwinkles

Average Composition of Fish (cooked)

Table 11.2

Fish type	Protein	Fat	Carbohydrate	Vitamins	Minerals	Water
White	17 - 20	0	0	B	1	70 - 80
Oily	17 - 20	13	0	A, D, B	2	65
Fish fingers (fried)	13.5	12.5	17	B	1.5	55.5

Remember the way you cook fish will change its food value — frying adds fat to it; coating fish in flour, breadcrumbs or batter adds carbohydrate, *e.g.* fish fingers.

Value for Money?

Fish is no longer a cheap food, but some varieties are cheaper and better value than others. Oily fish, such as herrings and mackerel, are cheap and very nutritious; salmon, on the other hand, is very expensive.

Some white fish is cheap and plentiful, other varieties, such as turbot and sole, are expensive.

When you buy whole fish, you must allow for the waste on cleaning, boning and skinning the fish. On the other hand, you save on fuel, because fish cooks very quickly.

Buying Fish

1. Fish must be absolutely fresh.
2. Always buy from a good clean fish shop.
3. It should not smell stale.
4. Its eyes should be bulging and bright (sunken eyes are a sign of stale fish).
5. Markings, such as spots, should be bright and clear.
6. The skin should be unbroken and moist.
7. The flesh should be firm.
8. The gills should be bright red. (A fish breathes through its gills. These are ear-like flaps at each side of its head).

Know your Fish

Most fish are best eaten at a certain time of the year, when they are 'in season'. They have a higher food value and better flavour at this time and are more plentiful and cheap.

Cod: *September to March.*

A large, round fish, with a greenish 'Connemara marble' coloured back and a white line running the length of the fish on each side.

Whiting: *All year.*

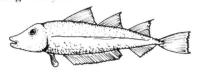

A smaller fish than cod, also round. It has a dark silver back and silvery white underside.

Sole: *All year*

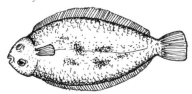

A flat fish, with a white underside. The upperside may be dark brown and rough (black sole) or pale brownish yellow (lemon sole).

Plaice: *All year except Spring.*

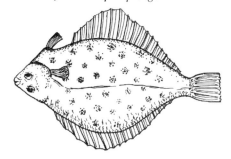

A flat fish, brownish grey in colour with bright orange spots when fresh, changing to brown as it gets stale.

Herrings: *July — February.*

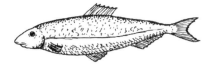

A fairly small round fish with a bluish-silver skin and lots of scales.

Mackerel: *All year.*

A larger round fish, with very definite striped markings on its back, which are a bluish colour.

Fish can be bought: (a) whole (b) as fillets (c) as steaks or cutlets.

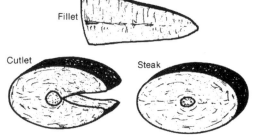

(a) Small fish are usually bought whole. They may be poached, grilled, fried or stuffed and baked.
(b) Fillets are long thin pieces cut from flat fish or round fish and lifted off the bone. A flat fish will have four fillets, a round fish, two. Fillets can be steamed, fried, grilled or baked.
(c) Steaks and cutlets are slices cut across the body of large round fish, *e.g.* cod or salmon, and include the bone. They may be grilled, fried, poached or baked.

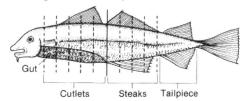

Preserved Fish

Fish may be preserved by: (a) smoking; (b) canning; (c) freezing.

Smoked Fish

The following fish can be smoked: cod/pollack; herrings (kippers); mackerel; haddock; trout.

When buying see that the fish is firm to the touch and shiny, without being sticky. It should have a pleasant odour.

Canned Fish

The most popular canned fish available are: salmon; tuna; sardines; mackerel; pilchards; as well as shellfish, such as prawns and crab.

Canned fish needs no cooking and should be added at the end of cooking time, in recipes where it is used. Canned fish is a good source of calcium and Vitamins A and D.

Frozen Fish

Many filleted fish, such as cod, plaice, whiting, *etc.* are available frozen. Also available are 'made-up' dishes, such as fish curry; fish in sauce; fish cakes and fish fingers.

Frozen fish is more expensive than fresh fish, but don't forget there is no waste — the fish is already cleaned and filleted, and in most cases coated and ready for cooking, so it saves time and trouble. Frozen fish is just as nourishing as fresh fish.

When buying:
  (a) Make sure the packet is unbroken and frozen solid.
  (b) Check the date-stamp to make sure it has not been too long in the deep freeze.
  (c) When you get home, put it straight into the freezer — before it has a chance to thaw out.
  (d) *Never* refreeze thawed or partially thawed fish.

To Defrost Fish: Defrost slowly in a refrigenerator for about 6 hours, without unwrapping. Prepared fish, *e.g.* breaded fillets or fish fingers, can be cooked from frozen.

Storing Fish

Fish should be eaten on the day you buy it. All fish, especially oily fish, goes stale very quickly. If you *must* store it:

  1. Remove wrappings.

  2. Lay fish on ice and cover with more ice in a suitable container in the refrigerator. It should be covered, to avoid flavouring other foods in the fridge.
  3. Use within 24 hours.

Preparing Fish

Cleaning

  1. *Flat fish* — cut a slit below the gills on the dark side and carefully remove gut.

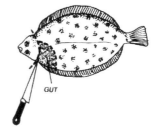

Round fish — remove head, if wished, slit from head to vent on underside and scrape out gut.

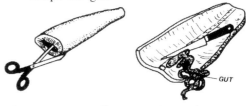

  2. Wash; rub off any black membrane or blood with salt.
  3. If skin is to be eaten, remove scales by scraping with a knife from tail to head. Rinse again.

  4. Cut off fins and tail with scissors.

5. If head is to be left on, remove eyes by slitting around socket with a sharp knife and easing out.
6. Rinse and dry.
7. Fresh-water fish may need to be rinsed several times.

Filleting Round Fish

1. Use a scissors to trim off fins.
2. Using a sharp knife, cut along the back, through to the backbone.

3. With the knife against the bone, cut downwards, along ribs, gradually paring away flesh.
4. Repeat with second fillet.

Filleting Flat Fish

1. Place gutted fish on board, with the tail towards the worker.
2. Using a sharp filleting knife, cut firmly down back, from head to tail.

3. Lifting flesh slightly with left hand, pare away left hand fillet, cutting flesh away from bone from head to tail, keeping knife close to the bone.
4. Turn head towards worker and repeat with second fillet.
5. Repeat on underside, removing two fillets.
6. Trim away loose edges from fillets.

Skinning a Fillet

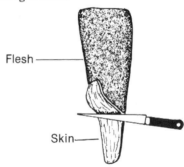

Flesh

Skin

Boning a Herring

1. Place gutted herring on board, skin side up.
2. Press firmly down length of backbone with thumbs, until bone is loose.
3. Turn fish over and peel off bone.

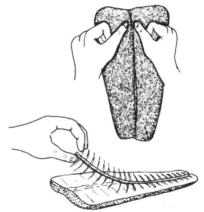

Cooking Fish

1. Fish must be absolutely fresh.
2. Wash and dry fish before cooking.
3. Fish cooks very quickly — be sure not to overcook it or it will break apart.
4. White fish needs to be well seasoned — a knob of butter, or a sauce will improve its food value and flavour.
5. Oily fish may be greasy and indigestible — lemon juice or a sharp flavoured sauce will help to counteract this.
6. You will know when the fish is cooked when it loses its transparent colour and becomes opaque. It also breaks apart easily.

Coatings for Fried fish	Suitable Sauces	Suitable Garnishes
1. Seasoned flour. 2. Oatmeal — perfect for herrings. 3. Egg and fine breadcrumbs. 4. Batter.	Parsley sauce. Cheese sauce. Egg sauce. Dutch sauce. Tomato sauce. Tartare sauce. Gooseberry sauce.	Lemons slices or wedges. Sprigs of parsley. Water lily tomatoes. Garden peas. Cucumber twists. Grated cheese.

Effects of Cooking

1. Protein coagulates (sets).
2. Fish becomes opaque.
3. Fish breaks apart easily.
4. Bacteria are destroyed.
5. Some minerals and vitamins dissolve into the cooking water — use it for sauces.

How to know when fish is cooked:
1 Transparent flesh becomes opaque
2. A creamy substance oozes from fish
3. It flakes easily and comes away from the bone

Fish Dishes

Fish is **never** boiled. The movement of the water would break up the flesh. Poach gently instead — the liquid in which the fish is cooked should be barely bubbling, on one side of the saucepan. The liquid can be water, a mixture of milk and water, or a *court bouillon* (a flavoured stock), which gives the best flavour. Only use just enough to come half way up the fish. Wrapping the fish in foil helps prevent it from breaking up and makes it easier to lift the fish in and out of the saucepan.

Poached White Fish

Ingredients

1 medium sized fish
  e.g. 500 g haddock
  or 4 cod steaks
1 Bayleaf
	1 slice onion
	Pepper and salt
	1 slice lemon
	Parsley

To cook: *Double sheet of tinfoil*

Method

1. Put saucepan containing poaching liquid to boil. Add onion, bayleaf and 1 slice lemon.
2. Wipe codsteaks or scale and clean haddock and wash.
3. Butter one side of foil, place fish in centre, season with pepper, salt and squeeze of lemon. Wrap foil loosely around fish, folding so that there are two long ends sticking out at each side.

4. Using foil 'handles', lower fish into poaching liquid and poach gently for 10-20 minutes, depending on thickness of fish (10 minutes to each 500 g + 10 minutes over).
6. Lift out, using handles or a fish slice.
7. Drain well, open foil, remove skin and bone from codsteaks. Lift onto warmed dish. Pour a little of the liquid in the foil over the fish.
8. Serve with boiled potatoes, buttered peas and a well flavoured sauce, such as Dutch sauce.

> **Note:** Fish may also be poached in the oven, in a covered dish. Allow 10-15 mins. per 500 g + 10 minutes over.

Steamed Fish

(Ideal for invalids, and slimmers)

Ingredients

4 medium fillets white fish
A little butter or margarine
Pepper and salt
Lemon juice

Method

1. Half fill saucepan with water and put to boil.
2. Butter plate.
3. Prepare fish. Wash and dry.
4. Place on buttered plate, season with pepper, salt and lemon juice (the fish can be left flat, folded in two, or rolled up).
5. Cover with buttered paper and second plate.
6. Place on saucepan of boiling water and steam for 15-20 minutes, depending on thickness of fish, until fish becomes white and creamy.
7. Drain well, place on warm serving dish and garnish with lemon wedges and parsley. Pour a little cooking liquid over, if wished.

Variation

Make up stuffing in following recipe and use to stuff fillets — cook for 10 mins longer.

Baked Stuffed Fish

Whole fish, fillets or cutlets can be cooked by this method. Whole fish suitable for baking include cod, haddock, mackerel, herring and trout.

Ingredients

A. 1 medium sized fish or
B. 4 cutlets of cod or
C. 8 fillets of fish (small)

Stuffing:

50 g breadcrumbs
1 tablesp. finely chopped onion
1 tablesp. finely chopped parsley
⅛ tsp. mixed herbs
Pepper & salt
25 g marg.
A little lemon juice
  or rind, grated

To garnish:
Peas/Lemon/Parsley

To serve:

Mâitre d'hotel butter

Method

1. Heat oven to 177° C (350°F), Gas 4.
2. Clean and prepare fish, trim fins, remove eyes. Wash well and dry.
3. Make stuffing: mix breadcrumbs, chopped onion, parsley, herbs and seasoning, in a small bowl. Melt margarine, and stir into crumb mixture. Finally add a little lemon rind or juice.

4. Place fish on well greased dish or tin.
5. A. Fill cavity of whole fish with stuffing and secure with skewers or stitch with a needle and white cotton.
   B. Fill cavity of each cutlet with stuffing and secure the thin 'flaps' with a cocktail stick.
   C. Lay four fillets on greased dish, spoon stuffing carefully onto each; flatten well down and cover with the other four fillets.
6. Brush fish with melted fat and cover with greaseproof paper or foil.
7. Bake for 20-30 minutes, depending on size or thickness of fish.
8. Remove bone from cutlets carefully; using fish slice, lift fish onto warmed serving dish.
9. Surround with freshly cooked peas and garnish with lemon wedges and parsley.

Note: Baking is a good way to cook fish when you want to avoid the strong smell of fish in the kitchen.

Grilled Fish

Ingredients

Herrings, mackerel or trout
Pepper, salt
Melted fat or oil

To garnish:

Lemon and parsley

To serve:

Maître d'hotel (savoury) butter
or gooseberry sauce

Method

1. Preheat grill.
2. Clean, scale and trim fresh herrings/mackerel/trout. Cut off heads. Wash and dry. Remove bone if wished.
3. Score the skin 3 or 4 times, brush with melted fat and sprinkle with pepper and salt.
4. Grease the bars of the grill. Place the fish, folded in two, under the grill and cook for about 4 minutes on each side.
5. Lift onto a hot dish, garnish with lemon wedges and chopped parsley.
6. Place a pat of maître d'hôtel butter on each fish.

Maitre d'hotel (savoury) butter

Ingredients

25 g butter
1 dessertsp. chopped parsley
Pepper, salt
1 tsp. Lemon juice

Method

1. Cream all ingredients together in a small bowl.
2. Shape into pats, and chill.

Grilled Kippers

(a tasty breakfast or supper dish)

Ingredients

Kippers
Butter
Boiling water

To garnish:

Lemon and parsley

Method

1. Trim tails and fins from kippers. Wash.
2. Place in a jug or bowl and pour boiling water over them.
3. Leave for 5 minutes, then drain and dot with butter.
4. Place under a hot grill for 1 minute, each side.
5. Serve on a hot dish, with savoury butter on top and garnish with lemon wedges and parsley.

Fried Fish

Only thin pieces of fish, such as fillets or steaks, are suitable for frying; small whole fish, such as herrings or trout, may also be fried.

Ingredients

4 large fillets plaice or whiting
1 tablesp. seasoned flour
1 egg
50 g fine breadcrumbs
Oil or butter for frying

To garnish:
Lemon
Parsley

To serve:
Dutch or tartare sauce

Method

1. Prepare, trim, wash and dry fish. Skin if wished.
2. Beat egg and pour into shallow dish.
3. Place breadcrumbs on large plate.
4. Coat fillets with seasoned flour, place in egg, brush all over with the egg and drain well.
5. Lay fish on breadcrumbs, turn and press breadcrumbs well in, making sure fish is covered completely. Shake surplus crumbs from fish.
6. Heat fat in frying pan, add fish and cook on medium heat until brown. Turn and fry other side until brown and fully cooked, adding extra fat if necessary.
7. Lift out carefully; drain on kitchen paper.
8. Serve on a warm dish, garnish with lemon wedges and parsley.

Deep Frying

Fillets of fish can be coated in egg and breadcrumbs, or batter, and deep fried at 180°C (350°C).

Goujons of Fish

(A tasty way to make fish go further)

Ingredients

4 fillets of plaice, sole or whiting
1 tablesp. seasoned flour
1 beaten egg
50 g fine breadcrumbs
1 tablesp. finely grated cheese
25 g butter
2 tablesp. cooking oil

Method

1. Prepare and skin fish. Wash and dry.
2. Cut into finger sized strips. Coat with seasoned flour.
3. Mix cheese with breadcrumbs, coat fish with egg and breadcrumbs.
4. Melt half the butter and oil in a frying pan. When hot, add half the fish and cook until crisp and golden brown, turning when necessary.
5. Repeat with remainder of fish, using the rest of the oil and butter.
6. Drain well on kitchen paper.
7. Pile onto a hot serving dish; garnish with tomato and lemon wedges.
8. Serve with chipped potatoes and french beans.

Stewed Fish

(Smoked cod or haddock 'au gratin')

Ingredients

400 g smoked cod or haddock.
225 ml milk ⎫
150 ml water ⎬ *375 ml cooking liquid*
Bayleaf, slice of lemon
Pepper, salt
75 g cheese
Browned crumbs
A little butter

Sauce:

25 g margarine
25 g flour
375 ml. milk/water

To serve:

Triangles of toast
Lemon wedges
Parsley

Method

1. Trim fish, remove any bones. Wash.
2. Place in bowl, cover with boiling water. Steep for 1 minute. Lift out and cut into large pieces.
3. Place fish and milk/water mixture in saucepan, with bayleaf, lemon and pepper. Do not add salt at this stage, as smoked fish is usually quite salty.

4. Bring slowly to the the boil, lower heat and simmer gently for 6 - 8 minutes. Remove bayleaf and lemon.
7. Lift out and place fish in greased heatproof dish.
8. Drain liquid into a jug, rinse saucepan and make sauce.
9. **Sauce:** Melt margarine, stir in flour, cook gently for 1 minute. Gradually add liquid in which fish was cooked, stirring all the time. Simmer for 3 minutes. Remove from heat and stir in most of the cheese. Taste and correct seasoning, adding salt if necessary.
10. Pour the sauce over the fish, lifting the fish to help the sauce spread easily.
11. Mix remaining cheese with browned crumbs and sprinkle over the fish. Dot with butter.
12. Bake in a hot oven for 10 minutes, or brown under the grill.
13. Place casserole on a large dish, garnish with triangles of toast, lemon wedges and parsley.

Fish Curry

Ingredients

400 - 500 g white fish
  (cod, haddock, monkfish)
25 g margarine
25 g flour
1 large onion
1 tomato
1 stick celery
1 dessertsp. curry powder
375 ml fish stock (made from skin and bones)
1 tablesp. tomato purée
1 tablesp. chutney
1 dessertsp. lemon juice
1 tablesp. raisins (optional)

To serve:
200 g long grained rice

Method

1. Prepare and finely chop onion and celery.
2. Melt margarine, add onion and celery and cook until beginning to brown.
3. Add curry powder and flour. Cook on a low heat for about 2 minutes, stirring all the time.
4. Gradually add stock, stirring all the time; then bayleaf, seasoning, tomato purée, chutney, lemon juice and raisins. Skin and chop tomato and stir in.
5. Bring to the boil, then simmer gently until vegetables are cooked (about 30 - 40 minutes).
6. Meanwhile prepare fish, remove bone and skin and cut into chunks.
7. Add to curry sauce and simmer very gently for about 10 minutes, until fish is cooked.
8. Serve on a bed of cooked rice; garnish with lemon and parsley.

5. Melt 25 g butter/margarine in a frying pan and fry fish fingers until slightly brown on each side.
6. Cut 4 oblong pieces of foil, about 9"× 12"; brush with oil.
7. Spread 1 tablesp. of vegetable sauce on half the foil. Place 2-3 fish fingers on top. Place any remaining sauce over them.

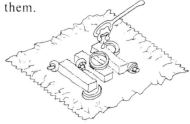

8. Fold over, seal well, place on tin and bake at 200°C (400°F), Gas mark 6, for 10 minutes.
9. Serve each 'parcel' on individual, warmed plates, with baked tomatoes; slit foil and garnish with parsley.

> *Note:* Fish fillets may be cooked in the same way.

Fish Fingers in Foil

Ingredients

8-12 frozen fish fingers	25 g flour
1 small onion	Salt, pepper
150 g mushrooms	125 ml milk
1 tablesp. parsley	2 tablesp. cream
50 g butter or margarine	

To serve:

Baked tomatoes

Method

1. Finely chop onion, mushroom and parsley.
2. Sauté in 25 g margarine until soft.
3. Blend in flour. Cook for 1 minute; gradually add milk and cream. Season.
4. Bring to the boil, then simmer for 3 minutes.

Reheated Dishes

Fish Cakes

Ingredients

200 g cooked fish
   (white or smoked)
200 g potato purée
½ teasp. grated lemon rind
1 teasp. lemon juice
Salt, pepper
Dessertsp. chopped parsley
Dripping (to fry)
Beaten egg (to bind)

To coat:

Egg and breadcrumbs

Garnish:

Lemon
Parsley

Method

1. Remove bones and skin from fish and flake with two forks.
2. Mix ingredients together well, binding with sufficient beaten egg to make mixture hold together.
3. On a floured board, form mixture into a roll. Cut in 8 and shape into flat cakes. Chill.
4. Coat with egg and breadcrumbs.
5. Cook in hot, shallow or deep fat, until golden brown and heated through.
6. Drain on kitchen paper.
7. Serve on a hot dish, garnished with lemon twists and parsley.

Fish Pie

Ingredients

400 g cooked fish	*1 teasp. lemon juice*
400 g potato purée	*1 teasp. butter or*
1 hard boiled egg	*margarine*
50 g cheese	*1 tablesp. milk*

Sauce:

25 g margarine	*Pepper, salt*
25 g flour	*Slice onion (optional)*
350 ml milk	*Bayleaf*

To garnish:

Sliced tomato
Parsley

Method

1. Remove bone and skin from fish and flake with two forks.
2. Chop egg, grate cheese.
3. **Sauce:** Melt margarine, add flour, cook for 1 minute, stirring to prevent burning. Slowly add milk, stirring all the time. Add seasoning, onion and bayleaf. Bring to the boil and simmer gently for 3 minutes.

4. Remove onion and bayleaf; add flaked fish, egg, cheese and lemon juice, keeping a little cheese back for decoration. Empty into greased dish.
5. Heat margarine and milk in saucepan. Add potatoes and mix well to soften and reheat.
6. Cover fish mixture with potato purée, sprinkle with grated cheese and bake at 200°C (400°F), Gas mark 6, for about 20-30 mins, until reheated through.
7. Halfway through, place sliced tomatoes around the outer rim of the fish pie.
8. Place pie dish on a hot dish which has a dish paper on it. Garnish with parsley.

Variation

Both Fish Pie and Fish Cakes may also be made from smoked fish or tinned salmon.

Kedgeree

(A substantial, breakfast, lunch or supper dish)

Ingredients

200 g smoked haddock	*1 teasp. curry powder*
(cooked)	*1 hard boiled egg*
25 g margarine	*Lemon juice*
200 g cooked long	
grain rice	

Garnish:

Cucumber and lemon slices

Method

1. Remove bones, fins, *etc.* from fish. Skin (if necessary) and flake.
2. Melt margarine, add curry powder. Cook for 1 minute, then add rice, flaked fish, lemon juice and chopped hard boiled egg.
3. **To serve hot:** pile into a hot dish.
   To serve cold: press into a clean mould, turn out on a serving plate.
4. Garnish with overlapping slices of lemon and cucumber and sprinkle with paprika.

12   All About Sauces

A sauce is a well flavoured liquid food. It may be thick — or thin; smooth — or textured; sweet — or savoury. It may be used to accompany food, or it may be part of a dish, as in stews. The main reasons sauces are served with food are:

1. To improve the appearance, taste and food value of plain food.
2. To moisten food.
3. To add variety and contrast to meals.
4. To bind food together.
5. To stimulate digestion.
6. To offset the richness of the food, *e.g.* apple sauce with roast pork.

The **food value** of sauces depends on the ingredients used — sauces made from eggs and milk, for example, would be more nourishing than sauces made with water.

A sauce should **suit the food** it is being served with. Some sauces are known to go well with certain foods — gravy with meat, for example, custard with many puddings, or mint sauce with lamb. Spicy sauces go well with foods which have little flavour; simple sauces are better with rich foods.

A good sauce will improve most food. A badly made sauce, which is lumpy or has no flavour, will ruin good food. If you want to make perfect sauces — follow the rules opposite.

Classifying Sauces

There are many types of sauces — most of them fall into one of these groups:

Roux sauces: such as white sauce, brown stewing sauce.
Custard sauces: made from eggs and milk.
Cold sauces: such as salad dressings.
Fruit sauces: such as apple sauce or jam sauce.
Miscellaneous sauces: including bread sauces.

Rules for Sauces

1. Carefully measure the correct amount of ingredients.
2. Follow the recipe exactly.
3. Cook the roux gently, to prevent burning.
4. Add liquid very slowly, stirring all the time — to prevent lumping.
5. Make sure the sauce is fully cooked — or it will taste raw and floury.
6. Season or flavour well, at the beginning of cooking time.
7. Use at once.*

*To Keep a Sauce Hot:** Stand the saucepan in a larger pan of simmering liquid. Dip a circle of paper in water and place straight onto the surface of the sauce. Cover with a lid. This will prevent a skin forming.

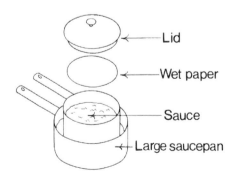

Lid — Wet paper — Sauce — Large saucepan

Roux Sauces

Roux (a French word) sauces contain equal amounts of fat and flour which are first cooked together to form a paste (or roux). The liquid is then added slowly — drop by drop, stirring all the time. The amount of liquid used depends on whether you want a thin **pouring sauce, a stewing sauce, a coating sauce,** or a very thick **binding sauce (or panard).**

The liquid used in white sauces is usually milk; stock or water is used for savoury or darker sauces.

A well made roux sauce should be:

1. A good colour.
2. Correct consistency (thickness).
3. Smooth, with no lumps.
4. Fully cooked.
5. Well flavoured.
6. Served hot.

Basic Roux Sauces

Ingredients

White Pouring Sauce:

25 g margarine
25 g flour
500 ml milk

White Stewing Sauce:

25 g margarine
25 g flour
375 ml milk

White Coating Sauce:

25 g margarine
25 g flour
250 ml milk

White Binding Sauce:
(Panard)

25 g margarine
25 g flour
125 ml milk

Seasoning: $\frac{1}{8}$ *tsp. salt/white pepper*

Method

1. Melt margarine in a small saucepan.
2. Add flour and cook over a *gentle* heat for one minute, stirring all the time. Add seasoning.
3. Remove from the heat and cool slightly.
4. Add milk, *drop by drop*, beating well after each addition to prevent lumps forming.

5. Return to heat and stir until sauce boils.
6. Reduce heat, cover and simmer gently for 5 minutes, stirring now and then.

Variations: (see next page).

Quick White Sauce

Place basic white sauce ingredients into a saucepan over moderate heat, bring to the boil whisking all the time with a wire balloon whisk. Boil for 5 mins.

Béchamel Sauce

*In French cookery, the milk used for making a
white sauce is first flavoured by 'infusing' spices
and other flavourings in it. This sauce tastes
much nicer than a plain white sauce — use it
for savoury pancakes or vol-au-vent fillings.*

Ingredients

2 cloves	*1 bay leaf*
Pinch powdered mace	*A small onion*

Sauce:

250 ml milk	*25 g flour*
25 g margarine	*Pepper and salt*

Method

1. Put cloves, mace, bayleaf, onion and seasoning into saucepan with milk. Leave on a very low heat to infuse (draw the flavour from the herbs and spices) for 15-20 mins. Strain liquid into a jug.
2. Rinse saucepan and make white coating sauce in the usual way, using flavoured milk.
3. If wished, 1 tablesp. cream or top of the milk can be stirred into the sauce just before serving.

Table 12.1

White Sauce Variations		
Sauce	**To each 500 ml basic sauce add**	**Serve with**
SAVOURY		
Caper sauce	1 tablesp. capers/chopped	Fish or Mutton
Cheese Sauce	50 g grated cheese/¼ tsp. made mustard	Fish/Cauliflower
Dutch Sauce	2 egg yolks/2 tablesp. vinegar (added very slowly)/¼ teasp. made mustard	Fish
Egg Sauce	1-2 hard boiled egg(s), chopped	Fish or Fowl
Mustard Sauce	1 teasp. made mustard, 1 tablesp. vinegar	Oily fish
Onion Sauce	Sauté 1 finely chopped onion in marg., before adding flour	Mutton or Tripe
Parsley Sauce	1-2 tablesp. finely chopped parsley	Bacon/ham or Fish
Shrimp Sauce	Small can shrimps, few drops anchovy essence.	Fish
SWEET		
Vanilla Sauce	½ teasp. vanilla essence, 2 teasp. sugar (leave out seasoning)	Steamed pudding

Brown Roux Sauces

Brown Pouring Sauce or Gravy

25 g dripping **or**	25 g flour
2 tablesp. sediment	500 ml stock
from meat	Pepper & salt

Method

1. Melt fat in a saucepan **or** drain off fat from roasting tin, leaving about 2 tablesp. of sediment from roast meat.
2. Add flour, stir in well, allowing it to brown over a low heat.
3. Gradually add stock, stirring all the time.
4. Season and bring slowly to the boil.
5. Simmer for 3-4 minutes and strain into a hot sauce boat.

Brown Stewing Sauce

(used as a basis for stews)

Ingredients

25 g dripping	Pepper & salt
25 g flour	1 teasp. Worcester Sauce
1 small onion	or tomato ketchup
375 ml stock	

Brown Binding Sauce

(used for rissoles)

Ingredients

25 g dripping	Pepper & salt
25 g flour	1 teasp. Worcester Sauce
1 small onion	or tomato ketchup
125 ml stock	

Method

1. Peel and finely chop onion.
2. Melt dripping, add onion, and cook gently until beginning to brown.
3. Add flour and seasoning, stir over a gentle heat until flour begins to turn sandy in colour. Be careful not to burn sauce at this stage.

4. Remove from heat and cool slightly.
5. Add stock very slowly, beating well to prevent lumps forming. Stir in sauce or ketchup.
6. Return to heat and stir until sauce boils.
7. Reduce heat and simmer for 5 minutes.

Variations

Curry sauce: see below.
Tomato sauce: see p. 113

The following sauces are variations on the above:

Curry Sauce

Ingredients

25 g fat
25 g flour
1 small onion (finely chopped)
1 dessertsp. curry powder
1 tomato (or 1 teasp. tomato ketchup)
1 small cooking apple
375 ml stock
1 dessertsp. chutney
Salt/1 teasp. lemon juice.

Method:

1. Melt fat, fry onion until beginning to brown.
2. Add flour and curry powder and cook over a low heat for 3 minutes, stirring all the time.
3. Remove from heat and cool slightly.
4. Gradually add stock, stirring all the time.
5. Bring to boil, add skinned, chopped tomato or ketchup, peeled, chopped apple, lemon juice, chutney and salt. Stir.
6. Simmer gently for 30-40 mins. Strain if wished.

Use for: Reheating meat
Cooking fish curry
Curried eggs

Tomato Sauce

Ingredients

25 g fat
1 streaky rasher or
  2 or 3 bacon rinds
1 small onion (chopped)
1 small carrot (chopped)
25 g flour
375 ml stock or water
4 med. tomatoes, canned or fresh
  or 1-2 tablesp. tomato purée
Salt/pepper/bay leaf

Method

1. Melt fat in saucepan, add bacon rinds or chopped rasher and fry until golden brown.
2. Add onion and carrot and fry gently until brown.
3. Add flour and cook over a low heat for 1 minute, stirring all the time.
4. Gradually stir in stock, sliced tomatoes or purée, salt, pepper and bayleaf.
5. Bring to the boil, skim and simmer for about 20 minutes.
6. Strain and correct seasoning. Correct consistency if necessary. If sauce is too thick, add a little more water and simmer for 2 minutes. If it is too thin, boil rapidly to reduce by evaporation.

Use with: Spaghetti   Chicken
           Hamburgers   Meat loaf
           Meat balls   Fish

Fruit Sauces

Jam Sauce

Ingredients

250 ml water
2 tablesp. jam or marmalade
Strip lemon rind
1 teasp. sugar
1 teasp. cornflour
1 tablesp. lemon juice

Method

1. Put water, jam and rind into saucepan.
2. Infuse for about 15 minutes. Strain.
3. Blend cornflour in bowl with lemon juice, add liquid, stirring to prevent lumping.
4. Return to heat, bring to the boil, stirring all the time. Simmer gently for 5 minutes.
5. Stir in sugar until dissolved. Add colouring if required.

Serve with: Steamed puddings
              Ice cream

Syrup Sauce

Ingredients

250 ml syrup from canned fruit
  e.g. pineapple, peaches, raspberries
1 teasp. lemon juice
2 teasp. cornflour or custard
  powder
Sugar to sweeten (if necessary)
A little chopped fruit e.g. peaches

Method

1. Blend cornflour into syrup. Bring to boil and simmer for 2 minutes.
2. Stir in sugar to taste, lemon juice and chopped fruit.
3. Serve in sauce jug.

Serve with: Steamed puddings

Apple Sauce

Ingredients

2 medium cooking apples
Strip of lemon rind
2 tablesps. water
1-2 teasp. brown or white sugar
25 g butter or margarine

Method

1. Peel, core and slice apples.
2. Put into a saucepan with the lemon rind and water. Cover. Stew over a low heat until soft. Remove rind.
3. Beat out lumps with a wooden spoon — or for a smoother sauce, rub through a nylon sieve or blend in a liquidiser.
4. Stir in sugar and butter and melt over a low heat.
5. Serve hot or cold in a sauce boat or small bowl.

Serve with: Roast pork

Gooseberry Sauce

Ingredients

200 g gooseberries   25 g sugar
125 ml water   Squeeze lemon juice

Method

1. Top and tail gooseberries; simmer with water and juice until soft (10 mins).
2. Sieve or blend in liquidiser. Stir in sugar.

Serve with: Baked or grilled mackerel or herrings

Other Sauces

Bread Sauce

Ingredients

250 ml milk   Blade of mace
1 small onion   4 peppercorns or pepper
2 cloves   Salt
1 bayleaf
35-40 g (about 6 tablesps. white breadcrumbs)
1 teasp. butter or margarine

Method

1. Infuse milk, peeled onion, cloves, bayleaf, mace, pepper and salt in a saucepan for 20-30 mins. Strain.
2. Return milk to saucepan, stir in breadcrumbs and return to heat, stirring now and then, until thick.
3. Stir in butter and serve.

Serve with: Roast chicken or turkey.

Mint Sauce

Ingredients

2 tablesp. chopped mint
1 teasp. brown sugar
2 tablesp. boiling water
2 tablesp. vinegar

Method

1. Put mint and sugar into small bowl.
2. Pour boiling water over and stir until sugar dissolves.
3. Cool, then stir in vinegar.

Serve with: Roast lamb

Butterscotch Sauce

Ingredients

100 g brown sugar
25 g butter or margarine
1 tablesp. cornflour or custard powder
Rind and juice of a lemon
250 ml water

Method

1. Dissolve cornflour in 2 tablesp. of measured water.

2. Place rest of water in saucepan with the sugar and stir over a gentle heat until dissolved.
3. Add butter and lemon rind and boil for 5 minutes.
4. Add blended cornflour, and stir until it boils. Add lemon juice and serve.

Chocolate Sauce

Ingredients

1 tablesp. cocoa (sieved)
50 g sugar
1 tablesp. cornflour
¼ teasp. instant coffee powder
or essence
2-3 drops vanilla essence
250 ml. milk or water

Method

1. Blend cocoa, sugar, cornflour and coffee with 2 tablesp. of measured milk or water. Add rest of water and put in saucepan.
2. Bring slowly to the boil, stirring all the time.
3. Boil for 1 minute, add vanilla essence and serve.

Both of the sauces above are delicious poured over ice cream.

Other recipes:

Maître d'hotel butter, p. 105
Custard sauces, p. 128-30
Salad dressings, p. 131

Over to you . . .

Fish

1. At your local fish shop, find out the prices of the following fish, and write them into your copy.
   Cod ....; Mackerel ....; Plaice ....;
   Whiting ....; Herrings ....; Sole ....
   Compare the cost of one fish, *e.g.* plaice, filleted and 'on the bone'.

2. Using your local or school library, find out as much as you can about the fishing industry in Ireland and write at least two pages about it into your copybook.

3. Find out the cost of 3 types of (a) frozen fish and (b) tinned fish. Compare them with fresh fish under the headings (i) food value; (ii) cost; (iii) convenience.

4. Look up some cookery books to find an unusual recipe for fish. Write it into your copybook and say how you would garnish it. (*Bord Iascaigh Mhara* are a good source of fish recipes).

5. Have you ever bought fish from a fish and chip shop? Find out the cost of a portion for one, and cost the same recipe if you were to cook it at home.

6. Give possible causes for the following faults in a white sauce.
   (a) lumps in the sauce;
   (b) a raw floury taste;
   (c) tasteless.

Sauces
List the three most important points to be remembered in order to obtain good results when making sauces.

7. What sauces would you serve with the following foods:
   Spaghetti; hamburgers; smoked cod; roast beef; steamed puddings; roast turkey.
   Write the recipe for *maître d'hotel butter* and list 3 foods it could be served with.

13   All About Vegetables

Many people look upon vegetables as a second rate food, since they usually act as an accompaniment to a meat or fish dish. This is a pity because vegetables are an important food in their own right. They are appetising and nourishing and supply the body with valuable vitamins and minerals.

In the past, vegetables were often cooked carelessly, swimming around in lots of water, until they were a soft tasteless pulp. Now we know better — cooking them in the minimum amount of liquid for the shortest possible time makes them twice as tasty and nourishing.

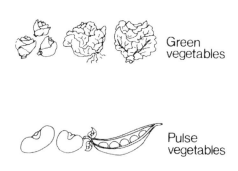

Root vegetables

Green vegetables

Pulse vegetables

Classification

Most vegetables can be placed in one of four groups. The food value and method of preparing and cooking the vegetables in each group are very alike.

Fruits

Table 13.1

Greens	Roots *	Pulses	Fruits
Cabbage	Carrots	Peas	Tomatoes
Kale	Parsnips	Broad beans	Peppers
Spinach	Swedes	French beans	Cucumber
Broccoli	Beetroot	Lentils	Marrow
Lettuce	Potatoes (tubers)	Dried peas	Courgettes
Brussels sprouts	Onion (bulbs)	Dried beans	Aubergine
Cauliflower			Pumpkin
			Sweetcorn

The classifcation here includes vegetables growing under the soil, e.g. tubers and bulbs.

Value in the Diet

1. Vegetables are a good source of Vitamins A, C and sometimes B.
2. They supply several minerals, especially iron and calcium.
3. They supply roughage.
4. Some provide protein (pulses).
5. Some provide energy (potatoes, roots and pulses).
6. They add variety, colour and flavour to our diet.
7. They supply large amounts of water.

All vegetables are deficient in fats. For this reason fat is often added in the final stages of cooking to improve flavour and food value.

Buying Vegetables

The importance of freshness cannot be over-stressed.

1. Vegetables must be as fresh as possible — buy from a good greengrocer who stocks fresh produce.
2. Vegetables should be firm, crisp and fresh looking, not bruised, withered or wilted.
3. Buy young, medium sized vegetables — large, old vegetables are tasteless.
4. Do not buy in large quantities — they do not keep well.
5. Avoid buying prepacked vegetables as these often hide blemishes, and plastic encourages mould growth.
6. Buy vegetables when they are in season — they are cheaper and at their best then.

Value for Money

While vegetables are cheaper than meat or fish, they are still rather expensive. Prices vary, depending on weather, production costs, demand, scarcity and quality. Prepacked vegetables tend to be more expensive. Greengrocers are a cheaper and more reliable source of fruit and vegetables than supermarkets. And of course, the cheapest way of all is to grow your own vegetables.

Vegetables in Season

Table 13.2

Spring*	Summer	Autumn	Winter
Potatoes	New potatoes	Potatoes	Potatoes
Spring cabbage	Cabbage	Cabbage	Cabbage
Onions	Spring onions	Onions	Onions
Mushrooms	Mushrooms	Mushrooms	Mushrooms
Cauliflower	Cauliflower	Cauliflower	Cauliflower
Lettuce (hothouse)	Lettuce	Lettuce	Lettuce (hothouse)
Celery	—	Celery	Celery
Parsnips/turnips	—	Parsnips/turnips	Parsnips/turnips
—	Carrots	Carrots	Carrots
—	—	Brussels sprouts	Brussels sprouts
—	Peas, beans	Beans	—

Vegetables tend to be scarce in spring – this is the time to avail of canned and frozen produce.

Table 13.3

Category	Food Value	Buying	Storing
Greens	Water 90 - 95% Vitamin A + C Good source of iron – also of calcium, potassium Cellulose	1. Crisp, fresh, green leaves 2. Not limp or withered 3. Not eaten by insects 4. Firm, closely-packed heads	1. Use immediately if possible. 2. Wash well, shake dry, place in plastic bag in salad drawer of refrigerator. *Or* 3. Place unwashed in a tightly covered tin or saucepan.
Roots (*incl.* **potatoes and onions**)	Water 70 - 90% Vitamin C (A in carrots) Protein 1 - 2% Carbohydrate 5 - 20% A little calcium and iron Cellulose	1. Firm, hard, with no bruises 2. Heavy for size 3. Good colour 4. Smooth undamaged skin 5. Not pliable or shrivelled 6. Not too large 7. No soil clinging	1. Remove from plastic bags. 2. Store in cold, dry dark ventilated place, *e.g.* larder. A kitchen is not ideal. 3. Use a vegetable rack.
Pulses	Water 75 - 90% Protein 2 - 5% Carbohydrate 4 - 10% Vitamin A + C Minerals: calcium, potassium	1. Hard crisp pods 2. Good green colour 3. Full but not bulging 4. Heavy for size 5. Not shrivelled	1. Store in tin or saucepan with tightly fitting lid. 2. Dried pulses are easy to store, but should be used within 6 months.
Fruits	Water 90 - 95% Protein 1% Carbohydrate 2% Vitamin A + C Minerals; iron	1. Hard, firm 2. Good bright colour 3. No withering or bruising	1. Wash, dry. 2. Store in salad drawer of refrigerator.

Grading Fruit and Vegetables

EEC standards of grading and labelling are now observed in our shops. These make sure that the produce is (a) sound, clean and free from soil and chemicals; (b) graded with produce of similar size; (c) clearly marked with quality, class, origin and variety.

Class extra — Best quality produce
Class I — Good quality
Class II — Marketable quality, but with possible defects of shape, colouring and blemishes
Class III — Marketable but inferior.

Methods of Cooking

Vegetables are cooked in order to soften them and make them more digestible. Boiling is the traditional way to cook most vegetables, especially greens.

Boiling

1. Place prepared, washed vegetables in boiling, salted water. (If the water is not boiling there will be greater loss of vitamins.)
2. It is not necessary to cover the food with water — about 4 cm water is usually sufficient.
3. Cover tightly with a lid and cook quickly.
4. Cook until just tender, but not mushy.
5. Drain well and serve at once.

Steaming

1. Prepare vegetables. Dice large vegetables and place in steamer over a saucepan of boiling water. Season.
2. Cook until just tender — 20–30 minutes according to type and size. (Steaming takes 1½ times as long as boiling.)

Stewing and Braising

Prepared vegetables are stewed gently in a well-flavoured sauce. Food value is retained, as most nutrients go into the sauce which is eaten.

Other Methods of Cooking Vegetables

Baking — potatoes; tomatoes; marrow.
Roasting in fat — potatoes and root vegetables.
Frying — chips and sauté potatoes; tomatoes; mushrooms.
Grilling — tomatoes; mushrooms.
Stir frying — a combination of frying and steaming frequently used in Chinese cookery. Vegetables are cooked to perfection, retaining crispness, colour flavour and food value.

Effects of Cooking

1. Cellulose is softened.
2. Starch is cooked and made more digestible.
3. Vegetables absorb water and swell.
4. If overcooked, they may break up.
5. Loss of vitamins, particularly Vitamin C.
6. Minerals dissolve into cooking water.
7. Loss of colour, flavour and texture.

To retain Maximum Food Value

1. Eat vegetables raw where possible.
2. Use freshest possible vegetables, in peak condition.
3. Prepare just before cooking.
4. Wash quickly and thoroughly, but do not steep.
5. Peel thinly — use a sharp knife to trim and shred. Do not tear — this damages cell walls, releasing oxidase, which destroys Vitamin C.
6. Cook quickly in minimum amount of liquid.
7. Cover with a lid, to reduce oxidation.
8. Do not overcook — vegetables should be tender, but not soft.
9. Do not keep warm for long or they will have little food value.
10. Never use bread soda when cooking vegetables — it destroys Vitamin C.
11. Use cooking liquid for sauces, soups, *etc.*
12. Add freshly chopped parsley to finished dish — to restore iron and Vitamin C.

Cooking Preserved Vegetables

It is now possible to buy most vegetables all the year round, thanks to modern food processing. When using any processed vegetables, follow the directions supplied for reconstituting, reheating or cooking.

A. Frozen vegetables

A wide variety of frozen vegetables is available. These are equal in food value to fresh vegetables, since so little time elapses between picking and freezing the produce. Frozen vegetables are cooked, from frozen, in a little boiling salted water, until tender. Add a knob of butter and seasoning at the end of the cooking time.

B. Tinned and Bottled vegetables

These lose Vitamin C in processing. Much of the mineral content dissolves into the preserving liquid, so use this up in gravies, *etc.* Many varieties, *e.g.* tomatoes, are cheaper than the fresh equivalent, and as tinned vegetables only need reheating, they save fuel.

C. Dried vegetables

A wide variety of dried pulse vegetables is available at delicatessen shops. These are a useful source of vegetable protein, but lack vitamins, which are lost in drying. For this reason, they are not a good substitute for fresh vegetables. Dried vegetables are steeped for several hours before cooking; some varieties must be boiled strongly for the first five minutes of cooking, to destroy harmful enzymes, then simmered very gently until soft.

Freeze-dried vegetables

A wider variety of vegetables can be freeze-dried than can be dried by traditional methods. This method is far superior in flavour, quality and food value.

Freeze-dried vegetables are light and easy to store and are quickly reconstituted (steeped to restore their water content). Follow directions on the packet for preparing and cooking.

COOKING GREENS
Table 13.4

Greens	Preparation	Cooking	Serving
Cabbage	1. Remove outer withered leaves. 2. Cut in quarters. 3. Wash under cold running water, separating leaves if necessary.	1. Cook in boiling, salted water — just enough to come half way up the vegetables. 2. Cook for 10 mins, until tender. 3. Drain in colander.	1. Toss in 25 g seasoned melted butter. 2. Serve *at once* in hot vegetable dish.
Kale	1. Remove withered leaves. 2. Strip leaves from thick stems. 3. Wash well under cold running water.	As above	As above
Brussels Sprouts	1. Cut a slice from base and peel off outer leaves. 2. Cut a cross on base of each sprout. 3. Wash well in colander.	As above (8 – 10 mins)	As above
Spinach	1. Pick through leaves, removing coarse stalks and withered leaves. 2. Wash well under cold running water.	1. Place in a large saucepan and heat gently. (There is no need to use water as enough clings to leaves.) 2. Season and cook gently, for 5 – 10 mins. 3. Drain well in colander.	1. Chop or purée in blender (if wished). 2. Pour a little cream or melted butter over.
Broccoli/ Cauliflower	1. Remove withered leaves. 2. Leave about 10 cm of leaves and stalk with each flour head. Cauliflower may be cooked whole or in flowerettes. 3. Wash well.	As for cabbage (8 – 10 mins)	1. Place in hot vegetable dish. 2. Pour melted butter over. 3. Cauliflower au Gratin — coat with cheese sauce and brown under grill or in oven (*see p. 111*).

COOKING ROOT VEGETABLES
Table 13.5

Root	Preparation	Cooking	Serving
Carrots	1. Top, tail and scrape. 2. Wash in cold water. 3. If large, cut in rings; if small, leave whole.	1. Cook until tender in boiling salted water (15–20 mins) 2. Drain.	1. Toss in melted butter or mash with butter or coat with white sauce. 2. Sprinkle with parsley.
Parsnips	As above	As above	As above
Swede Turnips	1. Peel thickly 2. Cut in chunks. 3. Wash in colander.	As above (20–30 mins)	1. Mash well, stir in 1 tablespn. cream and seasoning.
Beetroot	1. Wash carefully – do not break skin. Leave 2 cm stalk and root.	1. Place whole in boiling water. 2. Simmer for 1–2 hours, until tender, when skin peels off easily. 3. Peel.	1. Slice, place in hot vegetable dish. 2. Pour soured cream over. Sprinkle with chives. 3. Slice, serve in vinegar or vinaigrette dressing.
Onions	1. Top, tail, peel. 2. Rinse under cold water.	1. Cook whole in boiling salted water for 20–30 minutes. Drain. **or** 2. Slice and fry in butter or dripping, until soft and golden. Drain.	1. Serve in warm dish. Coat with white sauce or variation. **or** 2. Serve as an accompaniment to to steaks, grills, *etc.*
Boiled potatoes	1. Scrub well. 2. Peel thinly, (optional). 3. New potatoes should be scraped well.	1. Cook in boiling salted water, with or without jackets. Simmer until soft (15–20 mins). 2. Put mint in water with new potatoes.	1. Serve in hot vegetable dish. (Jacket potatoes are more nutritious.) 2. New potatoes: pour a little melted butter over and sprinkle with chopped mint.

COOKING ROOT VEGETABLES (continued)

Root	Preparation	Cooking	Serving
Creamed potatoes	As for boiled potatoes	1. As for boiled potatoes, without jackets. 2. Drain well. Mash. 3. Beat in 2 tblsp. milk, 25 g butter or margarine and seasoning.	1. Pile into hot dish. 2. Sprinkle with parsley.
Potato Croquettes	As for boiled potatoes.	1. As above. 2. Beat in egg yolk. 3. Shape into croquettes. 4. Coat with egg and crumbs. 5. Deep fry in hot fat for 3–4 mins. Drain well.	1. Serve at once. 2. Garnish with parsley.
Sauté potatoes	1. As for boiled potatoes. 2. Slice thickly.	1. Melt butter (50 g) or oil (3–4 tblsps.) in frying pan. 2. Add sliced potatoes. 3. Fry on each side, until golden brown.	1. Drain well. 2. Place in warmed serving dish. 3. Garnish with parsley.
Baked potatoes (medium or large)	1. Scrub potatoes well. 2. Prick with skewer. 3. Rub with salt and place on baking tray.	1. Bake at 200°C (400°F), Gas mark 6, for about 1 hour, depending on size, until soft when squeezed.	1. Cut a cross in the top of each. 2. Season and add a knob of butter and a sprinkle of chives.
Chipped potatoes	1. Scrub & peel potatoes. 2. Cut in thick slices, then lengthwise into chips. 3. Soak in cold water for 10 mins. Dry thoroughly.	1. Deep fry in hot oil for 5 mins. 2. Lift basket from oil and reheat. 3. Return to oil and deep fry for 1–2 mins to crisp.	1. Drain well on kitchen paper. 2. Sprinkle a little salt over. 3. Serve in hot dish.

COOKING PULSE VEGETABLES
Table 13.6

Vegetable	Preparation	Cooking	Serving
Peas	1. Shell and wash in cold water, using a colander.	Cook in boiling salted water until tender (about 10 mins) with a sprig of mint. Drain.	1. Toss in melted butter. Season. 2. Serve in hot dish.
Broad beans	1. Shell, wash in colander.	Simmer until tender (15–20 mins). Drain.	1. Toss in melted butter or coat with parsley sauce.
French Beans	1. Top & tail. 2. Wash under cold running water, in colander. 3. String mature beans.	Boil in salted water (10-15 mins.) Drain.	1. Toss in butter, season or melt 25 g margarine. 2. Sauté. 1 chopped onion + tomato mixed herbs, add beans. Serve in hot dish.
Marrowfat peas	1. Steep overnight, using soda tablet to help soften peas. Drain. 2. Wash well.	Simmer very gently for 10–15 mins, until cooked. Do not season. Drain.	1. Melt some butter, add seasoning and chopped parsley. 2. Place peas in hot dish, pour butter over.
COOKING OTHER VEGETABLES			
Baked Tomatoes	Wash well.	Bake in moderate oven for 15 mins.	
Corn on the cob	1. Pull off husk and silky threads. 2. Wash well.	Cook in boiling water for 7–10 mins. Drain.	Dribble melted butter over. Season.
Celery	1. Trim off root and leaves, wash well with brush. 2. Remove bruised or discoloured parts. 3. Slice into 5 cm pieces.	Cook in boiling salted water for about 20–30 mins, until soft. **or** Braise in brown sauce.	Coat with white sauce or braise in brown sauce. Garnish with parsley.

Colcannon

A traditional Irish recipe for Hallowe'en. Stir in some coins wrapped in foil and a ring, to see who will be next to marry!

Ingredients

400 g cooked potato
25 g butter or margarine
1 teasp. chopped onion
200 g cooked kale or cabbage
Pepper & salt
A little milk

Method

1. Mash potato; melt butter, sauté onion for 2 mins but do not brown.
2. Add potatoes, cabbage, seasoning and milk. Cream well together, until piping hot.
3. Pile onto vegetable dish, stir in 'favours'. Garnish with parsley.

Stuffed Tomatoes

Ingredients

8 medium tomatoes
50 g breadcrumbs
25 g margarine
1 slice finely chopped onion
25 g grated cheese or
   25 g chopped cooked ham
1 teaspoon parsley (chopped)
Pinch mixed herbs
Salt/pepper

Method

1. Wash tomatoes, cut slice from the smooth end of each for a lid.
2. Scoop tomato pulp into bowl, using a teaspoon.
3. Melt margarine; add onion, pulp, breadcrumbs, ham or cheese, herbs and seasoning. Mix well.
4. Pile mixture into tomato shells, replace lids.
5. Place on greased baking tin. Cover with greaseproof paper, greased.
6. Bake at 175°C (350°F), Gas mark 4, for 15-20 mins, until soft.
7. Serve as an accompaniment to grills, *etc.*, or as a savoury dish on freshly buttered toast.
8. Garnish with parsley.

Ratatouille

(A mediterranean vegetable casserole)

Ingredients

4 tablespoons cooking oil
1 large onion
1 green pepper
1 large aubergine
3 courgettes
4 large tomatoes
Salt/pepper
1 dessertspoon chopped parsley
Pinch oregano or mixed herbs
1 crushed clove garlic

Method

1. Peel and slice onion; wash, seed and slice pepper.
2. Wipe and slice aubergine and courgette.
3. Peel and slice tomatoes.
4. Heat oil in casserole, add onion and sauté gently for 5 minutes.
5. Add pepper and aubergine, followed by courgettes and tomatoes. Add herbs, garlic and seasoning to taste. Cover.
6. Gently stew ingredients for about 30 mins. Remove lid and simmer for about 10 more mins.
7. Serve at once, in the casserole in which it was cooked, or transfer to another dish and garnish with parsley. Serve with roast chicken, or grilled meat or fish.

Method

1. Peel, core and slice apples. Peel and slice onion.
2. Wash, trim and shred cabbage.
3. Put apple, onion, cabbage, raisins, sugar, seasoning into casserole. Pour over stock. Stir well.
4. Cover and bake at 180°C (350°F), Gas mark 4, for 1 hour, until cabbage is tender.
5. Adjust seasoning; stir in butter and serve from casserole. Garnish with parsley.
6. Serve with roast pork.

Casserole of Red Cabbage

Ingredients

1 small head red cabbage	25 g raisins
1 large onion	1 teaspoon sugar
1 large cooking apple	Salt and pepper
About 300 ml chicken stock	25 g butter

Over to you . . .

1. Plan a lunch menu for (a) summer and (b) winter, using vegetables in season.

   In the case of each menu, write a recipe for an unusual vegetable dish which could be served.

2. Make a list of all the methods you know for cooking potatoes.

   Write a recipe for a dish which uses up leftover potatoes (not from this book).

3. **Experiment**

   Careless preparation of vegetables can be very wasteful. Prepare, *i.e.* wash and peel, 300 g equal sized potatoes using a knife. Prepare another 300 g using a potato peeler. Weigh the potatoes after peeling, and find out which method is most economical.

4. Find out from your greengrocer the cost of the following vegetables per kilo (lb): potatoes; carrots; onions; swede turnips; mushrooms; lettuce; green peppers; cabbage; cauliflower; brussels sprouts; celery.

   Visit your local supermarket and compare costs.

   Perhaps all the students in the class could take part in the survey to find the cheapest greengrocer in the locality. Make a chart from the results and hang it up in the Home Economics room.

14　All About Salads

As most vegetables are more nourishing when they are eaten raw, what better way to serve them than in a crisp, refreshing salad? Salads are not only made from vegetables, though.

A salad can be made from a mixture of many **different foods** — vegetables, fruit, meat, fish, eggs, cheese and rice are all used in salads.

A salad can be a **complete meal** in itself or can **accompany** a main course such as grilled steak or roast chicken.

Value of Salads in the Diet

1. Rich in minerals and vitamins, especially Vitamin C.
2. They provide roughage (fibre) which prevents constipation.
3. They are cool and refreshing, providing a contrast in colour, flavour and texture, to cooked dishes.
4. They are ideal for summer meals, picnics and packed lunches.
5. They are quick and easy to prepare.
6. They are handy in emergencies.
7. They are useful for using up leftovers.
8. Many are low in kilocalories and therefore ideal for slimmers.

Rules for Salad Making

1. All ingredients should be very fresh.
2. Vegetables should be young and crisp and in peak condition.
3. Wash vegetables gently, dry thoroughly.
4. Handle as little as possible, to avoid bruising.
5. Arrange ingredients attractively, using colourful vegetables to garnish.
6. Use herbs, pickles, nuts and raisins to improve food value and add interest and texture.
7. Use a salad dressing to improve food value and flavour.
8. Prepare salads just before serving, or cover with cling film and chill in refrigerator until crisp.

Preparation

Remember many vegetables have been sprayed with chemicals to help them grow.

1. Wash all salad vegetables gently, but thoroughly, under cold running water.
2. Remove toughest outside leaves, coarse stalks and roots. Wash leaf by leaf, examining carefully for insects.
3. Shake dry in salad basket or clean teatowel.
4. Cooked vegetables should be just tender. Dice or slice.

Preparing 'Salad' Vegetables

Vegetables often used in salads are called 'salad vegetables':

Lettuce: Remove withered outer leaves (coarse leaves can be shredded). Wash leaves one by one under cold water. Shake dry.

Watercress: Pick away damaged roots and leaves. Wash very thoroughly (watercress often grows near polluted streams).

Spring Onions (Scallions): Cut off roots and tops of leaves. Peel away outer layer, wash and dry.

Cucumber: Wash well and slice thinly. Peeling is not necessary.

Tomatoes: Wash well. Slice or quarter, using a serrated knife. Remove green stem.

Radishes: Cut away top and root. Wash. Slice or leave whole.

Cabbage: Use hard white heads (Dutch cabbage). Wash well, dry and shred finely with sharp knife.

Other vegetables used in salads include carrots, celery, green and red pepper, avocado, fresh green herbs: (add flavour — try parsley, basil, chives), pickles (mixed pickles, beetroot, capers).

Serving Salads

Serve in a salad bowl *or* arrange attractively on a large dish *or* arrange on individual dishes. Toss in dressing or serve dressing separately.

Dressings

Salad dressings add flavour and food value. Do not toss salad in dressing until the last minute or the lettuce will go limp. Better still, serve dressing separately in a small jug or shaker, so that diners can help themselves.

Method

1. Wash, trim and dry ingredients. Place in polythene bag and chill in salad drawer of fridge.
2. Arrange attractively in a wooden salad bowl. Sprinkle with chopped parsley.
3. If wished, toss in French dressing.
4. Serve with grilled or roast meat or fish.

Summer Salad

(Serve for tea with brown soda bread)

Ingredients

1 lge head lettuce	*1 bunch spring onions*
2 eggs	*(scallions)*
4 tomatoes	*Cress or water cress*
Cucumber	*Parsley*
4-6 radishes	

Method

1. Hard-boil eggs for 10 mins. Cool and remove shells.
2. Wash, trim and dry lettuce, onions, cress and parsley. Place in plastic bag in salad drawer of fridge to chill.
3. Wash and slice cucumber, radishes, tomatoes.
5. Arrange attractively in a salad bowl or on individual plates.
5. Sprinkle with chopped parsley.
6. Serve French dressing or mayonnaise separately.

Simple Salads

Green Salad

Ingredients

1 large head lettuce
Bunch of scallions or chives
Cucumber (if wished)
Parsley

Tomato Salad

Ingredients

6 hard ripe tomatoes
1 medium onion
Fresh parsley or chives

Dressing:

French dressing or yoghurt dressing

Method

1. Skin tomatoes if wished. Slice thinly crosswise.
2. Peel and slice onions thinly, break into rings.
3. Arrange on flat dish with rings of onion and tomato overlapping.
4. Pour dressing over.
5. Sprinkle with parsley or chives.

Mushroom Salad

Ingredients

200 g mushrooms
1 tsp. parsley or chives

Dressing:
Juice ½ lemon
Salt/pepper
4 tblsp. olive oil
1 tablesp. mayonnaise (if wished)

Method:

1. Wash and trim mushrooms, slice thinly.
2. Blend dressing ingredients together in bowl.
3. Mix in mushrooms, chill in refrigerator for ½–1 hour.
4. Sprinkle with chopped chives or parsley.

Mixed Salads

Meat Salad

Arrange slices or rolls of cooked meat *e.g.* ham, beef, salami or chicken portions on plate, garnish with lettuce leaves, spring onions, tomato, cucumber, *etc.* Serve dressing separately.

Fish Salad

Place slices or fillets of cooked fish, such as cod, herring, smoked mackerel, trout or salmon, on a plate. Garnish with shredded lettuce, hard boiled egg, cucumber and tomato. Pour mayonnaise diluted with a little cream or tomato purée over fish. Garnish with lemon and parsley.

Shell fish such as mussels, prawns, scallops can also be used.

Winter Salads

The following salads are useful for times when salad ingredients are hard to get.

Potato Salad

Ingredients

½ kg waxy potatoes
*1 sml onion or a few scallions
  or chives*
Parsley
150 ml mayonnaise
1 tablesp. lemon juice
Salt/pepper
2 sticks celery (optional)

Method

1. Cook potatoes in their skins until just tender (about 15 mins).
2. Drain well, peel and cut into 2 cm dice.
3. Wash and dice celery. Peel and chop onion.
4. Place potatoes, onion and celery into a bowl.
5. Pour in mayonnaise, lemon juice and seasoning.
6. Using a tablespoon, carefully fold ingredients together.
7. Serve in salad bowl or dish. Sprinkle with chopped parsley.

Go easy on garlic!

The flavour of garlic is very strong. For a gentle hint of garlic in your salad, rub the inside of the salad bowl with a peeled clove of garlic, cut in two.

Russian Salad

Ingredients

½ *kilo mixed vegetables*
   e.g. potatoes, carrot, peas, beans
2 tomatoes
1-2 sticks celery
1 slice onion
Parsley

Dressing

4-6 tablesp. mayonnaise
2-3 tablesp. French dressing
Pepper/salt

Method

1. Cook prepared vegetables until *just* tender, but not soft, or use left over vegetables.
2. Dice into 2 cm squares.
3. Wash and dice celery. Chop onion.
4. Mix all vegetables carefully together in a large bowl.
5. Dilute mayonnaise with 2-3 tablespoons French dressing and fold gently into mixture.
6. Transfer to salad bowl and garnish with sliced tomatoes and parsley.

Coleslaw

(good with hamburgers, cold meat, flans, pizza)

Ingredients

1 small white cabbage   *1 apple (optional)*
1 large carrot   *Lemon juice*

Dressing:

150 ml French dressing
Salt/pepper

Method

1. Wash cabbage, cut in four, trim away stalk and shred finely.
2. Wash and shred carrots. Peel and grate onion.
3. Wash, core but do not peel apple. Dice and toss in lemon juice to prevent browning.
4. Place all ingredients into a bowl and carefully stir in dressing until vegetables are coated.
5. Transfer to serving dish, cover and chill in refrigerator until needed.

Waldorf Salad

Ingredients

2 red apples
50 g walnuts   **Dressing:**
3-4 sticks celery   *4 tablesp. mayonnaise*
2 tablesp. raisins   *2 tablesp. lemon juice*

Method

1. Wash, core and dice apples. Do not peel. Toss in lemon juice to prevent browning.
2. Wash and dice celery. Chop walnuts roughly.
3. Combine ingredients in bowl and moisten with mayonnaise. Chill before serving.

Salad Dressings

French Dressing (Vinaigrette)

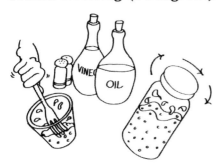

Ingredients

3 tablesp. corn or olive oil
1 tablesp. flavoured vinegar*
Salt/black pepper
Pinch sugar and/or mustard

* Use best quality oil and flavoured vinegars such as wine, cider or tarragon vinegar for best results.

Method

1. Put oil and vinegar into bowl. Blend well with fork.
2. Beat in seasonings.
3. Dressing ingredients can be shaken together in a screw-top jar and stored in the refrigerator.
4. Shake before use.

Yoghurt Dressing
(ideal for slimmers)

Ingredients

1 carton of plain yoghurt
2 teasp. lemon juice
Salt/pepper/pinch caster sugar
Chopped chives

Method

Blend ingredients together and chill until required.

Mayonnaise

Ingredients

1 egg yolk
2 tablesp. corn/olive oil
1 tablesp. vinegar/lemon juice
¼ teasp. made mustard
Salt/pepper
Pinch of caster sugar (optional)

Method

1. Oil and egg yolk should be at room temperature.
2. Blend mustard, salt, pepper and sugar with egg in small bowl.
3. Trickle on oil, drop by drop, beating vigorously.
4. When thick, add vinegar or juice, drop by drop, beating well.
5. Taste and correct seasoning.

Blender Mayonnaise

Ingredients

1 egg	*¼ teasp. salt*
125 ml oil	*¼ teasp. caster sugar*
1 tablesp. vinegar	*Pepper*
¼ teasp. mustard	

Method

Use whole egg, whisk with vinegar and seasonings. Pour oil slowly into mixture while machine is still running.

Over to you . . .

1. Plan an interesting and attractive dish which might encourage young children to eat salads.

   Write the recipe into your Home Economics copy — and include a sketch of how you would arrange and garnish the salad.

15 *All About Fruit*

Fruit is an ideal food for those with a sweet tooth. When you are feeling hungry it is a far better snack than sweets or biscuits, as it contains important vitamins and minerals and is far less fattening.

Uses of Fruit

1. Eat it raw — whole or in salads; for picnics and snacks.
2. Cold sweets — yoghurt, trifles, mousses, flans.
3. Hot puddings — stewed, baked or in tarts and pies.
4. Sauces — apple sauce, gooseberry sauce.
5. Preserves — jams and chutneys.
6. Fruit drinks — freshly squeezed juices, milk shakes.
7. For breakfasts — stewed prunes, with muesli.

Food Value

All fruit contains a lot of **water** (some fruits have over 90% water). The main reason fruit is important in our diet is because it has **Vitamin C.**

90% water

Some fruits also contain **Vitamin A** — usually bright coloured fruits such as apricots and peaches.

Fruit is rich in **minerals,** particularly **calcium** and **iron.** Dried fruit is a very good source of these.

Table 15.1

Composition of Fruit						
Fruit	**Water**	**Protein**	**Carbohydrate (Sugar)**	**Fat**	**Vitamins**	**Minerals**
Fresh	80 - 90%	trace	5 - 20%	0%	A + C	Calcium Iron
Canned	70 - 80%	trace	20 - 30%	0%	A + C (reduced)	Calcium Iron
*Dried**	15 - 25%	trace	50 - 60%	0%	A	Calcium Iron (increased)

*Note: Steeping alters the composition of dried fruit, raising the water content and lowering the sugar content.

Fruit, like vegetables, is rich in **cellulose,** which helps rid the body of waste and prevents constipation.

Because fruit has so much water it is **low in kilocalories.** If it is dried or canned, the sugar content is increased, doubling the kilocalories and lowering Vitamin C content.

Buying Fruit

1. Buy best quality fresh fruit.
2. Buy in small amounts and use up quickly.
3. Buy in season — when fruit is cheap and at its best.
4. Fruit should be *just* ripe, not over or under-ripe.
5. It should have a good colour.
6. It should be firm, not shrivelled or bruised.
7. Watch out for mould. If you buy a large quantity, check for damaged fruit or mould will quickly spread to others.
8. For grading fruit and vegetables *see p. 119.*

Why Fruit is Important in our Diet

1. It is a good source of vitamins, minerals and cellulose.
2. There is a wide variety available which add colour, flavour and texture to meals.
3. Cool and refreshing.
4. It is filling, yet low in kilocalories.
5. Fruit can be eaten raw or cooked, but raw fruit tastes better and has a higher food value.

Kilocalorie Content of some Fruits (per 100 g)

Table 15.2

Fruit	Kilocal.	Fruit	Kilocal.
Rhubarb	6	Apples	46
Lemons	7	Orange Juice	47
Grapefruit	22	Bananas	76
Melon	23	Canned pineapple	76
Raspberries	25	Canned peaches	88
Strawberries	26	Prunes	161
Oranges	35	Dates	248
Fresh Peaches	36	Sultanas	249

Effects of Cooking

1. Vitamin C content may be reduced by up to 25% (less than vegetables, due to acid content).
2. Texture is changed.
3. Cellulose breaks down, making some fruits more digestible.
4. Minerals dissolve into cooking liquid; be sure to use it.
5. Decaying organisms, such as moulds, are destroyed.

Preparation

1. Wash all fruit well to remove any traces of garden chemicals.
2. Prepare fruit at the last moment or Vitamin C will be lost.
3. Some fruits such as apples *must* be used at once or they will discolour.

4. Avoid peeling, unless absolutely necessary.
5. Remove cores, stones, *etc.* and any bruised parts.

Citrus Fruits

1. Wipe with damp cloth (if rind is to be grated). Dry.
2. Peel, removing all pith (white innner skin).
3. Section or slice, removing pips. Use at once.

Soft Fruit

(such as strawberries, raspberries, blackcurrants)

1. Pick out damaged fruit. Remove stalks.
2. Wash gently in colander. Dry carefully, using kitchen paper.

Hard Fruit
(such as apples, pears)

1. Wash, cut in quarters, peel and core.
2. Use at once, or cover with cold water, using a plate to hold apples under water.

Vitamin C Content of Fruit (per 100 g)

Table 15.3

Good sources	Vitamin C	Other Sources	Vitamin C
Blackcurrants	200 mg	Bananas	10 mg
Concentrated oranged juice	150 mg	Rhubarb	10 mg
Rose hip syrup	150 mg	Peaches	7 mg
Strawberries	60 mg	Apricots	7 mg
Oranges/lemons	50 mg	Apples	5 mg
Grapefruit, Gooseberries	40 mg	Grapes	4 mg
Raspberries/Melons	25 mg	Tinned fruit	3 - 10 mg

Rhubarb

1. Cut off leaves and base.
2. Wipe well with a clean, damp cloth.
3. Cut in slices 3-4 cm long.

Preserved Fruit

Many fresh fruits have a short season and are only available at certain times of the year. By preserving fruit we can have a far wider variety of fruit all the year round.

Fruit is available frozen and dried, as well as in cans and bottles. In the past, preserved foods were far less nourishing than fresh. Today canned and frozen fruits are almost as nourishing as garden fresh produce, due to modern methods of processing.

Frozen Fruit

Its **food value** is just as good as fresh fruit, but texture and appearance may be altered.

Buying:

1. Packs should be sealed and frozen solid.
2. Fruits in packs should remain separate.
3. Use within time on date stamp.

Thawing and Cooking

1. Thaw slowly in refrigerator, without opening.
2. Use as instructed on packet.

Canned Fruit

Vitamin C content may be reduced. Minerals may seep into canning syrup. Appearance and texture changes. High sugar level.

Buying:

1. Tins should have no bulges, dents or rust.

Using:

1. Serve fruit in its syrup, *or*
2. Drain syrup from fruit, by placing in a sieve over a bowl.
3. Use syrup to make sauce or glaze.

Dried Fruit

Vitamins B and C are almost totally lost. Colour changes (dried fruit darkens). High level of sugar. Many are rich in iron.

Buying:

1. Pack should be sealed.
2. Fruit should be a good colour, plump and not too dry looking, with no trace of sugary deposit.

Using:

1. Remove stalks. Wash gently in sieve.
2. Dry in clean teatowel or kitchen paper.
3. Steep overnight if necessary, *e.g.* apricots, prunes.

Over to you . . .

1. Find two recipes for interesting puddings using fresh fruit; write or stick them into your Home Economics copybook.

2. Make up an unusual fruit salad and write the recipe into your copy. Why is it better to serve fruit raw rather than cooked?

3. Name three ways fruit can be included in the diet, other than raw, or in puddings.

    What are the three most important points to remember when buying fruit?

16 *All About Milk*

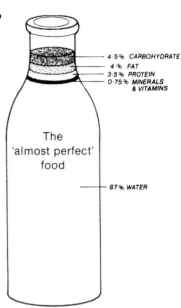

4·5% CARBOHYDRATE
4% FAT
3·5% PROTEIN
0·75% MINERALS & VITAMINS

The 'almost perfect' food

87% WATER

Milk is Nature's most important food, its purpose being to nourish young animals and babies during their first few months of life. Not only is milk good for babies however, but for older children and adults too. It is cheap and available everywhere — many people have it delivered to their door, fresh every morning.

Because milk contains so much **water** (**87%**) the amount of nutrients present is too low to make it a 'perfect' food. It also lacks Iron and Vitamin C.

Food Value

Milk contains all the nutrient groups:

Animal protein — for growth
Fat (in an easily digested form) — for energy
Carbohydrate (in the form of *sugar* only) — for energy.
Vitamins A and D (in the creamy part)
Vitamin B and a little **C**
Minerals — particularly **Calcium** for bones and teeth.

Milk in our Diet

Everyone benefits, nonetheless, from a daily drink of milk. Because milk contains all of the nutrients needed for *growth* — protein, calcium and vitamins — **children, teenagers and expectant mothers** should take a regular supply.

Mothers should make every effort to breastfeed their babies, as human milk is the perfect food for them and there is less danger of infection from carelessly sterilised bottles and milk.

Table 16.1

Approximate Composition	Water	Protein	Carbohy.	Fat	Vitamins	Minerals
Whole milk	87%	3.5%	4.5%	4%	A; D; B; a little C	0.7% (calcium)
Skimmed milk	90%	3.5%	5%	0.5%	B; a little C	0.6%

Babies can live on milk alone for the first few months of life — the period of greatest growth. By about three months, it is necessary to add extra energy foods *e.g.* baby rice or other cereals and by six months baby will need extra iron, *e.g.* egg yolk, sieved vegetables and Vitamin C (orange juice or rose hip syrup). *N.B.* — **Babies should never be fed dried skim milk or condensed milk,** only prepared dried **formula milk** or a fresh milk formula.

Milk is a good food for **invalids** because it is a liquid food, has all the nutrients required and is easy to digest.

Uses

1. Drinking alone, or in drinks (tea, coffee, milk shakes).
2. With breakfast cereals, porridge, *etc.*
3. For puddings (milk puddings, custards, bread puddings).
4. Sauces (white sauce, custard sauce).
5. To improve food value, add milk to soups, creamed potatoes, bread and cakes.
6. Savoury dishes (fish fricassée, quiches, batters).
7. As milk 'products' (yoghurt, cream, cheese).

Making Milk Safe

Because milk is a liquid food, it is easily infected with germs. For this reason, great care is taken at the farm, and during bottling, to keep milk pure. Cows must be tested to make sure they have not got T.B. (tuberculosis) or any other serious disease which might be passed from cows to people through infected milk.

To make really sure dangerous germs are destroyed, most milk we buy is **pasteurised,** that is, it is heated to 72°C (well below boiling point) for a short time, then cooled quickly and sealed in sterilised bottles. This kills the germs which cause disease.

Our milkman supplies:

1. **Pasteurised milk** — ordinary bottled milk.
2. **Skimmed milk** — milk with fat removed. Cheap and useful for slimmers.
3. **Buttermilk** — used for making bread.
4. **Jersey milk** — rich milk from Jersey cows.

In the shops we can buy milk which keeps longer:

Long lasting milk (U.H.T.) — in cartons, keeps unopened for weeks.

Evaporated and condensed milk — in cans, useful for cold sweets.

Dried milk, *e.g. Dairy bawn* — milk powder in packets.

These are useful for emergencies, for camping and caravaning.

The following products are made from milk:

Cream, Yoghurt, Ice cream, Butter, Cheese.

Cream

If you leave a bottle of milk standing for a day or so, you will see that the cream rises to the top. Cream can be skimmed from the top of milk or separated in the dairy by a special machine. Cream contains most of the fat from milk plus the fat soluble vitamins A and D.

Skimmed Milk

This is the liquid left behind after the cream is removed. It retains much of the 'good' of the milk — its protein, carbohydrate, Vitamin B and minerals — but it is much lower in kilocalories. This makes it a good drink for weight watchers and those on a low-fat diet.

Butter

This is made from cream. It takes 10 litres of milk to make 450 g (1 lb) of butter! Cream is churned about in giant churns so that the lumps of fat stick together and the remaining liquid — **buttermilk** — is drained off. Because buttermilk is quite acid, it is ideal for breadmaking.

Yoghurt

This is made by treating milk with a culture of harmless bacteria. This thickens the milk and gives it a refreshing, slightly acid taste. Yoghurt can be made from whole milk or from skimmed milk, in which latter case it will have little fat or fat-soluble vitamins A and D. This yoghurt is labelled low-fat yoghurt (low fat yoghurt does not always mean low **Calorie** yoghurt, though, as sugar may be added, which increases the kilocalorie content).

Yoghurt which is sweetened and flavoured with fruit is useful as a tasty 'instant' pudding. Plain yoghurt may be used as a salad dressing or in savoury dishes such as goulash or curry.

Ice cream

Most of the ice cream we buy contains dried, skimmed milk. Home-made ice cream, which has milk, cream and eggs, is much more nourishing, but higher in kilocalories.

Most milk products are perishable — look for the **'date stamp'** when you buy them to make sure they are fresh.

Storing Fresh Milk

Because milk is easily infected with bacteria, we must be extra careful to store milk correctly at home. Failure to do so could lead to an outbreak of food poisoning.

1. Never leave milk standing on the doorstep in the sun. Sunlight destroys Vitamin B and C and makes milk go 'off' more quickly.

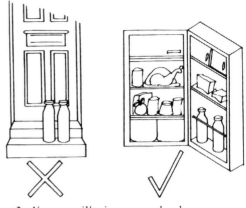

2. Keep milk in a cool place, *e.g.* a refrigerator. If you have not got one, put it standing in cold water in the coldest part of the house and cover it with a clean damp cloth.
3. Always cover milk and keep it away from strong smelling foods.
4. Keep milk in the bottle until you need it, then pour out just as much as you need into a clean jug. Replace the bottle cap each time.
5. Do not mix milk from different days together. The cap on the bottletop is stamped to show the day it was bottled: 1 - 7 (No. 1 = Sunday). Use each bottle in the correct order.
6. All milk containers, such as bottles and jugs, should be rinsed in cold water (hot water will set the milk), then washed in hot soapy water, rinsed and drained dry. Jugs should then be scalded with boiling water to sterilise them.

Keep Milk
COOL — CLEAN — COVERED

Effects of Heat on Milk

1. Some loss of Vitamin B and C.
2. Flavour changes.
3. Boiling destroys bacteria so the milk keeps longer.
4. Protein sets, forming a skin, which causes milk to boil over.

17   *All About Cheese*

Cheese was probably the first 'convenience food' — it is really a form of solid milk, containing most of the nutrients of milk in a concentrated form. Although most cheese is made from cow's milk — it can also be made from goat's, ewe's and even camel's milk! It is one of the most nutritious foods — its only disadvantage is that some may find it indigestible.

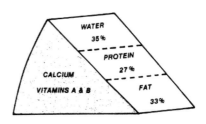

Food Value

Cheese is one of the best sources of **animal protein** — it contains more protein than most types of meat or fish.

It is a very good source of **calcium** — particularly important in the diet of pregnant women, children and adolescents, as it builds up strong bones and teeth.

It contains **Vitamin A** and some **Vitamin B** Because it has no carbohydrates, it is a good idea to serve it with a starchy food — cheese and crackers, for example, or cheese sandwiches.

Soft cheeses have more water, so the amount of other nutrients is less.

How Cheese is Made

1. A culture (harmless bacteria) is added to pasteurised milk.
2. Milk is heated slightly and rennet added to separate milk into curds and whey.
3. Curds are drained, chopped and salted, whey is drained off.
4. Cheese is pressed in moulds — lightly for soft cheeses, firmly for hard cheeses.
5. Cheese is left to mature, for flavour to develop.

Buying Cheese

Do not buy in large amounts — soft cheeses must be used up in 3–4 days as they go hard within a week. Cheese should not look dry or mouldy.

Composition of Cheddar Cheese   *Table 17.1*

Protein	Fat	Carbohydrate	Water	Minerals	Vitamins
27%	33%	0%	35%	4%	A and B

Types of Cheese

There are over 400 varieties of cheese known; differences in colour, texture and taste are due to the different milks and cultures used. Cheese can be placed in 3 groups:

Table 17.2

Hard	Soft	Processed
Cheddar *Cheshire* *Gruyere* *Edam* *Parmesan*	*Cottage Cheese** *Camembert* *Brie* *Stilton*	Cheese spreads Flavoured cheeses Mild, foil wrapped cheese *e.g. Galtee, Calvita* Sliced cheeses Smoked cheeses
Hard cheese has the highest food value and is also good for cooking, because of its strong taste and because it grates well.	*Cottage cheese is made from skimmed milk. It is easy to digest, low in kilocalories and therefore good for slimming diets.	Processed cheeses have a lower food value and milder flavour. They are really a diluted form of cheese with water whipped into them during manufacture.

Storing

1. Store in a cool place, wrapped loosely in greaseproof paper or foil, ideally in cheese compartment in refrigerator. Plastic wrapping makes the cheese sweat.
2. Use within a week. Vacuum packed cheeses must be used by date stamped on pack; once opened, they must be used within a few days.
3. Remove cheese from refrigerator one hour before use — to develop its flavour.
4. Hard pieces of cheese can be grated and stored in a screwtop jar for a week or ten days, for use in cooking.

Effects of Heat

1. Protein coagulates and shrinks.
2. Cooking for too long or at high temperatures makes cheese tough and indigestible.
3. Fat melts.

Cooking

1. Cook for the shortest possible time.
2. Avoid using high temperatures — cook gently.
3. Grate or slice thinly, to speed up melting.
4. Use hard cheeses for most cooking, as they grate easily.

For Tender Tummies!

Some people find cheese hard to digest — because of its high fat content. To make it more digestible:

1. Grate before using in salads and sandwiches.
2. Eat raw rather than cooked.
3. Eat with starchy foods, to make it less concentrated.
4. Season well, use mustard, pickles, *etc.* to stimulate digestion.
5. Chew thoroughly.

Advantages

1. High food value — good energy food — rich in protein and calcium.
2. Little preparation or cooking needed — saves time and fuel.
3. Little or no waste.
4. Good value for money — cheaper than meat and just as nourishing.
5. Wide variety — many flavours to choose from.
6. Adds flavour to insipid foods.

Uses

1. For snacks and salads; packed lunches and picnics.
2. In sauces — over vegetables and fish.
3. Main meals — omelettes, cheese flan, macaroni cheese, pizza.
4. Garnishes — over soup and spaghetti.
5. Last course of a meal — cheeseboard.

Welsh Rarebit

Ingredients

150 g cheese
25 g butter/margarine
½ tsp. made mustard
Salt, pepper
2 tablespoons milk/beer
4 slices toast

Method

1. Grate cheese. Make toast — keep hot.
2. Melt butter, stir in cheese, seasoning and mustard.
3. Gradually stir in milk/beer and heat gently, stirring all the time, until cheese has melted. Do not overheat.
4. Spread mixture over each slice of toast.
5. Place under a hot grill for about 1 minute until bubbling.
6. Serve on hot plate, with grilled tomatoes. Garnish with parsley.

Buck Rarebit

As for Welsh Rarebit but with a poached egg served on top.

Macaroni or Spaghetti Cheese

Ingredients

100 g macaroni or spaghetti
100 g grated cheese
Salt, pepper
½ teaspoon made mustard
1–2 tomatoes (optional)

Cheese sauce (stewing)
25 g margarine
25 g flour
375 ml milk

Method

1. Half fill a large saucepan with water and bring to the boil.
2. Add spaghetti and a little salt and boil for 12 minutes (spaghetti)/14–15 mins (macaroni), until tender. Drain in colander.
3. **Sauce:** Melt margarine in small saucepan, add flour. Cook for 1 minute on a gentle heat.
4. Gradually add milk, stirring all the time; simmer for 5 minutes. Stir in most of the cheese, the mustard and seasoning.
5. Stir in spaghetti/macaroni and empty into a greased pie dish.
6. Sprinkle remaining cheese on top. Arrange sliced tomato in a line down centre of macaroni.
7. Bake in a moderate oven at 375°F (190°C) Gas 5, until just brown (about 20 minutes) or brown under hot grill.
8. Place pie dish on a large plate. Garnish with parsley.

Cheese and Potato Pie

(A similar recipe — based on potatoes)

Ingredients

4 medium – large potatoes
1 onion
Salt, pepper
Browned crumbs

Sauce:

25 g margarine
25 g flour
375 ml milk or milk and potato water
75 g grated cheese

Method

1. Wash, peel and cook potatoes until almost soft. Drain and cut into large (2 cm) dice.
2. Peel and finely chop onion.
3. **Sauce:** Melt fat, sauté onion. Add flour and cook for one minute. Slowly stir in milk, bring to boil and cook for 5 minutes. Stir in most of cheese.
4. Mix in diced potato, empty into greased pie dish or casserole. Sprinkle with crumbs and left over cheese.
5. Bake in a moderate oven at 375°F (190°C) Gas 5, until just beginning to brown.
6. Serve with grilled rashers or baked fish. Garnish with parsley or chopped chives.

Vegetable Cheese

Make as for cheese and potato pie, using a mixture of left over vegetables — carrots, parsnips, turnips, cauliflower, potatoes, peas, celery, leeks or a packet of frozen mixed vegetables.

Quick Pizza

Ingredients

Scone Base:

200 g flour
½ teaspoon salt
1 teaspoon baking powder
50 g margarine
approx. 125 ml milk or water

Filling:

25 g margarine or 1 tablespoon oil
1 onion
300 g tomatoes or 1 tin tomatoes
Salt, pepper
100 g grated cheese
Pinch oregano or mixed herbs
50 g mushrooms (optional)

Methods

1. **Filling:** Peel and chop onion; skin and slice tomatoes.
2. Melt margarine/oil in saucepan and sauté onion and mushrooms if using.
3. Add tomatoes (and juice, if tinned) herbs and seasoning.
4. Simmer gently, while making dough.
5. Sieve flour, salt and baking powder into a bowl.
6. Rub in margarine with fingertips.
7. Moisten with liquid and mix to a fairly stiff dough.
8. Roll into a large round, 1 cm thick.
9. Place on **greased** tin, sprinkle cheese over, then spoon tomato mixture over cheese — covering it completely.
10. Bake in a fairly hot oven 200°C (400°C) Gas 6, for about 30 mins.
11. Serve in wedges, with a green salad.

Cheese and Bacon Quiche
(Quiche Lorraine)

(A quiche is a savoury pastry flan)

Ingredients

100 g shortcrust pastry
175 ml milk
2 eggs
Salt/pepper
Knob of margarine
3 rashers streaky bacon
100 g cheese
Pinch nutmeg
Tomato – to garnish

Method

1. Roll pastry to fit a 7″ flan case or pie plate.
2. Cut bacon into strips and sauté in margarine until beginning to brown. Drain on kitchen paper.
3. Beat the eggs, add seasoning and nutmeg and stir in milk.
4. Grate cheese and sprinkle over base of flan. Add bacon, then carefully pour over egg mixture.
5. Bake in a moderate oven 190°C (375°F) Gas 5, for about 30–40 minutes — until mixture is set.
6. Remove flan ring, serve on a hot plate, with a side salad. Garnish with tomato slices and parsley.

Other ways to Add Cheese

A slice on a hamburger.
Grated cheese mashed into baked potatoes.
Savoury pancakes, with cheese sauce.
Cauliflower au gratin.
Smoked fish au gratin.
Eggs mornay, *p. 147.*

Cheese and Pineapple Kebabs
(for parties)

Cut cheddar cheese into 2 cm cubes. Stick a cube of cheese, a cube of pineapple (from a can of pineapple chunks) and a grape onto each cocktail stick. Arrange sticks on a large grapefruit or melon.

Over to you . . .

Milk

1. Plan a day's menus for a school-going child which use milk at least once at each meal.

   State the reasons why milk is important in the diet of children.

2. Make a list of all the milk products available in your local shop/supermarket. Write the price beside each.

   Name a dish which could be made from each of the products listed.

Cheese

1. Suggest a suitable cheese dish for each of the following: (a) a supper snack; (b) a reheated dish; (c) a savoury dish suitable for a buffet party; (d) a foreign dish; (e) a packed lunch.

2. Make a list of all the cheeses you know, both Irish, continental, and find out as much as possible about how they are made and what they look and taste like. Write the results into your copybook, with pictures if possible.

18   All About Eggs

Eggs are one of the most useful foods because they can be used in so many ways, including:

Eating on their own: boiled, poached or scrambled for quick snacks; or in omelettes or quiches, for more filling meals.

Thickening: eggs will thicken or set mixtures, *e.g.* custards, quiches, cold sweets.

Holding air: when whisked or beaten, eggs will trap the air and hold it until the mixture sets, *e.g.* creamed cakes, sponges, meringues, mousses.

Binding: holding minced or soft foods together, *e.g.* hamburgers, fish cakes, potato croquettes.

Coating: covering food for frying with beaten egg and breadcrumbs or with batter, *e.g.* fish or chicken portions, fritters.

Adding richness: cakes, puddings and foods, such as mashed potatoes, are made richer and more nourishing by adding a whole egg or an egg yolk.

Glazing: brushing with beaten egg gives a nice shine to pastry dishes and scones.

Emulsions: eggs help to hold the oil and vinegar together in mayonnaise.

Eggs are a good substitute for meat or fish. They are ideal for picnics, salads and sandwiches and for feeding young babies and children, invalids and old people, as they contain most of the essential nutrients and are very easy to digest.

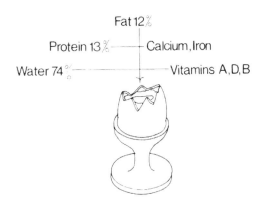

Fat 12%
Protein 13% — Calcium, Iron
Water 74% — Vitamins A, D, B

Food Value

Three quarters of every egg is **water**. The other quarter contains a good supply of body building **protein**, an easily digested form of **fat** (for energy), **Vitamins A, D and B** and the minerals **calcium, iron, phosphorus and sulphur.**

Eggs have **no carbohydrates,** so we often serve them with starchy foods to make them more balanced; poached or scrambled egg on toast for example, or omelette and chips. As eggs **lack Vitamin C** a salad could round off this meal, providing this vital vitamin as well as extra minerals.

Egg yolk contains **cholesterol,** which may harden the arteries of older people, so large numbers should not be eaten.

Table 18.1

Composition	Water	Protein	Carbohydrate	Fat	Vitamins	Minerals
%	74%	13%	0%	12%	A, D, B	1% (calcium, iron)

Buying eggs

Size

Eggs are **graded** by size from 1 - 7 (size 1 is the largest). Most cookery recipes are based on a size 3 egg.

Freshness

As well as having the size printed on it, each egg box has a label which states **the week** in which the eggs were laid. Weeks are numbered from 1 - 52 (January to the end of December). The higher the number, the fresher the eggs.

Quality and freshness are also judged by **class.** *Class A* eggs are the freshest unless they have an **extra** label as well, which means they are extra fresh. *Class B* eggs are not as good.

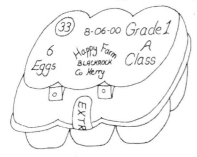

Testing for Freshness

If you buy eggs from shops where they are not packed in boxes, you must judge for yourself whether the eggs are fresh. Remember:

1. They should be heavy, for size.
2. They should have a rough shell.
3. If you break an egg onto a plate, the yolk should be high and rounded, the white should be jelly-like.
   If the yolk is flat, or breaks easily, and the white is thin and watery, the egg is not very fresh.

Fresh   Stale

How do eggs go stale?

Next time you break open an egg, look inside the shell. You will see a thin white membrane (skin) inside the shell with an air-space at the round end. This air space gets bigger the longer the egg is stored, because liquid from the white of the egg evaporates through tiny pores on the egg shell. The egg gets lighter as the air space expands so that stale eggs will actually float in water. A really bad egg will let you know — by its nasty smell.

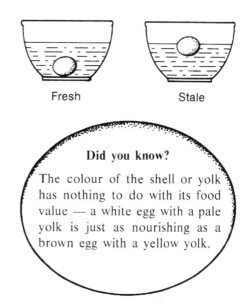

Fresh   Stale

Did you know?

The colour of the shell or yolk has nothing to do with its food value — a white egg with a pale yolk is just as nourishing as a brown egg with a yellow yolk.

Storing

Most eggs will keep for a few weeks, if they are stored properly:

1. In a cool place *e.g.* a fridge.
2. With the pointed end down — this keeps the yolk fresh longer.
3. Away from strong smelling foods.
4. Store egg yolks in a cup, covered with water; egg whites in a screw top jar in a fridge.

Note: Never wash eggs — this removes their natural protective covering.

Preserving

In the past, hens laid fewer eggs in winter, when the weather was cold. This meant that eggs were scarce and expensive in winter and plentiful and cheap in summer. So thrifty housewives preserved their eggs in summer. Today eggs are plentiful all the year round and the prices vary little.

To preserve eggs

1. Make sure they are very fresh and free from cracks.
2. Make up a solution of water-glass according to directions. Pack eggs pointed downwards into a plastic covered bucket. Cover completely with cold solution.
3. If you have a deep freeze you can freeze yolks and whites separately. Freeze in twos in small containers. Never freeze eggs (raw or hardboiled) in shells.

Effect of cooking

1. Protein coagulates and sets. The egg white becomes opaque (no longer transparent).
2. If eggs are cooked at too high a temperature, or for too long, they will curdle.
3. Overcooked eggs are difficult to digest. Hard boiled eggs get a dark green rim around the yolk. The white of overcooked eggs goes rubbery.
   A lightly cooked egg (*e.g.* soft boiled) is the most digestible form.

Rules for Cooking

1. Use eggs at room temperature. Remove eggs from the refrigerator about one hour before cooking.
   Cold eggs will be more likely to crack when boiled, curdle when cooked and will not whip up as well as eggs at room temperature.
2. Cook gently — rapid cooking causes curdling and toughness.
3. Cool hot mixtures before adding to egg.
   Always add warm mixture to egg — rather than the other way round, this way there is less chance of curdling.

4. When whisking egg whites, *e.g.* for meringue, make sure that the bowl, beater, *etc.* are free from any trace of fat or the whites will not whisk well.
5. For the same reason, when separating egg yolk from white make sure no yolk gets into white or volume will be less.

Separating Yolks from Whites

1. Have 2 bowls ready.
2. Crack egg shell sharply with knife or against edge of bowl.
3. Hold one egg shell upright over bowl, so that egg yolk will stay on it and carefully remove the other half. Most of the white will fall into the bowl.
4. Very carefully, transfer yolk from shell to shell, allowing white to drain away. Take care that the sharp edges of the shell do not break the yolk.
5. Place yolk in second bowl.

Safer way for beginners: Break egg onto saucer. Place egg cup over yolk and turn saucer side-ways so that white falls onto bowl below.

Recipes

For: Boiled; Poached; Scrambled; Fried Egg
— see p. 52/53

Curried Eggs

Ingredients

4 - 6 large eggs
200 g long grain rice
Salt
375 ml curry sauce, p. 00
Lemon and parsley to garnish.

Method

1. Make curry sauce. Leave to simmer.
2. Half fill a large saucepan with water. Bring to the boil.
3. Add washed rice and 1 teasp. salt. Boil for 12 mins, stirring now and then with a fork to prevent grains sticking.
4. Empty rice into strainer, pour hot water through to rinse off starch. Drain well.
5. Spread out on a greased dish and dry in a low oven 150°C (300°F) Gas 2, or grill, turned to low for about 15 - 20 mins. Toss now and then with a fork.
6. Hard boil eggs for ten minutes. Cool at once.
7. Shell and cut in half lengthwise.
8. Strain sauce or liquidise.
9. Make a border of rice on a warmed plate, placed halved eggs on top, cut side down and pour sauce over.
10. Garnish with lemon and parsley.

Eggs in Cheese Sauce (Eggs Mornay)

(used as a starter or as a savoury supper dish)

Ingredients

4 - 6 eggs
1 tablesp. breadcrumbs

Garnish:

Paprika and triangles of toast
250 ml cheese sauce (pouring)
25 g grated cheese

Method

1. Hardboil eggs for ten minutes.
2. Make cheese sauce.
4. Shell eggs. Cut in half lengthwise and place in a well greased dish.
4. Pour cheese sauce over eggs and sprinkle with breadcrumbs and grated cheese.
5. Brown in a hot oven 220°C (425°F) Gas 7, for 3 minutes, or under a moderate grill, if oven is not in use.
6. Sprinkle with paprika and garnish with triangles of toast.

Eggs Florentine (with spinach)

(used as a first course of a meal, or as a quick supper snack)

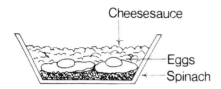

Cheesesauce

Eggs
Spinach

Ingredients

4 eggs
1 small pkt. frozen spinach
Pepper/salt
500 ml cheese sauce
A little grated cheese
Nutmeg

Method

1. Cook spinach, following directions on packet. Season.
2. Make cheese sauce.
3. Poach or soft-boil eggs. Shell if boiled.
4. Butter 4 individual heatproof dishes and divide spinach between them.
5. Place one egg on each and pour sauce over.
6. Sprinkle with cheese and brown under a hot grill.
7. Serve at once with a little grated nutmeg sprinkled on top.

Stuffed Eggs

Ingredients

4 hard boiled eggs
1 tablesp. mayonnaise
Pepper/salt

Fillings — choose from:

1 tsp. tomato purée
2 tsp. finely grated cheese
2 anchovies, well mashed
1 dessertsp. finely chopped ham
$\frac{1}{2}$ tsp. curry powder

Method

1. Half eggs lengthwise or crosswise. Cut a thin slice from base of each to help it stand easily.
2. Sieve egg yolk into bowl, mix with mayonnaise and one of the fillings.
3. Spoon back into egg whites or use a forcing bag.
4. **To serve hot:** Stick halves together, place in a greased dish and pour béchamel or cheese sauce over. Bake in a fairly hot oven—200 °C (400°F), Mark 6, until browned (about 15 mins.).
5. **To serve cold:** Serve halved eggs on a bed of lettuce leaves and garnish with tomatoes.

Omelettes

An omelette is one of the only egg dishes which is cooked quickly. It is basically a mixture of eggs and seasonings or flavourings, fried until slightly browned on the outside, but moist inside.

Rules for Omelettes

1. It is best to keep a small frying pan specially for making omelettes and pancakes. If this is not possible, a non-stick pan is ideal.
2. Avoid washing the pan — just wipe over after use with kitchen paper. This helps prevent sticking.
3. A palette knife or thin wooden spatula is the best utensil to use.
4. An omelette must be prepared and cooked quickly and served at once.

French Savoury Omelette

Ingredients for each person

2 eggs *1 tablesp. water*
Pepper/salt *Small knob butter*

To fry:

10 g butter

Flavouring 'fines herbs'

1 teasp. finely chopped parsley
¼ teasp. fresh herbs, e.g. chopped parsley, chives, tarragon

Method

1. Beat eggs *slightly* in a bowl, using a fork or wire whisk.
2. Add water, butter and herbs (if using).
3. Heat omelette pan, add butter and allow it to heat well.
4. Pour in mixture. As it begins to set, draw in from sides, allowing liquid mixture to run under. Repeat until all liquid has set, shaking frequently. Omelette should be moist and soft on the surface.
5. Fold omelette in three, slip onto a warm plate.
6. Serve at once, garnished with parsley.

Fillings

Make basic omelette, as above, omitting herbs.
Prepare fillings in a separate saucepan before cooking omelette.
Place fillings in centre of omelette before folding.

1. **Cheese:** sprinkle 2 tablesp. grated cheddar on omelette just before folding.
2. **Ham:** add 1-2 tablespoons ham to omelette mixture before cooking.
3. **Mushroom:** wash and slice mushrooms, sauté in a little butter.
4. **Onion and tomato:** Sauté 1 small sliced onion in a little butter for 1 minute; add 2 sliced tomatoes, cook for 2 minutes.
5. **Smoked haddock:** Flake haddock and heat with 2 tablesp. cream or top of milk.

Puffed Sweet Omelette

Ingredients for each person

2 eggs
2 tsp. water
2 tsp. caster sugar

To fry:

10 g butter or marg.

Fillings — choose from:

2 tablesp. jam (heated)	*Chopped pineapple*
2-3 tablesp. stewed fruit	*Fresh strawberries*
Sliced banana	*or raspberries*

Method

1. Separate eggs.
2. Beat yolks and sugar until creamy. Add water.
3. Stiffly beat egg whites, fold in egg yolk mixture.
4. Melt fat in omelette pan until sizzling.
5. Pour on omelette mixture and cook on a moderate heat until lightly browned beneath. Do not stir.
6. Brown top of omelette under a preheated grill or in a hot oven for a few minutes. Slide onto hot plate.
7. Slit the centre of the omelette, spread the filling on one half and fold other half over.
8. Serve at once, sprinkled with caster sugar.

Batter

A batter is a mixture of flour, eggs and a liquid (usually milk, or milk and water). The name 'batter' comes from the French word *'battre'* (to beat), which reminds us that the batter should be well beaten so as to take in as much air as possible. This air will make the batter rise on **cooking**, so no raising agent is needed. Batters can be thin or thick.

Batters

Ingredients

Thin batter:	Use for:
100 g flour	*Pancakes*
Pinch of salt	*Yorkshire pudding*
1 egg	
250 ml milk	

Thick (coating) batter:	Use for:
100 g flour	*Coating fish*
Pinch of salt	*Fritters*
1 egg	
125 ml milk/or milk	
and water	

Method

1. Sieve flour and salt into a bowl.
2. Make a hole in the centre of the flour and drop in the egg and 1-2 tablesp. of measured milk.
3. With a wooden spoon, stir the egg mixture in the centre of the bowl, allowing the flour to fall in gradually from the sides.
4. Slowly add about half the liquid, beating well to avoid lumping.
5. When half the liquid is added, beat with the front of the spoon for about five minutes to add air to the batter.
6. Stir in the rest of the liquid and use at once. If not required at once, pour into a jug and store in refrigerator until needed.

Pancakes

Ingredients

100 g flour	*1 egg*
Pinch salt	*250 ml milk*

To fry:	To serve:
Cooking fat. e.g. lard	*Caster sugar*
	Wedges of lemon

Method

1. Make batter and pour into a jug.
2. Brush pan with melted fat, wait for it to get really hot, then pour on sufficient batter to barely cover base of pan. Tilt pan to spread it evenly.
3. Fry over a medium heat until golden brown underneath, shaking now and then.
4. Toss pancake or turn with palette knife.
5. Fry second side until golden brown.
6. Slide onto a plate, kept hot over simmering water.
7. Sprinkle with castor sugar and lemon juice and roll up. Keep plate covered with lid.
8. Repeat with remainder of batter.
9. Serve pancakes on warm plate, with wedge of lemon.

Stuffed Pancakes

Like omelettes, pancakes can be filled with sweet or savoury fillings.

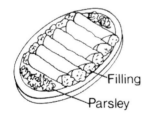
Filling
Parsley

Sweet: (serve with cream)

1. Stewed apple flavoured with cloves or cinnamon and sweetened with sugar.
2. Raspberries or sliced strawberries mixed with whipped cream.
3. Marmalade.
4. Bananas, fried in butter, with a little rum poured over.

Savoury:

1. 250 ml Béchamel (coating) sauce with one of the following ingredients stirred in, or cooked in it:

   (a) Chopped cooked chicken.
   (b) Smoked haddock and cheese.
   (c) Small tin of salmon, mashed well.
   (d) 200 g mushrooms sliced and stewed in sauce.

2. Mince, cooked in a curry sauce, *see p. 112.*
3. Bolognese sauce, *see p. 83.*

Fruit Fritters

Ingredients

100 g flour
Pinch salt
1 egg
125 ml milk & water

Fruit:

Apples - peeled, cored, sliced
Bananas - peeled, sliced lengthwise in two
Pineapple - drained slices

To serve:

Caster sugar

To fry:

Bath of oil or fat

1. Make batter. Heat fat or oil.
2. Slice fruit, drop into batter, lift out with a skewer and allow excess batter to drain off.
3. Lower carefully into hot fat. Fry until golden brown and cooked through.
4. Drain well on kitchen paper.
5. Sprinkle with caster sugar.
6. Serve in hot individual dishes.
7. Custard, cream or syrup sauce, *see p.113.* may be served with fritters.

Try PARSLEY in
stuffings and
garnishes

Try MINT with lamb,
new potatoes
or peas

HERBS ADD FLAVOUR TO YOUR COOKING

Try THYME
in soups,
salads,
stuffings

Try ROSEMARY
with lamb and
chicken in
salads

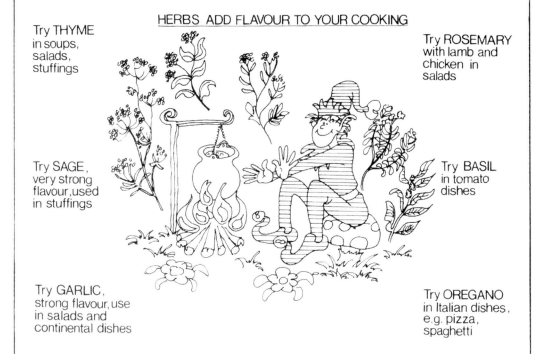

Try SAGE,
very strong
flavour, used
in stuffings

Try BASIL
in tomato
dishes

Try GARLIC,
strong flavour, use
in salads and
continental dishes

Try OREGANO
in Italian dishes,
e.g. pizza,
spaghetti

THEY ARE RICH IN IRON
AND VITAMINS A AND C

Try BAY LEAVES
in stocks, soups,
savoury dishes

Try CHIVES in
salads, soups,
omlettes

CURRY, a mixture of several spices including 'chilli', a very hot spice, used in stews called curries and other savoury dishes

Black and white PEPPER, used as a condiment and for seasoning savoury dishes

NUTMEG can be bought whole or ground, used in savoury and sweet dishes including cakes and biscuits

MUSTARD, used as a condiment (on the table) and in pickles and chutneys. It goes well with ham and cheese

CLOVES, dark brown spice, use whole and ground in apple dishes, sauces, cakes and biscuits

PAPRIKA, a red pepper, not hot, used in goulash and for garnishing, e.g. on rice

Add spice to your cooking

GINGER, use whole or ground in cakes, puddings and chutneys. It goes well with melon

CAYENNE, very hot red pepper, use sparingly in stews and devilled dishes

CINNAMON, a brown spice used in cakes and biscuits

19   All About Custards

A custard is a mixture of eggs and milk, cooked gently so that the egg thickens the milk without curdling.

Custards contain protein, fat, minerals and vitamins — they are nourishing, without being too fattening. They form the basis of many hot and cold sweets as well as savoury dishes, such as quiches.

Rules for Custards

1. The most important rule when cooking custards is to use a very low temperature — to prevent eggs curdling.
2. Eggs and milk must be really fresh.
3. Correct proportions are important — too much milk will prevent the custard setting.
4. Beat eggs just enough to mix yolks and whites. Do not whip them until frothy or there will be holes in baked and steamed custards.
5. Heat milk slightly, *then* pour warm milk over beaten eggs, rather than the reverse (to prevent curdling).

Consistency

Custard sauce should be a smooth pouring consistency.

Baked and steamed custards set to a smooth jelly-like consistency, with no holes. Steamed custards must be firm enough to stand on their own when they are turned out, therefore less milk is used.

Proportions

Custard sauce: 2 eggs/400 ml milk
Baked custard: 2 eggs/400 ml milk
Steamed custard: 2 eggs/200 ml milk

Custard Sauce

Ingredients

2 eggs	*2 teasp. sugar*
400 ml milk	*Vanilla*

Method

1. Beat eggs and sugar in bowl, using a fork.
2. Heat milk until steam begins to rise (it should not boil).
3. Pour milk over beaten eggs, stirring all the time.
4. Strain into the saucepan and stir over a *very gentle* heat until custard thickens. Too high a temperature here will curdle custard. You will know it is thick enough when it coats the back of the wooden spoon.
5. Add vanilla and serve at once in a warmed jug.

- If the sauce is to be served cold, place a damp piece of kitchen paper on the surface of the sauce to prevent a skin forming.
- To avoid the danger of curdling, a double saucepan can be used, with water in the

base; or the custard can be placed in a bowl, sitting over a saucepan of simmering water. This method will take longer, however.

- If the custard begins to curdle (you will know by the tiny grains which appear), empty at once into a clean bowl and whisk until smooth.

Quick 'Custard' Sauce

(This recipe uses custard powder, which consists of cornflour, colour and flavouring (no eggs). It is therefore not as nourishing as real egg custard but is handy in an emergency.)

Ingredients

2 tablesp. custard powder
1-2 tablesp. sugar
500 ml milk

Method

1. Put custard powder into a medium sized bowl with the sugar.
2. Blend with 2 tablesp. milk taken from the 500 ml.
3. Put rest of the milk into a saucepan, bring almost to boiling point, then pour over blended powder, stirring well.
4. Return custard to saucepan, bring to the boil, stirring all the time. Serve at once.

- Serve custard **hot** with fruit pies and tarts, steamed puddings, baked puddings, stewed or baked fruit.

- Serve **cold** with trifles, ice cream, stewed fruit, fruit flans.

Steamed Custard

Ingredients

2 eggs	*1-2 teasp. sugar*
200 ml milk	*Vanilla*

Method

1. Beat eggs and sugar in medium bowl.
2. Heat milk until steaming, pour milk over beaten eggs, stirring all the time. Add vanilla.
3. Strain into greased bowl, cover with foil and place in covered steamer or in a saucepan of *simmering* water* for about 20-30 minutes until set.
   (*To prevent curdling when using saucepan method, place bowl containing custard sitting on a large metal cutter, or on a wad of folded paper, so that the bowl is not directly in contact with the base of the saucepan. Place the saucepan to one side of the hot plate with the custard on the side furthest from the heat.)
4. Cool custard for 2-3 minutes before placing a plate on top of bowl, then turn quickly to unmould.
5. Serve with stewed fruit or cream.

Baked Custard

Ingredients

2 eggs	*1-2 tsp. sugar*
400 ml milk	*Grated nutmeg*

Method

1. Beat eggs and sugar in bowl.
2. Heat milk until steaming, pour over eggs, stirring all the time.
3. Strain into greased pie dish and grate nutmeg over. Wipe any spills from dish.

4. Place dish in a roasting tin, containing 3 cm cold water.

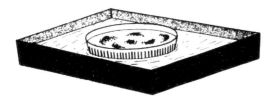

5. Bake at 350°F (175°C) Gas 4 for 30-40 minutes until set and beginning to brown.
6. Dredge castor sugar on top, and place on a plate with a d'oyley under pie dish.

Caramel Custard

Ingredients

3 eggs	*1 tablesp. sugar*
300 ml milk	*Vanilla*

Caramel:

100 g sugar	*1 tablesp. hot water*
150 ml water	

Method

1. Put sugar and water for caramel in a small heavy saucepan, and dissolve sugar slowly over a gentle heat, stirring all the time.
2. Boil syrup until it turns brown, add tablesp. hot water, then pour at once into a clean dry straight-sided tin or soufflé dish, turning dish until base and sides are evenly coated. (Use a cloth to protect hands when holding dish or tin).
3. Make custard as for baked custard, using the saucepan used for the caramel, and strain into dish.
4. Cover with foil and bake as for baked custard for 40-45 mins., until set.
5. Cool for a few minutes, then turn onto a warmed plate.
6. Serve hot or cold.

Bread Puddings

The following puddings are based on custards.

Bread and Butter Pudding

Ingredients

4 thin slices (75 g) of brown or white bread, buttered
1 egg
350 ml milk
25 g brown or white sugar
50 g sultanas or raisins
Nutmeg

Method

1. Cut bread into fingers and arrange a layer on base of pie dish. Sprinkle washed fruit on top. Arrange bread and fruit in layers with bread arranged neatly on top.
2. Beat egg and sugar, heat milk until steaming.
3. Pour over beaten egg, stirring well.
4. Strain over bread and leave to soak for 15-20 minutes if time allows. Grate nutmeg on top.
5. Place pie dish on a flat tin containing a little water and bake in a fairly moderate oven 350°F (175°C) Gas 4, for 30-40 minutes, until set and turning brown on top.
6. Serve on a plate with a d'oyley under pie dish.

Variations

1. Spread the bread with jam or marmalade.
2. Use grated lemon rind instead of nutmeg.
3. Use slices of cake instead of bread *e.g.* sponge cake, gingerbread.
4. Use left over sweet sandwiches, such as banana instead of bread and sultanas.

Queen of Puddings

Ingredients

75 g of breadcrumbs
2 egg yolks
350 ml milk
Small knob margarine
Grated rind of orange or lemon
1 dessertsp. sugar.

To finish:

2 tablesp. jam

Meringue:

2 egg whites
75 g castor sugar

Method

1. Beat egg yolks and sugar in a bowl.
2. Heat milk slightly, add butter and rind and pour over beaten egg, stirring all the time.
3. Place breadcrumbs in a well greased pie dish, pour custard over them and soak for 20 mins, if time allows.
4. Place on flat tin containing a little water. Bake in a moderate oven 350°F (175°C) Gas 4, until set (about 30 mins).
5. Heat jam in bowl in the oven, and spread over top of pudding.
6. Whisk egg whites until stiff, fold in castor sugar and pile roughly on top of pudding. Reduce oven heat.
7. Return to cool oven until meringue is set and lightly brown (about 20 minutes).
8. Serve on a dish with d'oyley under-neath pie dish.

Over to you . . .

Eggs

1. List 3 egg dishes suitable for breakfast and three dishes suitable for a main course.

   Find out the cost of one egg — size 1, 2, 3, 4; (this will be useful for costing recipes).

Custards

1. Compare a homemade egg custard sauce with the packet variety under the following headings: (a) cost for 400 ml; (b) flavour; (c) nourishment; (d) convenience. Suggest 2 ways you could introduce extra flavour to custards.

20 *All About Puddings and Sweets*

Puddings, although not essential to a nutritious diet, are traditionally served at the end of a meal. They should complement the meal and contrast with the main course in colour, taste and texture. There is a wide variety of puddings.

Hot sweet dishes are usually called **puddings. Cold sweet dishes** are called **sweets.**

Milk Puddings

These are made from milk, thickened with a starchy substance, such as rice. Other ingredients may be added to increase food value and flavour, such as eggs, sugar, margarine.

Food value

It is well known that milk is a very nourishing food. It follows that milk puddings are also very nourishing. They contain protein, carbohydrate, fat, Vitamins A, D, B and iron, but lack Vitamin C. For this reason, they should be served with fresh fruit, if possible, (this will also provide a contrast in colour and flavour).

Milk puddings are easy to digest. They are ideal for children, invalids and the elderly, but like many puddings they are high in kilocalories and should be avoided by those who have to watch their weight.

Milk puddings can be made from **Whole Grains,** *e.g.* Rice, or **Finegrains,** *e.g.* semolina. Whole grains take longer to cook than finegrains.

Proportions:

Wholegrain 50 g — to — 500 ml milk
Finegrain   40 g — to — 500 ml milk

Rules for Cooking Milk Puddings

1. Use correct proportions of fresh ingredients.
2. Wash whole grains in a sieve.
3. Grease saucepan to prevent rice sticking to the bottom.
4. Stir to prevent lumping — fine grains must be stirred constantly.
5. Cover and cook gently until thickened (rapid cooking curdles mixture).
6. Consistency should be set but creamy, neither stiff nor runny.
7. Grain must be thoroughly cooked before adding egg.
8. Cool mixture before adding to egg.
9. Bake in a moderate oven 175°C (350°F) Gas 4, until set.
10. Serve with fresh or stewed fruit.

Flavourings: Nutmeg, cinnamon, bayleaf (rice), vanilla.
Orange/lemon rind (juice would cause curdling.)

Rice Pudding

Ingredients

50 g short grain rice
500 ml milk
25 g sugar
13 g margarine
1 egg
Flavouring (nutmeg, bayleaf or vanilla)

Method

1. Put rice into strainer and wash under cold running water.
2. Grease a saucepan, add milk and rice, bring to boil and stir over a gentle heat, until rice softens and absorbs most of the milk (about 25-30 minutes).
3. Add sugar, margarine and flavouring. Mix well and allow to cool slightly.
4. Beat egg in a bowl, pour on rice, stirring all the time.
5. Pour into greased pie dish.
6. Bake at 175°C (350°F), Gas 4, until set and beginning to brown. Remove with a dry cloth.
7. Sprinkle with castor sugar. Serve on a dish, with a d'oyley underneath the pie dish.

Variation

Use recipe above for Sago or Tapioca pudding.

Semolina Pudding

Ingredients

40 g Semolina
500 ml milk
25 g sugar
13 g margarine
1 egg (separated)
Flavouring (vanilla or orange/lemon rind)

Method

1. Pour milk into a saucepan, bring to the boil.
2. Sprinkle in semolina, stirring all the time.
3. Stir over a gentle heat until thick (about 10 mins).
4. Remove from heat, add sugar, margarine and flavouring, stir for a few minutes to cool.
5. Separate yolk from white of egg, beat yolk in a bowl and pour in semolina, stirring all the time.
6. In a clean bowl, stiffly beat egg white, then fold into semolina mixture.
7. Pour into a greased pie dish and bake in a moderate oven, 175°C (350°F), Gas 4, until set and beginning to brown on top.
8. Sprinkle with castor sugar. Serve on a dish, with a d'oyley underneath the pie dish.

Variation

Other fine and powdered grains, such as **ground rice** may be cooked in the same way.

Easy Rice Pudding

Ingredients

40 g fine grain cereal
  or 50 g large grain cereal
25 g sugar
500 ml milk
13 g margarine
Cinnamon

Method

1. Wash large grain. Place grain, sugar, milk and margarine into a greased pie dish. Stir well.
2. Bake in a cool oven, 150°C (300 °F), Gas 2, for 1½-2 hours, stirring once or twice during first hour, with a fork, to prevent rice settling on base. Sprinkle with cinnamon and cook until set, and beginning to brown on top.
3. Serve as above.

Time Saver Tip!

Wipe splashes from dishes before baking — this saves time and energy removing burnt-in stains.

Milk Moulds

These are cold sweets made from milk, thickened with cereal, gelatine or other thickening agent, *e.g.* carageen.

Cornflour Mould (Blancmange)

Ingredients

40 g cornflour	*2 strips of lemon rind*
500 ml milk	*25 g sugar*

Method

1. Blend cornflour with 2 tablespoons of measured milk.
2. Put rest of milk in a rinsed saucepan with lemon rind and infuse for 15 minutes on a very low heat.
3. Strain onto blended cornflour, stirring all the time.
4. Return to saucepan, bring to boil, stirring continuously, and continue stirring while it boils, for 5 minutes.
5. Remove from heat and stir in sugar.
6. Rinse mould with cold water, then pour in cornflour mixture.
7. Place in a cold place to set.

To unmould:

8. Loosen around edges, place serving dish on top, turn upside down and shake firmly.
9. Decorate with fresh or stewed fruit.

Variation

Chocolate mould: Blend 1 tablespoon cocoa with cornflour.

Carrageen Mould

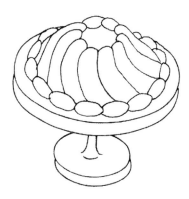

Ingredients

500 ml milk
13 g carrageen
Pinch salt
Thinly peeled rind from ½ lemon
25 g sugar
Beaten egg white
1 dessert spoon Irish liqueur

Method

1. Wash moss two or three times in cold water, changing it each time. Steep in cold water for 10 minutes.
2. Cut away hardened or black parts.
3. Put carrageen into saucepan, with salt and lemon rind.
4. Bring to the boil and simmer gently until it coats the back of a wooden spoon (about 10-15 minutes).
5. Stir in sugar and strain, without pressing, into a bowl.
6. Beat egg white until stiff, but not dry, and fold into carrageen mixture. Stir in liqueur if using.
7. Pour into a wet mould and leave in a cold place to set (placing mould in a bowl of ice speeds this up).
8. Serve with stewed fruit and decorate with whipped cream and crystallised violets.

Fruit Puddings

Stewed Fruit (Apples)

Ingredients

500 g fruit (4 medium apples)
Flavouring (cloves)
125 ml water
50 g sugar

Method

1. Dissolve sugar in water in a saucepan over a low heat, stirring all the time. Boil quickly for 3 minutes, without stirring.
2. Prepare fruit according to kind.
   Apples: Wash, quarter, peel and core. Cut each quarter in two, or in four if large.
3. Add fruit and flavourings to syrup, cover and cook *very gently* until fruit is soft—usually 5-10 minutes.
4. Serve hot or cold in a dessert dish or as an accompaniment to another pudding.

Oven stewed fruit

Place in an ovenproof dish, cover and cook in a moderate oven, 175°C (350°F), Gas 4, for about 20-30 minutes, until soft.

Stewed Dried Fruit (Prunes)

Ingredients

400 g fruit
400 ml water
About 50 g sugar

Flavouring:

Lemon or orange rind

Method

1. Wash fruit and soak overnight in cold water.
2. Next day, place fruit and steeping water into a saucepan.
3. Add flavouring if wished, then bring to the boil and simmer gently, until fruit is soft.
4. Add sugar and stir until dissolved. Empty into a dessert bowl and serve hot or cold.

Apple Purée

Ingredients

500 g cooking apples　　*2 tablesp. water*
¼ teasp. ground　　　　*50 g sugar*
　cloves (optional)

Method

1. Put prepared sliced apples and cloves into a saucepan, with water.
2. Cover and stew gently until dissolved.
3. Beat to a purée with a wooden spoon, rub through a nylon sieve or liquidise.
4. Serve in a hot dessert dish, with custard or cream.

Apple Snow

Ingredients

500 g cooking apples　　*50 g sugar*
2 tablesp. water　　　　*1 white of egg*
Grated rind of　　　　　*1 tablesp. of cream*
　1 lemon　　　　　　　*(optional)*

Method

1. Prepare and slice apples.
2. Stew with water and lemon rind until soft and pulpy, stirring frequently, to prevent burning.
3. Press through a sieve, or liquidise. Stir in sugar and leave until cold.
4. Beat egg white stiffy, and fold into apple purée.
5. Stir in cream and serve chilled in sundae glasses. Decorate with cherries and angelica.

Rhubarb Fool

Ingredients

500 g rhubarb
2 tablesp. water
50 g sugar

Custard:

125 ml milk
1 large egg
*   or dessertsp. custard powder*
125 ml cream

Method

1. Top and tail and wipe rhubarb. Cut in 3 cm lengths.
2. Stew in water until soft, stirring now and then. Add sugar.
3. Rub through a sieve or liquidise. Leave to cool.
4. Make custard sauce, *p. 152.* Cool and stir into rhubarb.
5. Whip cream and fold in.
6. Pour into individual sundae glasses, decorate with piped cream and chill before serving.

Variation:

Use apples or goosberries instead of rhubarb.

Baked Apples

Ingredients

4 medium cooking apples	*Cinnamon*
25 g sugar	*2 tablesp. water*
13 g margarine	

Method

1. Wash and remove cores from apples — **do not peel.**
2. Slit skin around 'equator' of each apple, with the point of a sharp knife.
3. Cream the margarine, sugar and cinnamon and press into central hole of apples.

4. Place on a greased tin or pyrex dish, add water.
5. Bake in a moderate oven, 190°C (375°F), Gas 5, until soft (about half an hour).
6. Lift skin from top half of apple and dredge with caster sugar.
7. Serve on a hot dish, with remaining syrup poured around. Serve custard sauce separately.

Variation

Fill centres with mincemeat (used for mince-pies).

Swiss Apple Pudding

Ingredients

125 g breadcrumbs (brown or white)
50 g margarine
50 g sugar (brown or white)
Grated lemon rind
3 large cooking apples ⎤
1 tablesp. water   ⎥ *stewed apple*
25 g sugar   ⎥
1 tablesp. lemon juice ⎦

Method

1. Prepare and stew apples in water and lemon juice until soft, stir in sugar (25 g).
2. Put breadcrumbs in a bowl, add sugar (50 g) and lemon rind. Melt margarine, pour into crumb mixture and mix well.

3. Place a layer of crumbs in the bottom of a greased pie dish, cover with half the apple. Cover with another layer of crumbs, then rest of apple.
4. Finish with a layer of crumbs. Bake in a moderate oven 190°C (375°F), Gas 5, for about 30 minutes, until top is crisp.
5. Serve in a pie dish on a plate with a d'oyley. Serve custard sauce separately.

Variation

Apple Charlotte: Layer sliced *uncooked* apples with crumb mixture, sprinkling sugar and lemon juice over each layer of apples. Bake for $\frac{3}{4}$ - 1 hour.

Apple Crumble

Ingredients

500 g apple (or other fruit)
Sugar (to sweeten)

Crumble:

150 g flour
50 g sugar (brown or white)
75 g margarine

Method

1. Sieve flour into a bowl. Rub in margarine, until it looks like fine breadcrumbs. Mix in sugar.
2. Prepare apples (or other fruit), slice and put in pie dish, sprinkling sugar between layers (more sugar will be needed for sour fruits, such as rhubarb and gooseberries).
3. Cover with crumble topping and bake in a moderate oven, 190°C (375°F), Gas 5, for about 35 minutes, until crumble begins to brown.
4. Serve in the pie dish, on plate with d'oyley underneath dish.
5. Serve custard sauce separately.

Quick variation

Use canned fruit or pie filling, draining off juice first. Use juice to make a syrup sauce.

Puddings using Madeira Mixture

Eve's Pudding

Ingredients

500 g cooking apples
  (or other fruit)
50 g sugar
Cloves
1 tablesp. water

Maderia mixture:

50 g margarine
50 g caster sugar
75 g flour
1 egg
$\frac{1}{4}$ teasp. baking powder
A little milk

Method

1. Peel, core and slice apples. Put into saucepan with water, sugar and cloves, and stew gently until half cooked.
2. Pour into greased pie dish and leave to cool.
3. Cream margarine and sugar together, until white and fluffy. Add egg, half at a time, beat well in. Finally, fold in sieved flour and baking powder. Add a little milk if mixture seems dry.
4. Spread mixture over cooled apples with a knife, then bake in a moderate oven, 190°C (375°F), Gas 5, for about 30-40 minutes, until mixture is fully cooked.
5. Sprinkle with caster sugar and serve on a plate, with a d'oyley under pie dish.

Pineapple Upside-down Pudding

Ingredients

1 can drained pineapple
(small size)
50 g margarine*
50 g brown sugar*
Cherries

Madeira mixture:

As for *Eve's Pudding*

Method

1. Cream margarine* and sugar * until well mixed. Spread over base of 18 cm (7") round cake tin.
2. Arrange pineapples and cherries on top.
3. Make madeira mixture, by creaming margarine and sugar. Add egg and beat well. Finally, fold in sieved flour and baking powder. If mixture is too dry, stir in 1 tablespoon pineapple juice.
4. Spread over pineapple slices, taking care not to lift them out of place.
5. Bake in a moderate oven, 190°C (375°F), Gas 5, until cooked through (about 30-40 minutes).
6. Turn directly onto a warmed dish. Serve with custard *or* use pineapple juice to make syrup sauce, thickening with blended cornflour, *p. 113.*

Variation:

Double madeira mixture for *Pineapple Upside-down* <u>Cake</u>.

Canary Pudding

Ingredients

50 g margarine	*1 egg*
50 g caster sugar	*¼ teasp. baking powder*
75 g flour	*1 tablespoon milk*
	or water

(Double quantities for larger pudding).

Method

1. Make madeira mixture (*see Eve's Pudding, p. 163*).
2. Empty into greased 500 ml pudding bowl.
3. Cover closely with foil or **greased** greaseproof paper, tied securely in position.
4. Steam for about 1-1½ hours.
5. Allow to cool slightly, then turn out onto a warmed plate. Sprinkle with caster sugar.
6. Serve with jam sauce or custard sauce.

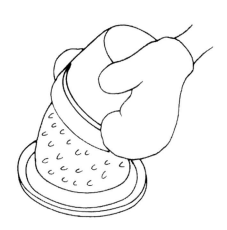

Variations

1. *Raspberry pudding:* Put two tablespoons of raspberry jam in the greased pudding bowl before adding mixture.
2. *Chocolate pudding:* Remove 1 tablesp. flour from recipe and add 1 tablesp. cocoa instead.
3. *Lemon/orange pudding:* Add grated rind of lemon/orange to mixture. Serve with lemon/orange sauce.
4. *Raisin or Sultana pudding:* Add 50 g raisins or sultanas.

Suet Puddings

These are less common now, as they take a long time to cook, and many consider them heavy and indigestible. This is often because they are not cooked for long enough. Suet puddings are usually cooked by **steaming**. Raising agents and breadcrumbs are added to give lightness.

Rules for Suet Puddings

1. Use correct proportions of fresh ingredients — suet especially should be very fresh, unless dried suet, *e.g. Atora,* is used.
2. Chop suet very finely to aid digestion. Lighter fats, such as margarine, are often used now, instead of suet, as they are less heavy and indigestible.
3. Consistency should be too soft to handle/too stiff to pour.
4. Only fill bowl three quarters full.
5. Bowl must be well sealed with a lid, to prevent entry of steam.
6. Long cooking is essential to melt suet and make pudding digestible — the richer the mixture, the longer it will take (minimum is 2-2½ hours).
7. Lift out carefully, using oven gloves; cool for a few minutes, then turn onto a warmed plate.
8. Serve piping hot with a suitable sauce, *e.g.* custard.

Basic Suet Pudding

Ingredients

50 g flour	*1 egg*
50 g shredded suet	*A little milk.*
50 g white breadcrumbs	*Flavouring, e.g.*
50 g caster sugar	*vanilla, lemon*
Pinch salt	*rind*
½ tsp. baking powder	

Method

1. Sieve flour, salt and baking powder into a bowl.
2. Chop suet finely, add with breadcrumbs and sugar and mix well.
3. Beat egg, add flavouring and 1 tablespoon of milk. Mix into dry ingredients, adding more milk if necessary, to give a 'dropping consistency'.
4. Empty into greased pudding bowl — do not overfill.
5. Cover with foil or greased paper, which has been pleated in the centre to allow for rising, and tie securely.
6. Steam continuously for at least 2 hours. Cool slightly, then tu.. into a warm serving dish.
7. Sprinkle with caster sugar and serve with custard sauce.

Variations

This basic pudding would not be very tasty, so add one of the following ingredients and/or flavourings.

1. *Sultana Pudding:* 50-75 g sultanas.
2. *Chelsea Pudding:* 50 g raisins, 50 g currants: 1 dessertsp. treacle.
3. *Marmalade Pudding:* 1 tablesp. marmalade, added before egg.
4. *Lemon Pudding:* add grated rind and juice of 1 lemon.
5. *Ginger Pudding:* add 1 teasp. ground ginger with flour. Stir in 1 tablesp. each treacle and golden syrup with egg.

Traditional Plum Pudding

Basic Suet Pudding with fruit garnish

Plum Pudding

Ingredients

50 g flour
100 g suet
100 g breadcrumbs
100 g brown sugar
100 g raisins
100 g sultanas
50 g currants
25 g mixed peel
25 g chopped or flaked almonds
Rind and juice of $\frac{1}{2}$ a lemon
Rind and juice of $\frac{1}{2}$ an orange
1 large cooking apple — peeled and grated
$\frac{1}{2}$ tsp. mixed spice
$\frac{1}{4}$ tsp. salt
2 large eggs
2 tablesp. whiskey/brandy
Stout or milk to mix

Method

1. Chop suet. Clean raisins (if not prewashed). Skin and chop almonds. Make breadcrumbs. Grate apple and lemon rind. Squeeze juice from orange and lemon.
2. Sieve flour, salt and mixed spice into bowl.
3. Add all dry ingredients, apple and rind and mix well. Add beaten eggs, spirits and mix to a dropping consistency with stout.
4. Cover with plate, and leave overnight.
5. Pour into greased 1 kilo pudding basin. Do not fill more than $\frac{3}{4}$ full.
6. Cover securely with greased paper and foil and steam for at least 5 hours.
7. When cold, wrap in foil and store.
8. Steam for at least 2 hours on day of serving. Pour a little whiskey or brandy over and set alight.
9. Garnish with a sprig of holly.
10. Serve brandy butter in a small dish.

Variation:

Margarine may be substituted for suet to make a lighter pudding.

Cold Sweets

Fruit in Jelly

Ingredients

1 packet jelly
370 ml boiling water
Lemon juice
Fresh fruit (e.g. banana, grapes)
* or Canned fruit, drained.*

Method

1. Place jelly square in bowl and dissolve with boiling water, stirring often. Make up to just under a pint with lemon juice and syrup from canned fruit, or with cold water. Place on ice to cool quickly.
2. Prepare fruit and cut into neat pieces. Dip banana slices in lemon juice first, to prevent browning.
3. Pour 2-3 tablespoons of jelly into the base of a mould, which has been rinsed in cold water.
4. Arrange fruit attractively on jelly, the best side of fruit facing down. Place mould on ice to set jelly.
5. Pour a little more jelly over and leave to set.
6. Add half the remaining jelly and fruit, and, when set, add the other half.
7. If time is short, jelly and fruit can be arranged in individual glasses.
8. To unmould jelly, dip in water which is just too hot for hands, place plate on top and invert mould, giving a sharp jerk to loosen jelly.
9. Decorate with piped fresh cream or serve with icecream.

Banana Split

Ingredients per person

1 banana   *Icecream*
2 tablesp. strawberry jam   *1 chocolate flake*
2 tablesp. water

Method

1. Place jam and water into a saucepan and heat gently, stirring all the time.
2. Cut banana in two, lengthways. Place on long dish.
3. Place a scoop of icecream on top and sieve strawberry syrup over. Sprinkle with chocolate flake.

Peach Melba (for 4)

Ingredients

2 large peaches or
* 1 medium can peaches*
2 tablesp. raspberry jam
2-3 tablesp. drained syrup
* from can (or water)*
4 scoops icecream
Wafers
Cake decorations e.g.
* hundreds and thousands*

Method

1. Make raspberry syrup — dissolve jam in syrup or water over a low heat, stirring all the time.
2. Peel, stone and slice peaches, or drain canned fruit.
3. Place peaches in bottom of 4 sundae glasses.
4. Place a scoop of icecream on each and strain syrup over.
5. Decorate with cake decorations and wafers.

Apricot Eggs

Ingredients

1 can halved apricots   *Swiss Roll*
* or peaches*   *Medium carton cream*

Method

1. Drain fruit.
2. Cut swiss roll into 8 slices. Place on serving dish.

3. Whip cream until almost stiff. Spoon cream onto each slice and top with an apricot half.

Trifle

Ingredients

Stale sponge or madeira cake (about 6 slices)
Jam
Fresh fruit (e.g. banana, orange, grapes)
  or 1 small can of fruit cocktail
Flavouring (sherry if wished)

To decorate:

1 small carton cream
Sugar (to sweeten)
Grated chocolate or flaked almonds

Custard:

150 ml milk
1 teasp. sugar
1 egg or
1 dessert spoon custard powder

Method

1. Cut sponge into fingers, spread with jam and sandwich together.
2. Make custard — warm milk, pour over beaten egg or blended custard powder, return to heat to thicken (do not boil egg custard). Add flavouring.
3. Prepare fruit according to kind, or open and drain tin.
4. Place sponge fingers in base of dessert bowl. Pour over juice from tin and/or a little sherry.
5. Arrange fruit on top, keeping back some for decoration.
6. Pour custard over — leave to cool.
7. Whip cream until thick, spread over custard or pipe a decoration, if wished, using a piping bag and large rose pipe.
8. Decorate with grated chocolate and fruit or almonds.

Easy Chocolate Mousse

Ingredients

2 eggs
50 g chocolate

Method

1. Place chocolate in basin over saucepan of simmering water, until melted. Cool.
2. Carefully separate eggs. Stir egg yolks into warm chocolate.
3. Whip egg whites until stiff. Fold gently into chocolate mixture.
4. Pour into sundae glasses and leave to set in a cold place.
5. Decorate with grated chocolate and whipped cream.

Pineapple Soufflé

Ingredients

1 packet of lemon jelly
1 medium tin pineapple chunks
1 medium carton cream
  or small can evaporated milk
A little sherry (if wished)

To decorate:

Whipped cream
4 pineapple pieces
Cherries

Method

1. Drain pineapple through sieve.
2. Dissolve jelly in 200 ml boiling water. Make up to 300 ml with syrup from pineapple and stir. Leave in a cold place until beginning to set.
3. Chop pineapple into small pieces, keeping back 4 for decoration.
4. Whip cream or evaporated milk until fairly thick.
5. When jelly begins to set around the edges, whip to a froth, add cream and whip until well mixed. Stir in pineapple and sherry if using.

6. Pour at once into a soufflé dish or dessert dish, which has been rinsed out in cold water. Leave to set.
7. Decorate with piped cream, pineapple and cherries. Place dish on a plate with a d'oyley beneath.

Variations

1. *Strawberry Soufflé:* Use strawberry jelly and 400 g strawberries (sieved).
2. *Raspberry Soufflé:* Use raspberry jelly and 200 g canned or fresh raspberries (sieved).
3. *Orange Soufflé:* Use orange jelly and a can of mandarin oranges.

Lemon Cheesecake

Ingredients

150 g digestive biscuits
75 g margarine
1 lemon
200 g cream cheese
125 ml cream
50 g caster sugar

Method

1. Crumb biscuits in blender, or place in plastic bag and crush with a rolling pin.

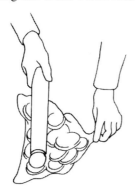

2. Melt margarine in saucepan, stir in biscuit crumbs. Use to line base and sides of 20 cm (8″) flan case or shallow dish. Chill.
3. Wash and dry lemon. Cut 2 slices from centre of lemon for garnish. Grate rind and squeeze juice.
4. Cream cheese with sugar in a bowl. Stir in lemon rind and half the juice. Whip cream until thick and fold into mixture. (Reserve enough for decoration.)
5. Spread mixture over crumbs and chill before serving.
6. Decorate with whipped cream and twists of lemon.

Fruit Flan

Ingredients

Sponge:

2 eggs
50 g caster sugar
50 g flour

Filling:

Fresh fruit (e.g. strawberries,
raspberries, bananas or grapes)
or canned fruit (e.g. peaches,
mandarin oranges)

To decorate:

Whipped cream

Method

1. Grease flan tin, dust with a little caster sugar and flour.
2. Whisk eggs and sugar together in bowl until thick (mixture should hold the figure 8 for a few seconds).
3. Sieve flour and fold in gently. Pour into flan tin.
4. Bake in moderate oven, 190°C (375°F), Gas 5, until firm (about 15-20 minutes).
5. Remove carefully and cool on a wire tray.

6. Whip cream until fairly stiff and spread over centre of flan.
7. Arrange prepared fruit on top and decorate edges with more stiffly whipped piped cream.

Fresh Fruit Salad

Ingredients

1 red skinned apple
1 pear
1 orange
1 banana
1 tablesp. lemon juice
10 green grapes
10 black grapes
250 ml water
100 g sugar

Method

1. Put the sugar and water into a saucepan and stir over a low heat until dissolved. Boil for three minutes. Allow to cool.
2. Wash apple and cut in four, using a stainless steel knife. Remove core but do not peel. Cut into slices, dip in lemon juice and add to syrup.
3. Cut pear in four, peel, core and dice. Add to syrup.
4. Peel orange and cut away flesh from membranes. Peel and slice banana. Dip in lemon juice and add to syrup.
5. Wash, halve and stone grapes; add to fruit salad.
6. Chill and serve with whipped cream or natural yoghurt.

For puddings and sweets using pastry, see following chapter.

Over to you . . .

1. Suggest a pudding suitable for the following occasions: (a) an invalid menu; (b) a children's dinner; (c) a formal dinner party; (d) an economical meal; (e) a picnic lunch.

   In the case of *one,* write a recipe for a sauce to accompany it.

2. Name a pudding you could make from each of the following fruits: gooseberries; rhubarb; lemons; bananas; raspberries; prunes. Write an unusual recipe for a pudding using dried fruit.

3. What sauce would you serve with the following: apple tart; ice cream; pineapple upside down cake.

   What are the advantages of serving a sauce with a pudding?

4. Write a note on the advantages and disadvantages of suet puddings.

   Suggest methods of decorating the following: (a) a suet pudding; (b) a fruit tart; (c) apple snow; (d) trifle.

21   All About Pastry

Pastry is a mixture of flour and fat (shortening), mixed together with just enough water to bind it. Richer pastries may have extra ingredients such as egg yolk and sugar.

The simplest kinds of pastry are:
1. **Shortcrust pastry.**
2. **Suet pastry.**

Other types include:

> **Flaky pastry**
> **Rough-puff pastry**
> **Puff pastry**
> **Choux pastry**

Ingredients

Pastry has three basic ingredients:

Plain flour: This is always used for pastry. Self-raising flour would make pastry soft and doughy, instead of crisp and light. (Exception: suet pastry).

Fat: Most fats can be used for pastry — margarine, butter, lard, cooking fats and even oils. A mixture of lard (or cooking fat) and margarine gives best results.

Water: Poor pastry generally results from adding too much, or too little, water. Too much will make the mixture too wet to roll and if you bake the result, it will be hard and tough. Too little will make a pastry which breaks up easily, making it impossible to roll out.

To make sure you use *just* the right amount, add it in a spoonful at a time, mixing well between each addition. Mix to a **stiff** rather than a soft dough for really crisp pastry.

Light as air!

Baking powder is not used in pastry (except suetcrust), so its lightness depends on how much air you can put into it.

To make really light pastry it is important to trap as much air as possible into the pastry while making it. When this goes into the hot oven, the air will expand and rise, making the pastry light. Air is enclosed by:
(a) Sieving flour
(b) Raising hands well above the bowl when 'rubbing in'.

Keep it cool!

Everything used for pastry making should be cold — the ingredients, utensils and your hands (rinse them in cold water before you begin). The kitchen should be cool too — it's almost impossible to make good pastry in a warm room. If you are baking a few things, start with the pastry, before the heat of the oven warms the room. Keep fat in the refrigerator until just before using and use iced water, or water straight from the cold tap.

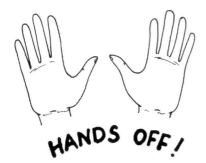

Handle pastry as little as possible. Put fat into flour and cut into very small pieces with a knife, then rub in with the tips of the fingers, until it looks like fine breadcrumbs. Use a knife to mix pastry; it is cooler, and gives a better consistency. Only knead it just enough to bring the dough together. Roll pastry lightly and evenly with a forward/backward motion (rolling sideways makes pastry rise unevenly). Do not stretch pastry; use the rolling pin and knife to lift or turn.

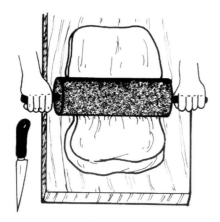

Let it relax!

Even the minimum of rubbing in and rolling warms and stretches the pastry. Leave it in the refrigerator for at least 15 minutes to cool and relax, while you get on with the filling. This will make the pastry light and 'short' textured and will reduce the possibility of shrinking. If you are leaving pastry in a refrigerator for longer than 20 minutes, store it in a floured plastic bag to prevent hardening. Pastry freezes very well.

Turn up the heat!

Bake pastry in a hot oven (to burst starch grains so that the fat is absorbed). If the oven is too cool, the fat will melt and run out of the pastry before the starch bursts, making it greasy and hard.

Reduce heat after 10–15 minutes to allow the filling to cook and to prevent burning.

Remember! When a recipe asks for 100 g pastry — it refers to the amount of flour — not the sum total of ingredients in the pastry.

Summary

1. Use correction proportions.
2. Introduce lots of air.
3. Everything must be cold.
4. Handle as little and as lightly as possible.
5. Use a knife.
6. Roll lightly and evenly
7. Take care adding water.
8. Rest pastry in a cool place before baking.
9. Never stretch pastry.
10. Bake in a hot oven.

Tip!

It's a good idea to make double the quantity of pastry at one time, you can store the extra in a plastic bag in the refrigerator for a day or two, until you need it.

Shortcrust Pastry

This pastry can be used for sweet and savoury dishes, puddings, tarts, flans and pies. Short crust pastry should be 'short', *i.e.* brittle in texture, and light and crumbly to eat. The following five recipes may all be used in recipes which call for shortcrust pastry.

Shortcrust Pastry

Ingredients

200 g plain flour
¼ teaspoon salt
100 g fat (50 lard, 50 margarine)
Cold water (about 3 tablespoons)

Method

1. Sieve flour and salt into a bowl.
2. Cut fat into flour with knife, then rub with fingertips, until mixture looks like fine breadcrumbs. (**Do not rub too much**).
3. Add water, very little at a time, and mix with a knife to a smooth stiff dough.
4. Turn onto a *slightly* floured board and knead lightly until smooth.
5. Turn upside down and roll lightly to required shape.

Brown Shortcrust

(for savoury dishes)

Ingredients

100 g plain flour   *100 g fat*
100 g wholemeal   *Cold water*
¼ teaspoon salt

Method

Make as above, but do not sieve wholemeal.

Rich Shortcrust

Ingredients

200 g plain flour
¼ teaspoon salt
1 level tablespoon icing sugar
125 g margarine
1 teaspoon lemon juice
1 egg yolk
2 tablespoons water

Method

1. Sieve flour, salt and sugar into bowl.
2. Cut margarine into the flour, then rub in lightly until mixture is like fine breadcrumbs.
3. Add 1 tablespoon water to egg yolk, mix into flour with a knife, then add lemon juice and mix well.
4. Add second tablespoon water if required, mix to a stiff dough. Knead lightly.
5. Roll on a floured board into required shape.

Cheese Pastry

Ingredients

200 g flour   *100 g fat*
¼ teaspoon salt   *50 g hard cheese, grated*
¼ teaspoon mustard   *1 egg yolk*
Cayenne pepper   *Cold water*

Method

Make as for rich pastry, sieving mustard and pepper with flour. Mixing in cheese before moistening ingredients. Use for quiches, savoury flans, cheese biscuits, *etc.*

Cheese Straws

1. Roll out pastry 3 mm thick.
2. Cut in strips 10 cm × 1 cm wide.
3. Place on greased tin and bake in a moderate oven 190°C (375°F), Gas 5 for 10-15 minutes — until biscuit coloured.
4. Serve in a tall glass as a party 'nibble'.

Tips!

Reduce temperature slightly when cooking cheese pastry as it burns easily.

All-in-one Shortcrust Pastry

Ingredients

255 g plain flour | 150 g softened margarine
Pinch salt | 2 tablesp. cold water

Method

1. Place margarine, water and half the flour (sieved) into a bowl and cream with a fork.
2. Sieve in remaining flour and mix to a stiff dough.
3. Knead until smooth and roll as required.

Suet Pastry

This may be used for sweet or savoury dishes. The fat used is suet, which is not rubbed in, but shredded into very small pieces and mixed into the dough.

Suet pastry is the only pastry to use a raising agent, *i.e.* baking powder. Breadcrumbs are also added to lighten it. It is usually steamed (*e.g.* apple dumpling, steak and kidney pudding) but may be baked.

Suet Pastry

Ingredients

150 g flour
$\frac{1}{4}$ teaspoon salt
$\frac{1}{2}$ teaspoon baking powder
50 g suet
25 g fine white breadcrumbs
Cold water

Method

1. Sieve flour, salt and baking powder into a bowl.
2. Mix in finely chopped suet, and breadcrumbs.
3. Mix to a stiff dough with cold water, using a knife.
4. Knead on a lightly floured board, then use as required.

Rough Puff Pastry

Ingredients

200 g plain flour
$\frac{1}{4}$ teaspoon salt
125 g fat (half margarine/
  half lard or cooking fat)
125 ml cold water (approx.)
1 teaspoon lemon juice

Method

1. Sieve flour and salt into a bowl. Put water in refrigerator to chill.
2. Put fat into flour and cut into pieces, 1 cm square. **Do not rub in.**
3. Add lemon juice and enough water to make a fairly soft dough.
4. Turn onto a floured board and knead lightly until smooth.
5. Roll into a long strip, fold pastry in three, turning up end of pastry first.
6. Seal open edges with rolling pin, then turn pastry a quarter turn.
7. Roll out into an oblong and repeat the whole process four more times.
8. Leave in a cold place for about 20 minutes, then roll into required shape.
9. Bake in a hot oven, 230°C (450°F), Gas 8, for first 10 minutes; reduce heat to finish cooking, according to recipe.

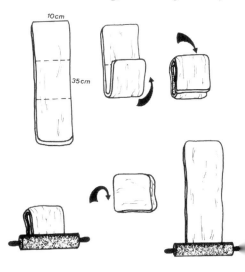

Frozen Pastry

As pastry freezes very well, bought frozen pastry is a good substitute for home made pastry, especially the more difficult pastries, such as puff pastry.

Remember:
  (1) Allow time to thaw pastry fully.
  (2) Roll very thinly.
  (3) Bake in a very hot oven.

To Line a Tin or Plate

  1. Roll pastry about 5 mm thick, so that it is a little larger than the plate.
  2. Lay pastry on plate, easing down into 'bowl' of plate. **Do not stretch.** Trim off extra pastry with sharp knife. Lift pastry off.

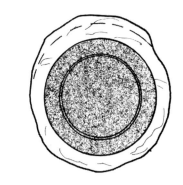

  3. Use 2 cm wide trimmings to line rim of plate, brushing first with cold water.
  4. Damp top of pastry strip and return circle of pastry to plate, pressing firmly in position.
  5. Flake and decorate.

Pastry decorations

To Bake Blind

This means to bake pastry in a flan case before the filling is added. Line flan case, easing pastry into place. Trim off extra pastry. Prick base with fork. Place a sheet of greaseproof paper over pastry in flan ring and fill with dried peas or rice, to weight the pastry down and prevent it rising. Bake at 200°C (400°F), Gas 6, on top shelf, for about 15 minutes. Remove paper and beans and return to oven for 5 minutes to dry pastry out.

Baking blind

Recipes using Pastry

Open Jam Tart

Ingredients

150 g shortcrust pastry
  (150 g flour: 75 g fat)
2 tablespoons jam
Egg (to glaze)

Method

1. Grease a 20 cm (8") ovenproof plate or tin.
2. Make pastry. Roll out a little wider than the plate.
3. Place pastry on plate and trim off edges with the back of a knife. Lift off pastry.
4. Use thin strips of pastry to line edge of plate, placing cut edge outwards. Brush with water to make them stick.
5. Damp strip and lay the round of pastry on top, pressing edges together. Flake and decorate.
6. Roll out remaining pastry and cut into long even strips.
7. Spread jam on deep part of plate only and use strips to decorate, arranging them like a lattice, or twisting them and forming them into a cartwheel.

8. Chill in refrigerator for 15 minutes. Brush with beaten egg.
9. Bake in a hot oven — 220°C (425°) Gas 7, for 10 minutes, reduce to moderate and cook for 15 minutes more until golden brown and crisp.
10. Serve with whipped cream or custard.

Apple Tart

Ingredients

200 g shortcrust pastry
  (200 g flour/100 g fat)
3 medium cooking apples
Sugar (to sweeten)
Cloves (3–4)
Egg (to glaze)

Method

1. Grease large plate. Make pastry (*p. 173*). Chill in refrigerator.
2. Divide pastry in two, roll out each half and place one half on plate. Return both pieces of pastry to refrigerator.
3. Peel, core and slice apples. Place on pastry, sprinkling sugar and cloves on top.
4. Brush edge of pastry with water and cover with second round of pastry, pressing well together.
5. Trim, flake and decorate. Cut a slit across the centre, to allow steam to escape.
6. Brush with beaten egg, place on a flat tin and bake in a hot oven, 230°C (450°F), Gas 8, for 10 minutes. Reduce to moderate, 190°C (375°F), Gas 5, to finish cooking (about 25 minutes more)
7. Serve with whipped cream, ice cream (*à la mode*) or custard.

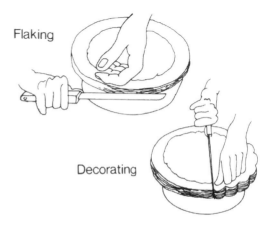

Flaking

Decorating

Variations

1. Similar tarts can be made from rhubarb, gooseberies, blackberries, blackcurrants, mincemeat or mixtures of these.
2. *Apple Pie:* use 5 apples, 100 g pastry, and make in a deep pie dish, using pastry to cover top only.
3. Make with canned pie fillings, *e.g.* cherry pie filling.

Brushing pastry

Apple Cobs

Ingredients

200 g shortcrust pastry
   (200 g flour/ 100 fat)
   or rich shortcrust pastry
Caster sugar and egg white — for frosting.

Filling:

4 medium cooking apples   15 g margarine
25 g sugar   Cinnamon

Method

1. Grease tin, make pastry and chill.
2. Roll pastry into 30 cm square. Cut in 4.
3. Peel and core apples, mix margarine, sugar and cinnamon in a small bowl and fill into centre of apples.
4. Place apples in the centre of each square, damp edges and gather up around the apple, sealing the edges well. Leave an opening at the top and use trimmings, if any, to make two leaves for each cob.

5. Place on greased tin and bake in a hot oven, 230°C (450°F), Gas 8, for 10 minutes; reduce heat to moderate, 190°C (375°F), Gas 5, and cook until pastry is golden brown and apples soft (15–20 minutes). Five minutes before end of cooking, brush with stiffly beaten egg white and sprinkle with caster sugar. Return to oven to dry frosting.
6. Serve on a warm dish, with custard or cream.

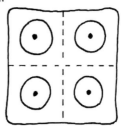

Mince Pies

Ingredients

200 g rich shortcrust pastry
2–3 tablesp. mincemeat
Beaten egg to glaze
Icing sugar

Method

1. Roll out pastry less than 5 mm thick.
2. Using 2 cutters — 1 slightly larger than the other — cut into rounds.
3. Press larger rounds into greased patty tins and put a teaspoon of mincemeat on each.
4. Damp edges and place smaller rounds on top, sealing well with a fork (or flake and decorate).
5. Brush with beaten egg and prick top with fork.
6. Bake in hot oven, 230°C (450°F), Gas 8, for 10 minutes; reduce to moderate and bake until pies are cooked (about 15 minutes more).
7. Cool on a wire tray, arrange on a plate with a d'oyley underneath and sprinkle icing sugar over. Serve warm.

Bakewell Tart

Ingredients

100 g shortcrust pastry, p. 173
2–3 tablespoons jam, lemon curd
  or stewed fruit

Madeira:

50 g margarine
50 g caster sugar
75 g flour
1 egg
¼ teaspoon baking powder
Vanilla
1 dessertspoon water (approx.)

Method

1. Grease plate. Make pastry. Line plate with pastry, using trimmings to line edge of plate. Flake and decorate and place in refrigerator.
2. Cream margarine and sugar. Beat egg slightly.
3. Add half the egg, beat well in.
4. Add 1 tablespoon sieved flour, stir well in.
5. Add rest of egg, beat well. Add vanilla.
6. Sieve flour and baking powder and *fold* gently into mixture. **Do not beat.**
7. If mixture is too stiff, add a little water, to make a soft dropping consistency.
8. Spread jam on base of pastry, cover with madeira mixture. Brush pastry with a little egg or milk.
9. Bake in a moderate oven, 190°C (375°F), Gas 5, for 40–45 minutes, until golden brown and cooked through.
10. Serve with custard sauce.

Apple Amber Pudding

Ingredients

100 g Short or Rich short pastry
4 medium cooking apples
13 g margarine
Grated rind of half lemon
25 g sugar
1 egg yolk
1 dessertspoon water

Meringue:

1 egg white
50 g caster sugar

Method

1. Make pastry and use to line a greased plate or flan tin. Flake and decorate edges. Chill.
2. Peel, core and slice apples. Put apples, water, rind and margarine into saucepan and stew gently until soft.
3. Beat to a pulp with wooden spoon or sieve if wished.
4. Cream egg yolk with sugar, and add to apple mixture. Mix well and pour into pastry case. Bake in fairly hot oven, 200°C (400°F), Gas 6, for 15 minutes; reduce heat and cook at moderate, 190°C (375°F), Gas 5, for 15 minutes.
5. Beat egg white until stiff, fold in caster sugar and pile or pipe on top of apple.
6. Return to cool oven, 100°C (200°F), Gas ½, for 20-30 minutes, to cook meringue.

Apple Dumpling

Ingredients

150 g suet pastry
3 medium cooking apples
2–3 tablespoons sugar
Cloves or cinnamon
1–2 tablespoons water

Method

1. Grease a small pudding bowl (130 cm) and prepare greaseproof paper, foil, *etc.*, for top.
2. Cut one third off pastry, knead each piece and roll larger piece into a circle large enough to fit bowl. Ease gently into bowl, pressing well against sides.
3. Peel, core and slice apples. Put into pastry lined bowl and sprinkle with sugar and spice. Add water.
4. Roll smaller piece of pastry into a circle large enough to cover bowl, brush edges with water and lay on top, pressing edges well together.
5. Pleat greased paper or foil and tie onto top of bowl.
6. Have ready a saucepan one third filled with boiling water. Lower bowl into water, and steam for 2–2½ hours.
7. Turn onto hot dish, dredge with caster sugar and serve with custard sauce.

Savoury Pastry Dishes

Sausage Rolls

Ingredients

200 g shortcrust pastry	*Pepper and salt*
200 g sausage meat	*Egg (to glaze)*

Method

1. Roll pastry into oblong, approx. 300 cm × 160 cm.
2. Divide sausage meat in two and roll into two long 'sausages', the same length as pastry.
3. Cut pastry in two on the length, and place sausage meat in centre of each. Damp cut edges of pastry.
4. Roll pastry around sausage meat towards cut edges, press lightly to seal. Cut in lengths 5 cm or 10 cm long.
5. Flake edges, glaze with beaten egg and cut two slits on the top of each sausage roll.

6. Place on a greased tin. Bake in a fairly hot oven, 220°C (425°F), Gas 7, for 10 mins; reduce to moderate, 190°C (375°F), Gas 5 and cook for about 15 minutes more.

7. Serve on warmed dish, on a dish paper.

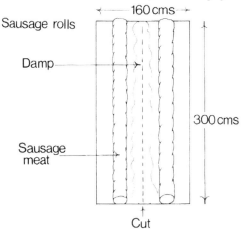

Sausage rolls

Damp

160 cms

300 cms

Sausage meat

Cut

Cornish Pasties

(ideal for picnics and packed lunches)

Ingredients

200 g short pastry   Egg (to glaze)

Filling:

100 g lean beef (minced)
1 small chopped onion
1 medium potato, diced
1 medium carrot, diced
Pepper, salt

Method

1. Make pastry. Chill.
2. Roll pastry out to 5 mm in thickness (slightly thicker than a 50 p coin). Using a small saucepan lid, cut circles of pastry, rolling out trimmings to make a further circle.
3. Divide filling ingredients between pasties, seasoning with pepper and salt.
4. Damp edges and bring them together on top of pastry, leaving a hole in the centre. Press well together and crimp.
5. Brush with beaten egg. Place on greased tin and bake in fairly hot oven, 200°C (400°F), Gas 6, for 20 minutes; reduce to 180°C (350°F), Gas 4, for about 20–25 minutes more, to cook filling.
6. Serve hot or cold with a green salad.

22   All About Cereals

Cereals are the seeds or grains of grass plants.

Cereal products

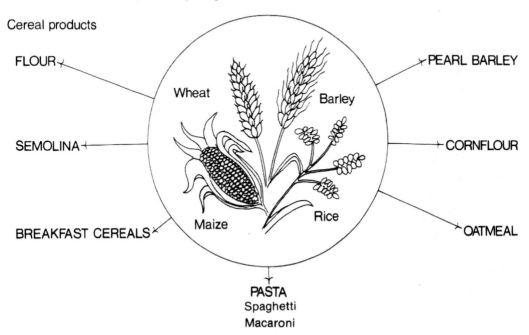

FLOUR

SEMOLINA

BREAKFAST CEREALS

Wheat

Maize

Barley

Rice

PEARL BARLEY

CORNFLOUR

OATMEAL

PASTA
Spaghetti
Macaroni

The cereals we eat include:

Wheat	Rice
Oats	Maize
Barley	Rye

Food Value

The main nutrient in cereals is **carbohydrate** in the form of **starch,** so they are a good source of energy. Whole cereals contain **cellulose** in the outer husk, but this is often removed in processing. Cereals also contain **vegetable protein,** a little **fat, B group vitamins** and several minerals including **iron, calcium and phosphorus.** Cereals should be served with an animal protein food, such as milk, eggs or cheese, to improve their food value.

Some cereals, *e.g.* rice, are cooked in liquid, which is absorbed by the cereal. This alters the food value by increasing the water content considerably and reducing the amount of protein and carbohydrate.

Average composition of Cereals

Table 22.1

Protein	Fat	Carbohydrate	Vitamins	Minerals	Water
7 - 14	2 - 7	70 - 77%	B group	iron calcium	12%

The Effect of Cooking on Cereals

1. Moist heat causes grains to swell and burst.
2. Grains absorb water.
3. Starch becomes digestible.
4. Cellulose is softened.
5. Dry heat, *e.g.* baking, causes starch grains to burst, releasing starch, which absorbs fat, *e.g.* in pastry making.

Advantages of Cereals

1. Cheap yet filling.
2. Easy to prepare, to cook and to store.
3. No wastage.
4. Good source of energy.
5. Unprocessed cereals — a good source of fibre.

Disadvantages of Cereals

1. High in kilocalories.
2. Can be insipid.
3. Process cereals are not a well balanced food.

Wheat

Wheat is the most important cereal and is used to make bread, one of our staple foods.

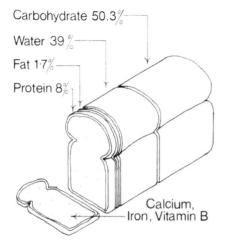

Composition of white bread

Carbohydrate 50.3%

Water 39%

Fat 1·7%

Protein 8%

Calcium, Iron, Vitamin B

Structure of a Wheatgrain

Each grain has 3 basic parts:

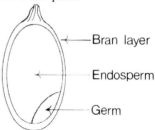

Bran layer

Endosperm

Germ

1. **The germ:** the most nutritious part, contains most of the protein, fat and Vitamin B.
2. **Endosperm:** mainly **starch** with a little protein, which is called **gluten.**
3. **Bran:** layers of cellulose make up this outer layer. It also contains Vitamin B and minerals.

Why we need Bran

It is now well known that bran is a very important substance in our diet. This is because the cellulose it contains provides dietary fibre (roughage) which helps move food along our intestines. Bran is removed from many cereals during processing, *e.g.* white flour and rice, so that these foods lack valuable vitamin B and fibre.

Today in western countries, many people suffer from problems like constipation and from serious diseases of the bowel, just because they do not eat enough fibre. We should try to eat wholemeal bread rather than white bread, because of its extra fibre content.

Flour

Wheat is ground down (milled) to make flour. There are 4 basic types of flour:

1. **Wholemeal flour** contains the whole grain (100%), which is cleaned, then crushed. Nothing is taken away and nothing is added. Wholemeal flour and bread are rich in vitamin B and dietary fibre.

2. **Wheatenmeal or brown flour** has about 85% of the grain left. Some of the rough outer layers of bran are removed.
3. **White flour** retains only 73% of the total grain — the germ and bran have been removed by repeated crushing and sieving. All that is left is the starchy endosperm, which also contains much of the protein (gluten).
4. **Self-raising flour** is white flour which has a raising agent (baking powder) added to it.

What is left of the Wheatgrain?

Percentage of total grain left in:

wholemeal   brown   white
flour   flour   flour

Rice

Rice is imported from the East and the U.S. It is one of the least nourishing cereals, especially white 'polished' rice, which has the germ and bran removed. In eastern countries, where some people live almost entirely on white rice, many suffer from malnutrition, including the disease beri-beri caused by lack of Vitamin B_1 (thiamine). Rice may be used in sweet and savoury dishes. Several forms are available:

1. **Long grain (Patna) rice** — used in savoury dishes, as the grains remain fluffy and separate when cooked.
2. **Short grain (Carolina) rice** — round grains which become soft and sticky during cooking. This is good for puddings.

3. **Brown Rice** — whole grain rice with only the outer husk removed. It has a chewy texture and nutty flavour. It takes longer to cook than white rice — about 40 minutes, instead of 12. Brown rice is more nourishing than polished rice, as it contains more Vitamin B, protein and dietary fibre.

To Cook Rice (for Savoury Dishes)

(50 g per person)
1. Wash in sieve under cold running water.
2. Put into a saucepan containing plenty of boiling salted water. Return to boil, cook for 11-12 minutes until tender, but not too soft. **Do not overcook.**
3. Strain through a sieve, rinse with cold water. Drain. Spread out on a large dish and allow to dry in a moderate oven for 20 minutes, turning now and then with a fork.

Maize

Maize is used to make cornflour, popcorn, corn oil; it is also eaten as a vegetable (corn on the cob).

Oatmeal

Used mainly for porridge and biscuits.

Cereal Products

Semolina: From wheat; used for milk puddings.
Pearl barley: Barley is polished to remove the husk. It is used to thicken soups and stews.

Cornflour: Flour made from maize (corn); cannot be used alone for baking, as it has no gluten. Cornflour is used to thicken soups, and custards.

Rolled oats: Oats are ground between heated rollers, which flatten and partly cook them. These are used for porridge, biscuits, muesli, and for coating fish.

Breakfast cereals: These are processed cereal foods, made from wheat (*Weetabix*), maize (*Cornflakes*), oats (*Readybrek*) and rice (*Rice Krispies*). They have been precooked and many have added vitamins. If cereals are served with milk, they make a nourishing and satisfying breakfast dish. Those which contain the whole grain and bran are more nutritious.

Sago, Tapioca, Arrowroot: These are starchy foods which are used in puddings and for thickening soups, in a similar way to cereals. But they are **not** cereals; they come from parts of tropical trees and plants.

Pasta: This is made from ground semolina. It is mixed with water to form a paste, which is pressed into different shapes and dried. Brown pasta is now available, this is made from wholemeal flour.

To Cook Pasta

(60–70 g uncooked pasta per person)
1. Cook pasta in a large saucepan containing lots of fast boiling water and 1 teaspoon salt.
2. To prevent pasta sticking together, add 1 tablespoon oil to the cooking water.
3. Cook for 10–15 minutes. Cook wholemeal pasta for at least 15 minutes. Stir now and then. Pasta should not be too soft — cook it *al dente* (Italian for 'with a bite').
4. Toss in butter before serving.

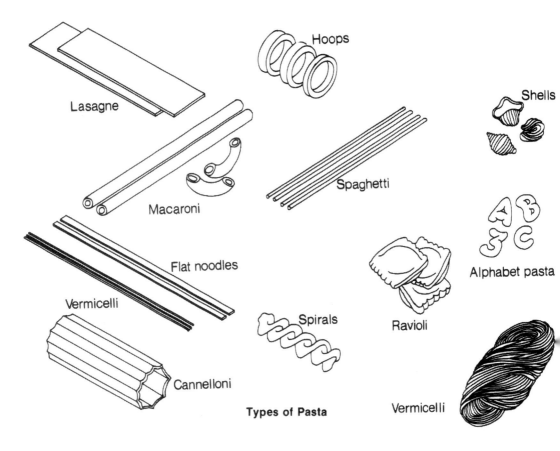

Types of Pasta

Hoops · Lasagne · Shells · Macaroni · Spaghetti · Flat noodles · Alphabet pasta · Vermicelli · Spirals · Ravioli · Cannelloni · Vermicelli

Recipes Using Cereals

Rice

Kedgeree, *p. 108.*
Rice pudding, *p. 133.*

Pasta

Macaroni cheese, *p. 141.*
Spaghetti Bolognese, *p. 83.*

Oats

Porridge, *p. 55.*
Flapjacks, *p. 201.*

Wheat

Bread, cake recipes, *Chapter 23.*

Risotto

Ingredients

200 g long grain rice
1 onion
50 g mushrooms
50 g margarine
750 ml chicken stock
25 g Cheddar or Parmesan cheese
Pepper, salt

Method

1. Peel and chop onion finely. Wash and slice mushrooms.
2. Melt margarine in a saucepan, add onion and mushrooms, and sauté for a few minutes until beginning to brown.
3. Meanwhile wash rice in a sieve under cold water. Drain.
4. Add rice to saucepan and heat gently, stirring for a few minutes.
5. Add stock and stir well. Cover and simmer gently for about 20 minutes, until all the stock has been absorbed.
6. Meanwhile, grate cheese, stir most of it into the cooked rice and serve at once.
7. Serve in a hot dish or casserole, sprinkle a little cheese over. Garnish with parsley.

Variations

1. Add 2–3 chopped streaky rashers, with the onion.
2. Add 3 skinned, chopped tomatoes, for final ten minutes.
3. Add 100–200 g of left-over cooked chicken or ham for final 10 minutes.
4. Add a few prawns, or a packet of mixed frozen vegetables, after 10 minutes.

Fried Rice

Ingredients

200 g long grain rice
1 medium onion
50 g cooking fat or
   2 tablespoons oil
50 g frozen peas
1 egg
Pepper/salt
Soy sauce (optional)

Method

1. Cook rice in boiling, salted water for 10 minutes. Drain. Chop onion into medium sized pieces.
2. Melt margarine in a large frying pan, add onion and fry gently for 5 minutes, without browning. Stir in rice.
3. Add peas, seasoning and sauce, if using. Cook for 5 minutes, stirring all the time.
4. Beat egg and pour into rice, stirring all the time, until egg sets in little pieces.
5. Serve in individual rice bowls or on a large vegetable dish.
6. Garnish with chopped spring onions.

23 All About Baking

Home baked bread and cakes, when well made, have a better food value, flavour and appearance than bought produce. They are cheaper and there are no mystery additives — you know just what is going into them.

But to get good results, it is important to follow the basic rules. Baking is the area of cookery most likely to go wrong if you do not keep exactly to the recipe. Ingredients have been carefully balanced to give correct results. Always use good quality ingredients:

Flour: Wheat flour forms the main structure of bread and cakes. White flour is the most popular, but with greater emphasis on fibre in the diet, wholemeal is now being used a lot more, not just for bread, but in pastry, cakes and biscuits.

Flour should be fresh and dry — sieve it before use to enclose air. Self-raising flour has raising agent in it, so there is no need to use baking powder. It may be used for plain cakes and scones, but is not suitable for rich cakes or for pastry.

Fat: Fat helps cakes stay fresh longer. Margarine is suitable for most plain and rich cakes — it is easy to cream and has a good flavour. Butter is expensive and difficult to cream but gives a rich flavour. Soft margarines are often used for 'all in one' recipes, but do not use soft fats and spreads for normal baking.

Sugar: Castor sugar is the most suitable sugar for baking, as it is fine, and blends well. Granulated (table) sugar and brown sugar are difficult to cream. Brown sugar gives a spicy flavour — use it for dark fruit cakes and gingerbread.

Eggs: Eggs add food value to cakes. They also help to hold air, making your baking light and spongy. Eggs must be fresh, and at room temperature before using. Remove from refrigerator 1 hour before use. Use size 2-3 for most baking.

Dried fruit: *e.g.* raisins, sultanas, currants. Today, most dried fruit comes ready washed in 500 g packets. If not, put it into a sieve and rinse under warm running water. Shake well and dry thoroughly in a low oven. Cool before use. Stalks must be carefully removed from all dried fruit before use.

Cherries: Rinse in warm water and dry before chopping.

Raising Agents

A raising agent is something added to baked foods, to make them rise. Bread and cakes without a raising agent would be hard, flat and unpalatable. A well risen cake

(a) looks more attractive;

(b) is light and spongy;

(c) is more pleasant to eat.

There are 4 raising agents used in cooking:

Air
Bread Soda
Baking Powder   THINK! ABBY
Yeast

The aim of a raising agent is to produce a gas in the dough. When this is put in the oven, the heat makes the gas expand; it becomes lighter and starts to rise, pushing the dough or mixture upwards, until the heat of the oven sets it.

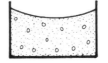 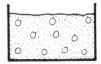

Gas made in dough . . .   Gas expands . . .

Rises . . . until oven heat forms a crust

Natural Raising Agents

Air

In most baking, we try to get as much air as possible into the mixture, in order to make it light:

1. By sieving the flour.
2. By rubbing fat into flour high over the bowl.
3. By creaming and beating cakes and batters.
4. By whisking egg mixtures, *e.g.* sponges.

In pastry and whisked sponges, the only raising agent used is air, so the lightness of this depends on the amount of air we put in.

This air expands and rises in the hot oven, until a crust forms on the pastry or the eggs in the sponge set.

Chemical Raising Agents

Other raising agents depend on a **chemical reaction** to make a gas in the dough. This is the reaction you learn about at science class; **when an alkali and an acid are mixed and moistened, carbon dioxide is produced.**

$$\textbf{ALKALI} + \textbf{ACID} + \textbf{LIQUID} = \textbf{CO}_2$$

1. Bread Soda

The action of bread soda in baking works this way:

Breadsoda + Sour Milk = CO_2
(ALKALI)   (ACID) (LIQUID)

If you have no sour milk, you can use **lemon juice** to produce acid, or **cream of tartar** (a white acid powder):

Breadsoda + Cream of Tartar + Milk = CO_2
 (ALKALI)   (ACID)   (LIQUID)

Cream of tartar gives more accurate results than sour milk, as the amount of acid is known — use in the proportion: 1 teaspoon cream of tartar to $\frac{1}{2}$ teaspoon bread soda.

Bread soda is used to raise soda bread, plain scones and some cakes, *e.g.* gingerbread.

2. Baking powder

Baking powder has an alkali and an acid mixed together, in just the right proportion, with rice flour added to prevent them reacting together in the tin.

Baking Powder + Milk or Eggs = CO_2
 (ALKALI + ACID)   (LIQUID)

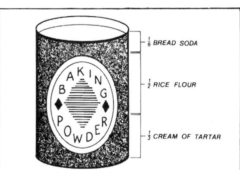

- **Use raising agents carefully.**
- **Store all raising agents in airtight containers.**
- **Replace lid tightly.**

Correct proportions are important. Too little leaves your baking flat and unpalatable. If too much is used, the gas expands too quickly and passes out through the top of the cake before the heat has time to set it, and the cake sinks. Too much raising agent also gives an unpleasant taste.

When too much raising agent is used . . .

Gluten

Raising agents could not work if it were not for a very important protein in wheat flour, called **gluten.** When this is moistened, it becomes quite elastic, allowing the dough to stretch upwards as the gas expands, until the oven heat sets it.

Oven Heat

The oven must be at the correct temperature *before* putting in a cake.

Allow 15 minutes heating up time. For most recipes, this means turning on the oven before you start to make the cake.

When the oven is too hot, it causes burning, hard crusts and cracks on cakes.

When the oven is too cool, it causes gas to escape before the crust forms, resulting in heavy unrisen cakes.

Avoid opening and closing the door unnecessarily. Do not slam the oven — the cold air may cause the cake to sink.

Rules for Baking Bread and Cakes

1. **Prepare tin** before you start; grease or line it, *p. 200.*
2. Use **correct proportions** of **fresh ingredients.** Weigh accurately.
3. The amount of **raising agent** is vital to the success of a recipe.
4. **Sieve flour** and raising agent together to mix well.
5. The **correct consistency** is very important — for bread add most of the liquid at the same time for a good soft dough.
6. Avoid **overhandling** and overkneading.
7. **Correct oven temperature** is important — preheat before moistening ingredients.
8. Arrange shelves in correct position — most cakes are baked in the centre of the oven.
9. Once mixture is moistened and raising agent added, **do not delay before baking.** Avoid opening oven door, particularly during first 10 minutes.
10. **Time baking accurately** and test to see if its done, before removing from oven.
11. Cool on a wire tray.

Is it cooked?

Table 23.1

Bread	Cakes	Sponges
Hollow sound underneath when tapped.	Inset a dry skewer: it should come out dry.	Surface springs back when lightly pressed with finger.

Soda Bread

Characteristics of good Soda Bread

Question:	*What should well-made soda bread look and taste like?*
Answer:	It should be light, spongy and well risen, with a golden brown crust. There should be no yellowish spots or damp streaks. It should have a good flavour, without a strong soda taste.

Soda Bread

Ingredients

400 g plain flour
½ teaspoon salt
½ teaspoon bread soda ⎫
250 ml sour milk ⎬
    or
½ teaspoon breadsoda ⎫
1 teasp. cream of tartar ⎬
250 ml fresh milk ⎭

Method

1. Sieve flour, salt and raising agent into a bowl (rub soda first in the palm of hand to remove small lumps).
2. Add most of milk and mix to a soft dough with a wooden spoon, adding more milk if necessary.
3. Empty onto lightly floured board and knead gently, until smooth underneath and free from cracks.
4. Turn smooth side up, flatten into a round, about 5 cm thick.
5. Place on a lightly floured tin. Cut a cross on the top and brush over with a little milk.
6. Bake in a fairly hot oven, 220°C (425°F), Gas 6, for about 40 minutes.
7. Cool on a wire tray.

Brown Soda Bread (Wholemeal Bread)

Ingredients

300 g wholemeal
100 g plain flour
½ teaspoon salt
½ teaspoon bread soda ⎫
250-300 ml sour milk ⎬
    or
½ teaspoon bread soda ⎫
1 teaspoon cream of tartar ⎬
250-300 ml milk ⎭

Method

Make as for white soda bread. Mix wholemeal in to sieved flour and raising agent before adding milk.

Faults	Reasons
Brownish, yellow spots	Too much bread soda *or* soda not blended in
Damp patches	Over-sour clotted milk used *or* not fully cooked
Flat, unrisen cake	Not enough raising agent *or* dough too dry
Crust too hard	Temperature too high *or* baked too long

Soda Bread and Fruit

Add 100 g raisins or sultanas to either of recipes above, before liquid is added.

50 g margarine and 50 g sugar may be added for a richer bread.

Scones and Cakes

There are 4 basic methods of making cakes:

1. **The rubbing-in method** — for plain scones and cakes.
2. **The creaming method** — for richer cakes.
3. **The whisking method** — for sponge cakes and meringues.
4. **The melting method** — for gingerbread.

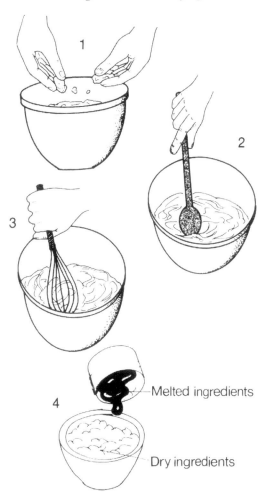

Melted ingredients

Dry ingredients

1. The Rubbing-in Method

This is used for plain cakes, which do not have a lot of fat, *e.g.* scones, rock buns, and pastry. The flour is sieved into a bowl with the raising agent. The fat is cut into small pieces then rubbed in with the tips of the fingers, until the mixture looks like breadcrumbs. All dry ingredients are added before the liquid (eggs/milk).

Special points

Be careful when adding liquid. Do not make the mixture too dry, or too wet. In many cases you will have to roll it out.

Scones (pronounced skons) are called after a town in Scotland. They are quick to make and bake and are a good substitute for bread.

Remember: The dough should be soft. The scones should be rolled out quite thickly (at least 1 cm).
They should be cooked at the top of a fairly hot oven.

Brown Wholemeal Scones

Ingredients

100 g wholemeal
100 g plain flour
¼ teaspoon salt
¼ teaspoon bread soda
50 g margarine
25 g caster sugar
About 100 ml sour milk

Method

1. Sieve flour, salt and bread soda into a bowl. Stir in wholemeal.
2. Add margarine, cut in small pieces, then rub into flour.

3. Stir in sugar and mix well.
4. Add enough sour milk to make a soft dough.
5. Turn onto a floured board, knead until smooth underneath.
6. Turn smooth side up and roll into a circle 1.5 cm thick.
7. Cut into 8 triangles, place on a greased tin and brush over with milk.
8. Bake in a fairly hot oven, 215°C (425°F), Gas 6, for 15-20 minutes.
9. Cool on a wire tray. Serve on a round plate with a d'oyley or in a bread basket, lined with a paper napkin.

Tea Scones

Ingredients

200 g flour
⅛ teaspoon salt
1 teaspoon baking powder
50 g margarine
25 g castor sugar
1 egg or egg yolk
A little milk (about 2 tbsps.)

Method

1. Sieve flour, salt and baking powder into a bowl.
2. Rub in margarine, until it looks like breadcrumbs, then stir in sugar.
3. Beat egg and milk in a small bowl.
4. Add to mixture (keeping back a little for glazing) and mix to a soft dough, adding more milk if necessary.
5. Turn onto a floured board; knead lightly, until smooth underneath.
6. Roll out to at least 1 cm in thickness, and cut into rounds with a small cutter.
7. Place on a greased tin, brush with egg. Bake in a fairly hot oven, 215°C (425°F), Gas 6, for about 15 minutes.
8. Cool on a wire tray. Serve on a round plate with a d'oyley or in a bread basket lined with a paper napkin.

Variations:

Sultana Scones: Add 50 g cleaned sultanas, with sugar.
Cheese Scones: Add 50 g grated cheese instead of sugar.

Milk Rolls

Ingredients

As for Tea Scones (above)

Method

1-5. As for Tea Scones.
6. Divide dough in two. Roll out each piece into a thin round (about 5 mm) and cut each into 6 or 8 triangles.
7. Dampen points with milk and roll from wide end to point, pressing lightly to hold.
8. Bake as for Tea Scones (7 and 8).

Raspberry Buns

Ingredients

200 g plain flour
⅛ teasp. salt
1 teaspoon baking powder
75 g margarine
75 g castor sugar
1 egg
2-3 tablespoons milk
1-2 tablesps. raspberry jam

Method

(This is a slightly richer version of the tea scone recipe.)
1. Sieve flour, salt and baking powder into a bowl.
2. Rub in margarine, then stir in sugar.
3. Beat egg and milk in a small bowl.
4. Add to mixture, keeping back a little for glazing. Mix to a soft dough, adding more milk if necessary.

5. Turn onto a floured board, and knead lightly until smooth.
6. Form into a roll and cut into 10 pieces.
7. With a floured thumb, make a hole in the centre of the cut side of each piece.
8. Drop about ¼ teasp. jam into hole and carefully draw edges up over jam. Press well to seal.
9. Place on a greased tin, brush with beaten egg, sprinkle granulated sugar over and bake in a fairly hot oven, 215°C (425°F), Gas 6, for 15-20 minutes.
10. Serve on a round plate with a d'oyley underneath.

Coconut Buns

Ingredients

200 g flour	75 g castor sugar
⅛ teasp. salt	50 g coconut
1 teasp. baking powder	1 egg
75 g margarine	2-3 tablesp. milk

To decorate:

1-2 tablesp. warmed jam
2-3 tablesp. coconut

Method

1. Sieve flour, salt and baking powder into a bowl.
2. Rub in margarine, stir in sugar and coconut and mix well.
3. Beat egg in bowl, add a little milk and pour into centre of mixture, adding enough milk to make a fairly stiff dough.
4. Using two forks, pile into 10-12 cakes on a greased baking tin, or use greased patty tins.
5. Bake in a fairly hot oven, 215°C (425°F), Gas 6, for about 20 minutes.
6. Place jam and coconut on 2 plates, invert buns onto hot jam, then onto coconut.
7. Serve on a round plate with a d'oyley underneath.

Rock Buns

Ingredients

200 g flour
⅛ teasp. salt
1 teasp. baking powder
¼ teasp. mixed spice
75 g margarine
75 g sugar
25 g mixed peel
75 g currants or sultanas
1 egg
2-3 tablesp. milk

Method

1. Sieve flour, salt, baking powder and spice into bowl.
2. Rub in margarine. Add sugar, peel and fruit and mix well.
3. Beat egg in bowl, add milk and pour into the centre of mixture, adding enough to make a fairly stiff dough.
4. Using two forks, pile into 10-12 cakes on a greased tin, or use patty tins.
5. Bake in a fairly hot oven, 215°C (425°F), Gas 6, for about 20 mins. Cool on a wire tray.
6. Serve on a round plate with a d'oyley.

Drop Scones

Ingredients

200 g flour
¼ teasp. breadsoda
¼ teasp. salt
25 g castor sugar
1 egg
About 250 ml sour milk

Method

1. Sieve flour, salt, breadsoda into a bowl. Mix in sugar.
2. Make a well in the centre of the flour, drop in the egg and a little sour milk. Beat well, adding more milk, until mixture reaches a dropping consistency.

3. Heat and grease a frying pan or griddle.
4. Drop batter, in tablespoons, onto hot surface, and cook until well risen and brown underneath.
5. Turn and cook other side. Keep warm on a covered plate over boiling water, until all are cooked.
6. Serve at once, on a hot plate, with butter and golden syrup or honey. Dredge with castor sugar.

Doughnuts

Ingredients

200 g flour
$\frac{1}{8}$ teasp. salt
1 teasp. baking powder
50 g margarine
50 g castor sugar
1 egg
2 tablesp. milk

To fry:

Bath of oil

To Finish:

Castor sugar and cinnamon

Method

1.-5. As for Tea Scones *p. 191.*
6. Roll dough 1 cm thick, cut into rounds about 6 cm across, then cut a small round (2 cm) from the centre of each.
7. Fry in deep fat at 175°C, for about 10 mins, turning once.
8. Drain well and toss in cinnamon flavoured castor sugar.
9. Serve hot or cold on a plate with a d'oyley.

Country Apple Cake

Ingredients

200 g flour
$\frac{1}{8}$ teasp. salt
1 teasp. baking powder
$\frac{1}{8}$ teasp. cinnamon or ground cloves
75 g margarine
50 g castor sugar
1 egg
2 large cooking apples
1-2 tablesp. milk (if required)
Granulated sugar (to sprinkle)

Method

1. Sieve flour, salt, baking powder and spice into a bowl.
2. Rub in margarine, until mixture looks like fine breadcrumbs.
3. Peel, core and chop apples finely.
4. Beat egg and add to mixture with apples and sugar.
5. If mixture is too dry, add a little milk to make a stiff dough.
6. Put mixture into a greased sandwich tin and sprinkle granulated sugar over.
7. Bake in a moderate oven, 190°C (375°F), Gas 5, for about 40 minutes until golden brown.
8. Serve hot or cold with butter.

2. The Creaming Method

This method is used for richer cakes, which have a large percentage of fat (often equal in weight to the amount of sugar). Madeira cakes, fruit cakes, puddings and small cakes, *e.g.* queen cakes, can be made by the creaming method.

The fat and sugar are **creamed** or beaten together with a wooden spoon or electric mixer, until they become white and fluffy. This process, which may take up to 10-15 minutes, traps air in the mixture, so that the cake becomes light. A raising agent (baking powder) is also added. The whisked eggs are added a little at a time and beaten well into the mixture. The flour and baking powder is then **folded** (*i.e.* very gently stirred using a metal spoon) into the mixture. Beating at this stage would knock the air out of the mixture and make it close textured instead of spongy.

Basic Madeira Mixture

Ingredients

A. Small Amount

50 g margarine
50 g castor sugar
75 g flour
¼ teasp. baking powder
1 egg
About 1 dessertsp. water

B. Large Amount

100 g margarine
100 g castor sugar
150 g flour
½ teasp. baking powder
2 eggs
About 1 tablesp. water

C. Rich Mixture

100 g margarine
100 g castor sugar
100-125 g flour
¼ teasp. baking powder
2 eggs

Flavouring:

Vanilla
Orange rind
Lemon rind

Method

1. Light oven. Prepare tins, *p. 200.*
2. Cream margarine and sugar together in a bowl, until soft and creamy.
3. Beat eggs in a small bowl, add gradually to creamed mixture, beating after each addition. If there is a danger of curdling (or for very large amounts), add a little flour, alternately with eggs. Add flavouring.
4. Sieve flour and baking powder onto a sheet of kitchen paper. Fold into mixture using a tablespoon.
5. If the mixture appears dry, add water.

Queen (Fairy) Cakes

Make madeira mixture A or B; put spoonfuls of mixture into well greased patty tins or paper cases. Bake in a fairly hot oven, 200°C (400°F), Gas 6, for about 20 minutes. Decorate as wished.

Variations:

Cherry Cakes: As for queen cakes (B), adding 50 g chopped cherries (washed, dried and chopped) at the end of recipe.
Chocolate Cakes: Rich madeira mixture (C), adding 25 g cocoa with flour.
Coconut Cakes: Fold 1 dessertsp. coconut into mixture B.
Coffee Cakes: Dissolve 1 dessertsp. coffee powder in 1 dessertsp. boiling water or use coffee essence. Stir into Mixture B.

Victoria Sandwich

Ingredients

Rich madeira mixture (100 g flour)
2 tablesp. jam (warmed)

Glacé Icing:

150 g icing sugar
Boiling water.

Method

1. Prepare 2 x 18 cm (7") tins. Light oven.
2. Make madeira mixture and turn into prepared tins.
3. Bake in a fairly moderate oven, 180°C (350°F), Gas 4, for 20-25 minutes.
4. Cool on a wire tray, spread with jam while still warm and sandwich together.

5. Put icing sugar in bowl, add a little boiling water, beat well (it should be the consistency of thick cream).
6. Spread over cake and decorate with cherries or chocolate buttons.

Variations:

Orange Sandwich: Use grated orange rind in cake and decorate with orange glacé icing.
Lemon Sandwich: Use grated lemon rind and decorate with lemon flavoured glacé icing.

Light Fruit Cake

Ingredients

Basic madeira (Mixture B)
½ tsp. mixed spice
Grated rind of ½ lemon
200 g sultanas
25 g mixed peel
25 g chopped cherries
25 g chopped almonds

Method

1. Make as for basic madeira (Mixture B).
2. Stir in fruit and flavourings.
3. Pour into prepared 18 cm (7″) cake tin. Bake in a fairly moderate oven, 160°C (325°F), Gas 3, for about 1¼ hours.
4. Cool slightly in tin, then turn onto wire tray.

Welsh Cheese Cakes

These are little individual Bakewell tarts. They are called 'cheese cakes' because, instead of jam, they are sometimes filled with Lemon Curd, which in the past was known as Lemon Cheese.

Ingredients

75 g shortcrust pastry
  (or use leftover scraps)
Raspberry jam or Lemon Curd

Madeira:

50 g margarine
50 g caster sugar
75 g flour
¼ teasp. baking powder
1 egg
About 1 dessertsp. water

Method

1. Grease patty tins. Make pastry. Chill.
2. Roll pastry out thinly, cut into rounds with a large cutter and use to line 9-10 patty tins. Put a half teaspoon of jam or lemon curd on each.
3. Cream margarine and sugar.
4. Add egg, a little at a time, beating well after each addition.
5. Fold in sieved flour and baking powder, adding water (if necessary).
6. Place a heaped teaspoonful of mixture into each pastry case.
7. Bake in a moderate oven, 190°C (375°F), Gas 5, for about 20 minutes.
8. Cool on a wire tray.

Variation:

Fill with stewed fruit *e.g.* apple or rhubarb, instead of jam.

All-in-One Mixtures

Also called 'one stage' mixtures. This is a quick easy method of making creamed mixtures. The flour and baking powder are sieved into the bowl and the other ingredients are added and beaten together until light and fluffy. Easy creaming or easy spread margarines should be used (they should be removed from the refrigerator a half an hour before use). Self-raising flour may be used instead of plain flour and baking powder.

All-in-One Victoria Sandwich

Ingredients

175 g soft margarine
175 g caster sugar
175 g self-raising flour
3 eggs

Filling:

Warmed jam

Decoration:

Icing sugar (to dredge on top)

Method

1. Prepare tins and set oven to 180°C (350°F), Gas 4.
2. Place all cake ingredients in a mixing bowl and beat with a wooden spoon until well mixed (2-3 minutes).
3. Divide mixture between two tins and bake in pre-heated oven for 25-35 minutes.
4. Cool on a wire tray.

All-in-One Chocolate Cake

Ingredients

175 g soft margarine (easy creaming)
175 g caster sugar
175 g self-raising flour
3 eggs
1 tablesp. cocoa ⎫
2 tablesp. boiling water ⎬ *blended and cooled*

Method

1. Prepare tins, light oven to 180°C (350°F), Gas 4.
2. Place all ingredients together in a mixing bowl and beat for 2-3 minutes with a wooden spoon.
3. Divide between two 18 cm (7") tins.
4. Bake in a preheated oven for 25-35 minutes. Cool on a wire tray.

3. The Whisking Method

This method is used for fatless cakes, *e.g.* sponges.

Eggs and sugar are whisked together until they are thick and creamy. You will know the mixture is ready when the beater leaves a trail on the mixture.

(A hand whisk, rotary whisk or electric whisk may be used.) During this time air is trapped in the mixture, which will expand in the oven and make the sponge light.

The flour is lastly folded in with a metal spoon, using a gentle cutting motion. **Do not beat in flour.**

Although air is the only raising agent in sponges, some recipes include a small amount of baking powder for extra lightness.

Fault!
Sponge is dry and hard.

Reason:
Baked too long *or* overbeaten.

Fault!
Sponge is flat, with lots of holes.

Reason:
Flour beaten in, air knocked out *or* too much raising agent.

Sponge Sandwich

Ingredients

3 eggs
75 g caster sugar
75 g flour
¼ teasp. baking powder

Filling:

2 tablesp. jam
125 ml cream whipped and sweetened

Method

1. Prepare tins, light oven.
2. Whisk eggs and sugar together. When using a hand whisk, place bowl over a saucepan of hot (not boiling) water, to speed up thickening.
3. Whisk until thick and creamy (mixture should hold imprint of beater). Remove from saucepan and whisk until cold.
4. Sieve flour and baking powder and gently fold into mixture.
5. Divide mixture between two greased 18 cm (7″) sandwich cake tins. Bake in a moderate oven, 190°C (375 °F), Gas 5, for about 15 minutes.
6. Cool on a wire tray; spread one half with jam, the other with cream and sandwich together. Dredge with icing sugar.

Swiss Roll

Ingredients

As for sponge sandwich

Method

1. Line a large swiss roll tin, *p. 200.*
2. Make sponge mixture, pour into prepared tin, smoothing out well into corners.
3. Bake in a moderate oven, 190°C (375°F), Gas 5, for about 10 mins. Heat jam.
4. Prepare sheet of greaseproof paper on damp tea towel. Dredge with caster sugar.
5. When cooked, turn sponge onto paper, peel off lining paper in strips.
6. Trim edges away and score a line on the cake, as shown.

Trimming a swiss roll

Trim off crusts and score a line on cake 2cms. from worker

7. Spread with heated jam, spreading well out to the sides.
8. Roll up, tucking cake well in at first to get a tight roll, and working away from you. Be sure not to enclose paper, as you roll.
9. Leave swiss roll wrapped in paper for 1-2 minutes, to set, then remove paper and dredge with caster sugar. Cool on a wire tray.

Variation:

Add grated rind of orange to mixture when whisking. Spread with apricot jam, softened (in a bowl) with a little orange juice.

Fruit Flan: see p. 169.

4. The Melting Method

Only a few recipes use this method, *e.g.* gingerbread. The dry ingredients are put into a bowl, and the ingredients which melt are placed in a saucepan over the heat. The melted ingredients are then poured into the bowl, and everything mixed well. Cakes cooked by this method are cooled in the tin.

Fault!   Cracks on top.   **Reason:**   Oven too hot *or* mixture too dry.
Fault!   Cake sunk in middle.   **Reason:**   Oven too cool or mixture too wet.

Gingerbread

Ingredients

200 g flour	75 g brown sugar
$\frac{1}{4}$ teasp. salt	1 tablesp. treacle
$\frac{1}{4}$ teasp. breadsoda	1 tablesp. golden
1 teasp. ground ginger	syrup
50 g sultanas	1 egg
75 g margarine	A little sour milk

Method

1. Sieve flour, salt, bread soda, and ginger into a bowl. Mix in sultanas.
2. Melt margarine, treacle, syrup and sugar over a very low heat — **do not overheat.**
3. Pour liquid into centre of dry ingredients. Add egg and enough milk to give a soft dropping consistency.
4. Pour into a well-greased loaf tin or square cake tin.
5. Bake in a moderate oven, 190°C (375°F), Gas 5, for about 35-40 minutes.
6. Cool in tin, then cut into about 15 squares.

Boiled Fruit Cake

Ingredients

200 g margarine
200 g brown sugar
100 ml water + 1 tablesp. lemon juice
400 g fruit, e.g. raisins, sultanas, mixed peel
2 eggs, beaten
300 g flour
½ teasp. breadsoda
½ teasp. salt
½ teasp. mixed spice
½ teasp. ground nutmeg

Method

1. Put margarine, sugar, lemon juice and water into a saucepan over a low heat, stir until sugar is dissolved. Add fruit and simmer for 5 minutes.
2. Cool, stirring now and then.
3. Sieve flour, salt, breadsoda and spices into a bowl.
4. Make a well in the centre, pour in beaten egg, then cooled fruit mixture. Mix well together, to make a dropping consistency.
5. Turn into lined 20 cm (8") square, or 23 cm (9") round, tin.
6. Bake in preheated oven, 160°C (325°F), Gas 3, for about 1½ hours.
7. Cool in tin, then turn out, remove paper, wrap in foil and store in an airtight tin.

Fillings and Icings

Butter Filling or Icing

Ingredients

100 g icing sugar
50 g margarine
Flavouring

Method

1. Cream margarine very well.
2. Sieve in icing sugar and beat until soft and creamy.
3. Beat in flavouring.

Chocolate Butter Filling or Icing

Ingredients

50 g icing sugar
50 g cocoa
50 g margarine
Vanilla

Method

1. Sieve icing sugar and cocoa and add to creamed margarine.
2. Add vanilla and beat well.

Variations

Coffee filling: Add 1-2 dessertsp. coffee essence.
Orange filling: Add grated rind of orange and orange colouring.
Lemon filling: Add grated rind of lemon and yellow colouring.

Glacé or Water Icing

Ingredients

200 g icing sugar
Boiling water
Colouring (as required)
Flavouring (as required)

Method

1. Sieve icing sugar into a bowl.
2. Add boiling water gradually, beating well, until it has the consistency of thick cream.
3. Beat in colouring and flavouring (if required).

Preparing Tins

A well prepared tin will prevent cakes sticking, making it easy to remove cakes without breaking them.

1. **Flouring:** Tins used for breads and other very low-fat baking, such as plain scones, should be floured.
2. **Greasing:** Use melted cooking fat and brush over tin. Suitable for small plain cakes.
3. **For cakes cooked in shallow tins and plain cakes:** Line the base (only) of the tin with greaseproof paper.
4. **For small sponge cakes:** Sprinkle the greased tin with equal amounts of flour and caster sugar, shaking out surplus.
5. **For large creamed cakes:** Line the tin completely with greased greaseproof paper.

Baking Biscuits

Homemade biscuits are cheaper and more nourishing than the bought variety.

Remember!
1. Grease tins well, as biscuits break easily when they are lifted from tins.
2. Do not overcrowd, allow space for biscuits to spread.
3. Bake in a *very* moderate oven.
4. When cooked, biscuits are a pale beige colour. If you leave them to brown, they will be overdone.
5. Biscuits do not crisp until they are cold.
6. Leave them on the baking tin for 2-3 minutes, then lift off with a palette knife and cool on a wire tray.
7. Store in an airtight tin. Never store in the same tin as cakes or bread, as the biscuits will go soft.

Lining a square tin

Lining a round tin

Lining a swiss roll tin

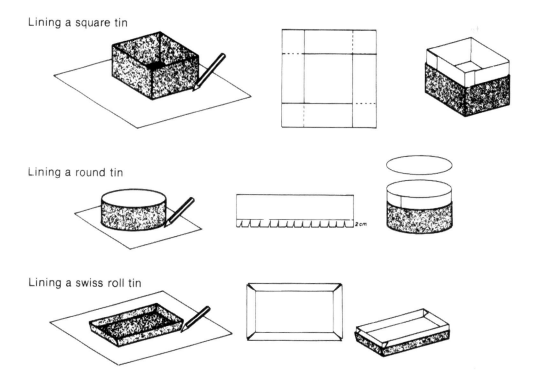

Shortbread

Ingredients

100 g flour
50 g cornflour or rice flour
50 g caster sugar
100 g butter or margarine
  (butter gives a better flavour)

Method

1. Sieve flour and cornflour into a bowl.
2. Mix in sugar.
3. Rub in butter, then squeeze mixture together with fingers, until it clings together.
4. Roll into a ball, then roll or press it into a smooth round, 1.5 cm thick. It can be pressed directly into a greased sandwich tin.
5. Crimp the edges, by pinching all around between finger and thumb. Cut into 8 sections, and prick surface with fork.
6. Bake in a very moderate oven, 160°C (325°F), Gas 3, for 15-20 minutes, until a pale fawn colour.
7. Cool on tin for a few minutes, then, using a palette knife, carefully lift onto a wire tray to cool.
8. Sprinkle with caster sugar.

Note: Biscuits may also be cut into fingers, or into rounds (with a cutter).

Flapjacks (Oatmeal Biscuits)

Ingredients

225 g rolled oats
Pinch salt
100 g butter or margarine
25 g caster sugar
2 tablesp. golden syrup

Method

1. Beat butter and sugar in mixing bowl, until soft and creamy.
2. Stir in syrup, then rolled oats and salt. Mix well.
3. Put mixture into greased Yorkshire tin, pressing down well with the back of a metal spoon.
4. Bake in a moderate oven, 175°C (350°F), Gas 4, for about 35-40 minutes, until golden.
5. Cut into squares or fingers and cool in tin.
6. Lift out carefully and store in an air-tight tin.

Ginger Snaps

Ingredients

50 g margarine
25 g caster sugar
1 tablesp. golden syrup
100 g flour
$\frac{1}{4}$ teasp. baking powder
$\frac{1}{2}$ teasp. ground ginger

Method

1. Melt margarine, sugar and syrup slowly in a saucepan.
2. Sieve flour, baking powder and ginger into mixing bowl.
3. Stir in syrup. Mix well.
4. Shape into about 20 small balls, the size of a walnut. Place on a greased tin, allowing space for them to spread. Flatten slightly.
5. Bake in a moderate oven, 180°C (350°F), Gas 4, for about 15 minutes, until set and a good brown colour.
6. Cool a little before lifting onto a wire tray.

Melting Moments

Ingredients

100 g butter or margarine
75 g sugar
Grated lemon rind
1 egg yolk
125 g flour
¼ teasp. baking powder
Crushed cornflakes (about 2 handfulls)

Method

1. Cream butter and sugar, beat in lemon and egg yolk.
2. Sieve in flour and baking powder and mix to a smooth dough.
3. Shape into small walnut-sized balls. Roll in cornflakes.
4. Place on greased tin, allowing space to spread.
5. Bake in a moderate oven, 180°C (350°F), Gas 4, for 20 minutes. Cool on wire tray.

Over to you . . .

Pastry

1. Write a note on pastry. What precautions must you take in order to obtain perfect pastry? What is the difference between **shortcrust** and **suet-crust** pastry?

2. Describe how to bake pastry 'blind'. Name four dishes which need pastry cases which have been baked blind. Write a recipe for a savoury dish baked in this way.

Cereals

1. Draw a diagram of a cereal grain, showing its main constituents. Write a note on the importance of fibre in the diet. Name two cereal dishes which could be used for the following: (a) a breakfast; (b) a pudding; (c) a savoury dish. Give the recipe for a dish using pasta.

2. Compare **white bread** with **wholemeal bread** under the following headings: (a) cost; (b) food value; (c) flavour. Write a recipe for a pudding or savoury dish which uses bread or breadcrumbs.

Baking

1. Why are home baked bread and cakes superior to bought products? Compare home made and bought cakes under these headings: (a) cost; (b) flavour; (c) appearance and texture; (d) convenience.

2. Explain in your own words how a raising agent works. What are the results of careless use of raising agents.

3. List the six most important rules to remember when baking bread and cakes. Find out the current cost of the following: (This is useful for costing recipes).

Plain White flour	Dried fruit
Wholemeal flour	Tin baking
Caster sugar	powder
Margarine	Salt
Porridge oats	Milk
½ doz. eggs.	

4. Which cake making method is used for each of the following: (a) Raspberry buns; (b) sponge flan; (c) flapjacks; (d) Welsh cheesecakes; (e) gingerbread; (f) Victoria sandwich; (g) Swiss roll; (h) Christmas cake.

24   All About Convenience Foods

'Convenience food' is a general name given to any food which has been prepared in some way before we buy it.

Canned, bottled and frozen foods, dried foods, such as packet soups and sauces, cake mixes, instant desserts and even bottles of ketchup are all convenience foods.

Advantages

1. **Time saving** — ideal for those who work and cook.
2. **Labour saving** — meals are easier to prepare and cook.
3. **No waste/saves fuel** — due to shorter cooking time.
4. **Helpful for beginner cooks, the elderly** and **handicapped people.**
5. **Useful in emergencies** — for unexpected visitors, when you are unable to shop.
6. **Easy to store** — will keep for a long time in cupboard or freezer.
7. **Provide a wide variety** — *e.g.* unusual and foreign dishes.
8. **Quality is standard** — usually high.

Disadvantages

1. **Flavour not as good as fresh food** — can be bland.
2. **Food value** — certain vitamins and minerals may be lacking.
3. **Lots of additives** — particularly in dried foods.
4. **Lot of money wasted** — on advertising and packaging.
5. **Portions** — often small and less than package suggests.
6. **Quality of some foods** (*e.g.* meat pies) **inferior** — pastry soggy, little meat.

Cost

This varies. Prepacked foods are sometimes more expensive than the homemade variety, sometimes less so. Frozen vegetables can work out just as cheap as fresh, when you allow for the large amount of waste on, say, fresh peas. It may be cheaper to make your own cream of chicken soup from left over bones, but homemade asparagus soup would be much more expensive than buying a packet.

Homemade marmalade is usually cheaper, lemon curd is much dearer to make. A tin of tomatoes is usually cheaper than 500 g fresh tomatoes.

Food Value

This varies also. In the past, before enough was known about how to preserve food, many packaged and canned foods were far inferior, in food value and flavour, to fresh foods. There have been great improvements in food processing in recent years and, today, most frozen and canned foods are equal in value to freshly cooked foods. Dried foods may suffer some vitamin losses, particularly Vitamins B and C. In all cases, protein, fat and carbohydrate remain the same.

Many processed foods lack dietary fibre or roughage, *e.g.* biscuits and cakes contain lots of white flour and sugar. At home, you can include more unprocessed ingredients, such as brown flour, in your baking.

Additives

Almost every package or tin you pick from a supermarket shelf will have a list of contents printed on the label. Among them are likely to be chemicals, which are added to improve the colour, flavour and appearance of the food, or to make it keep longer.

Although there are laws controlling the use of such chemicals in our food, we cannot be sure that these will not effect us, after eating them for several years, or that a mixture of chemicals from different foods might not react in our body, causing serious problems.

The safest course is to keep our use of convenience foods to a minimum, and to do our best to eat fresh, unprocessed foods, as far as possible.

Wise use of Convenience foods

It is only common sense to make use of modern aids and ideas which will cut down the amount of work we have to do, particularly if we lead a very busy life, for example, if we work all day and have to prepare a meal when we get home.

1. Rely on convenience foods for helping you in emergencies, rather than for everyday use.
2. Use with fresh food to supplement normal cooking, *e.g.* freshly stewed apples with custard powder sauce.
3. Keep convenience foods for more complicated recipes, where there are several processes, *e.g. Eve's Pudding* — using a cake mix topping over fresh apple; *Lemon Meringue Pie* — using lemon mix with homemade pastry and meringue; *Bakewell Tart* — using fresh pastry and madeira mix or vice versa; *Shepherd's Pie/Fish Pie* — using instant mashed potato for topping; *Lasagne* — using tinned Bolognese sauce; Sauce mixes for fish pie, chicken pie, *etc;* Pie fillings — for crumbles, flans and fools.
4. Mix convenience foods and fresh together in one mixture, *e.g.* fresh and tinned vegetables in a casserole; fresh and tinned or frozen fruit in a fruit salad.

5. Think before you buy. Some fresh foods are quicker to assemble or make than the so called convenience food, *e.g.* freshly made shortcrust pastry is quicker than thawing a block of frozen pastry.
6. Use your initiative. A soup mix can be used in a stew or casserole; a pie filling can be puréed into a sauce; a can of sieved apple, meant for baby, makes delicious apple sauce.
7. When planning meals, avoid a complete meal of convenience foods. Have 2-3 fresh or homemade, to every one convenience, food. Try to include a fresh salad, to add the vitamins missing in many processed foods.

A menu over-using convenience foods

Canned tomato soup

Beef Curry & Rice (frozen)

Instant dessert
Instant topping

A better choice — mixing fresh and ready prepared foods

Egg mayonnaise (bottled mayonnaise)

Beef casserole (using dried casserole mix)
Freshly baked potatoes

Baked apples
Caramel custard (mix)

* Golden Rule *

READ DIRECTIONS **CAREFULLY**
AND FOLLOW THEM **EXACTLY**

Frozen Food

Manufacture

Best quality food is frozen within hours of harvesting. There is a very wide range of frozen foods available as almost all foods can be frozen.

Food value

Similar to fresh (sometimes better, if 'fresh' fruit and vegetables have been lying around in a shop for a few days).

Quality

Appearance and flavour are good. The texture of some fruits is soft. There is some drip loss on thawing.

Cost

Frozen foods are quite expensive, but there is no waste whatsoever.

Buying

Food packaging on frozen foods must be sealed and frozen solid. It is essential to buy from a reliable source — careless shopkeepers may not be particular about keeping food properly frozen. It should be stored below the load-line, or in cabinets with closed doors.

Storing

Frozen food must be stored in a deep freeze or 'star marked' refrigerator for not longer than the recommended time.

Thawing and Cooking

N.B. Follow directions on packets for best results.

Vegetables: These are already partly cooked (blanched). No thawing is necessary — cook from frozen in a minimum of boiling salted water. **Do not overcook.**

Fruit: Thaw in package, slowly, in the frigerator. Use at once — texture may be better if used *before* completely thawed.

Meat: Thaw slowly to prevent loss of juices. Thaw completely — insufficiently thawed and undercooked frozen meat and poultry is **highly dangerous.**

Fish: Leave in package, and thaw slowly in refrigerator until portions can be separated. For best results, cook while there is still a little ice left in fish. Certain items, *e.g.* coated fish or fish fingers can be cooked from frozen.

 N.B. **Never refreeze thawed food.**

Canned Food

Manufacture

Food is canned soon after harvesting, *e.g.* in fish factories on ships or near ports; in vegetables factories in the middle of fruit and vegetable growing regions.

Food value

Newer methods of canning ensure that the food value of canned goods is almost as high as that of cooked fresh foods, with Vitamin C only reduced as much as it is in cooked foods.

Quality

Appearance and texture of canned foods are not as good as frozen; fruit and vegetables tend to get soft and mushy. Taste varies. Colouring and other additives are often used.

Cost

Canned foods are relatively cheap, especially when you remember that there is no waste and very little fuel needed to heat them.

Buying

Never buy damaged cans — they should be neither dented, rusted, leaking nor bulging. Note the net weight of foods and check the unit price when comparing tin sizes. Large sizes are often best value.

Storing

Store in a cool dry place. Canned foods keep for at least 1 year.

Using

As they are already cooked (due to heat processing), canned foods need only be reheated. Use canning liquid for sauces and soups.

Cost

Dried foods are relatively cheap, but cost varies.

Buying

Each container must be sealed and airtight; note any date stamping.

Storing

Store in a cool dry place, keeping packet sealed. Once opened, use up quickly.

Using

Most dried foods, *e.g.* vegetables, are rehydrated, *i.e.* steeped in water, to soak back the liquid lost during drying. Cook according to directions on packet.

Dried Foods

These are the oldest form of convenience food — raisins and other fruits have been dried for thousands of years.

Manufacture

Food is cut into small pieces and dried in warm ovens. A more modern method of preserving is — **freeze drying,** in which food is frozen first, then dried. This gives a better colour, texture, flavour and food value.

Food Value

There is some loss of Vitamins A, B and especially C, in varying amounts, depending on food and method of processing.

Quality

This has been improved in recent years, due to more advanced processes, *e.g.* freeze drying.

Cake Mixes

These are handy for beginner cooks, to give them confidence.

Manufacture

Flour, salt, raising agent, dried fat and sugar are mixed together and packaged. Unfortunately these are the cheapest ingredients. The more expensive ones, *e.g.* eggs and milk, still have to be added.

Food Value

This is similar to fresh. No Vitamin C; many additives used.

Quality

Cake mixes are often very sweet with a standard, bland taste.

Cost

On the whole they are expensive, not really good value for money. The yield from packages is often disappointing.

Buying

Each packet must be sealed and absolutely fresh. See that the shop uses them in rotation.

Storing

Store in cool dry place.

Using

Follow the directions on the packet, especially relating to liquid proportions. Use them to make more complicated dishes simpler.

Over to you . . .

1. Visit your local supermarket and make a list of the various cake mixes available, together with the cost of each. Make up two cake mixes and the equivalent homemade cake. Compare cost, flavour, convenience.

2. **Project**
   Find out about one of the following Canned and Bottled foods; Dried foods; Frozen foods. Write up results in your Home Economics copybook.

3. Make two lots of sausage rolls — one using bought rough puff pastry; one using home made rough puff pastry. Compare the results — under the following headings: flavour; texture; 'shortness'; length of time to make and cook; cost.

4. Plan a menu for a teenage party using at least *six* convenience foods. Write the cost of each food named. Give the method of making up *one* of the dishes for which you use a convenience food.

5. Compare frozen food with dried food. Write out your comparison under these headings: food value; quality; flavour; texture; cost; convenience; storing.

6. Write a half page on the advantages and disadvantages of 'take-away' foods, *i.e.* foods such as fish and chips, which you can buy ready to eat.

7. Find out the cost of eating dinner at a local hotel or restaurant. Work out the cost of making the same meal using convenience foods. Now work out the cost of making the meal using all fresh foods. What conclusion do you come to?

8. Make a list of items you would consider necessary to have in your store cupboard for emergency meals. Give the cost of each.

25 *All About Packed Meals*

Many people, particularly school children, eat a packed lunch everyday. When a packed meal is one of your main daily meals, it is very important that it should be a proper meal, not just a snack. A well-planned packed lunch can be just as nourishing and tasty as a cooked meal.

Food value

Like all meals, a packed meal should supply a well-balanced mixture of all the basic nutrients.

Protein: meat, fish, eggs, cheese or milk.

Carbohydrate: usually in the form of bread or a roll.

Fat: supplied in the spread *e.g.* butter and fillings.

Minerals and Vitamins: In order to supply the important protective nutrients include some fresh fruit or raw vegetables, *e.g.* lettuce, tomato.

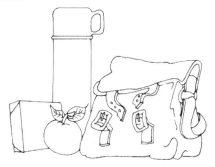

Planning a Packed Meal

1. It should be nourishing (see above).
2. Avoid snack foods *e.g.* sweets, biscuits and fizzy drinks, as they contain little nourishment and it is unlikely you will be able to wash your teeth for some time after eating them.

3. Foods used should keep well.
4. They should be tasty and attractive looking.
5. They should be easy to pack and carry — pack carefully in rigid airtight containers. Place heaviest foods at the bottom, to prevent food getting squashed.
6. Include napkins, seasoning and cutlery when packing picnics.

N.B. After your picnic or packed meal, **PUT YOUR LITTER IN A BIN OR CARRY IT HOME.** Do not spoil your school or the countryside by leaving your litter behind you.

Packaging

Modern packaging has made it easier to pack meals well — plastic lunch boxes, aluminium foil, polythene bags, vacuum flasks and storage jars make it possible to pack and transport a very wide range of foods. Insulated bags keep food cool for picnics.

Make use of empty margarine tubs, *etc.* for carrying tasty salads and desserts.

Sandwiches

Many different ways have developed of enclosing a filling in bread, since about 200 years ago when the 4th Earl of Sandwich called for some meat between two slices of bread, so that he didn't have to leave the gaming tables.

There are many types of sandwiches:

1. Single
A tasty savoury or sweet filling, between 2 slices of bread.

2. Double Decker
3 slices of bread are used with a different, but complementary, filling in each of the two layers, *e.g.* chicken and lettuce on top, grilled bacon and tomato slices beneath.

3. Club Sandwiches
4 or more slices of bread, with fillings between.

4. Rolls
Crisp bread rolls, filled with suitable filling.

5. Toasted Sandwiches
Filled sandwiches, carefully toasted under a grill or in a sandwich toaster — certain fillings, *e.g.* lettuce, are unsuitable.

6. Pinwheels
Thin slices of fresh bread, with crusts removed, are spread with a smooth filling, paté, cream cheese or smoked salmon. They are then rolled up like a Swiss Roll, and chilled, before cutting in 1 cm slices.

7. Open Sandwiches
Smörrebrod — from Denmark: these are more substantial and are eaten with a knife and fork. A generous amount of filling is arranged attractively on a base of bread or cracker. Suitable garnishes are added to create a colourful display.

There are three parts to a sandwich:

(a) Bread.
(b) Spread.
(c) Filling.

(a) Bread

This must be fresh. Ready sliced pan is quick and neater than cutting from a loaf. Use brown, white or wholemeal. Try Vienna bread, French rolls and crusty rolls for a change. Allow at least 2 rounds (4 slices) per person.

(b) Spread

This acts as a waterproof layer and prevents moist fillings making the bread soggy. Soft margarine is easy to spread but butter must be at room temperature, or creamed first, to make it easy to spread (a mixture of both, creamed together is a cheap alternative to butter). The spread can be seasoned and flavoured instead of the filling, *e.g.* beat grated lemon rind, mustard, *etc.*, into the spread.

(c) Fillings

Try to have a combination of soft and crisp textures. Fillings should be tasty and well seasoned. Be generous with filling but do not overfill. Moisten dry fillings, *e.g.* meat, with a little sauce, *e.g.* chutney or mayonnaise.

Meat in sandwiches should be very thinly sliced, *e.g.*

Thinly sliced roast lamb and mint jelly.
Thinly sliced beef, lettuce and onion rings.
Chicken/Turkey with chopped apple, celery, mayonnaise.
Roast pork, apple sauce, onion rings.
Ham, pickles, lettuce.
Ham, mustard, cress.
Salami and lettuce.

Fish

Tinned salmon, with cucumber and mayonnaise.
Sardines, mashed with lemon juice and mayonnaise.
Flaked tuna, with chopped apple, lemon juice and mayonnaise.

Salad sandwiches — lettuce, tomato, onion, mayonnaise.

Cheese — Cream cheese and kipper and lemon juice; and
— cheddar cheese with chutney or pickles.

Egg — hardboiled egg, mashed with chives and mayonnaise.

Chopped apples, dates, shredded lettuce and mayonnaise.
Peanut butter, cucumber.
Raspberry jam, mashed banana and lemon juice.

Tips for Sandwich Making

1. Soften butter.
2. Cut bread into thin slices and lay out in matching pairs.
3. Butter one side of each slice, right to the edge.
4. Prepare filling and season well.
5. Spread on generously, but do not overfill.
6. Place second slice on top and press firmly together.
7. Stack 4 or 5 sandwiches together for cutting.
8. Using a really sharp knife (or electric carving knife), cut sandwiches in halves, either square or diagonally, and then in halves again. For special occasions remove crusts first with sharp knife.
9. Serve at once. Garnish savoury sandwiches with parsley, cress or watercress.

To Store

Wrap well in cling film or foil. Store in a cool place until required (wrapping in a damp teatowel will help keep them cool and fresh). Keep overnight in refrigerator. For longer periods, store in freezer — meat and fish sandwiches freeze well; egg white and mayonnaise do not. Frozen sandwiches will thaw out in 1-2 hours, wrapped.

Table 25.1

A Week of Packed Lunches		
Monday	*Tuesday*	*Wednesday*
Cheese sandwiches made with brown bread	*Ham roll with lettuce and tomato*	*Tomato Soup*
Tub of apple & celery salad	*Carton of yoghurt*	*Quiche Lorraine*
Flapjack	*Slice of fruit cake*	*Tub of coleslaw*
Chilled milk or fruit juice	*Drinking chocolate*	*Wholemeal bread*
		Orange

Thursday	*Friday*
Beef broth/wholemeal roll	*Chicken/Rice/Tomato Salad*
Rye crackers with cheese or paté	*(in Mayonnaise)*
(or Cornish pasties and tomato)	*with wholemeal bread*
Slice of gingerbread	*Apple*
Fruit juice	*Packet peanuts*
	Chilled milk

Over to you . . .

1. List some precautions to be taken when packing meals in order to be sure that the food is in the best possible condition when eaten. Name five packing materials you might use — giving the cost of each item.

2. Plan a packed lunch for: (a) a man who does heavy manual work; (b) a child at primary school; (c) a group of four teenagers, going on a hike. All of them will be eating a cooked dinner in the evening.)

3. Plan a day's menu for a caravan/boat outing for one day, a menu which will not keep anyone in the kitchen too long. Cooking facilities are limited to two boiling rings.

4. Make a list of five nourishing salads which could be included in a packed lunch. Give the main ingredients in each salad. Name five different types of bread/rolls, *etc.*, which could be included in each lunch.

5. On a snowy winter's day you are travelling a long distance by car with your family. Plan a nourishing packed midday meal suitable for such a day (include drinks).

6. Snack foods have a bad reputation. List six nourishing snack foods you could include in packed lunches. In each case, write the current price.

7. Make a list of all the items, apart from food, which should be included when preparing a substantial packed meal.

26   All About Cooking for Invalids

Those who are unwell, or recovering from an illness, require a diet which contains a lot of nourishment in little bulk. They need easily digested food, particularly **protein foods,** to help rebuild tissues, and foods rich in **Vitamin C,** to aid healing and recovery. (Vitamin C also helps prevent bed sores). Patients who are confined to bed use **little energy,** so energy rich foods should be kept to a minimum.

It is essential to follow any instructions given by the doctor. As a general rule, patients with a **high temperature** have little appetite and require **liquid foods** only — milk, fruit juices and clear broths. As they begin to recover, **gradually introduce solid foods,** in easily digestable form.

General Rules

1. Follow doctors orders.
2. Use best quality fresh food.
3. Choose highly nourishing foods, with little bulk, *e.g.* eggs.
4. Serve foods which are easy to digest — avoid greasy foods, highly spiced foods or heavy, rich, indigestible foods.
5. Introduce variety, while always considering the patient's individual tastes.
6. Cleanliness is essential; everything used should be spotless when preparing and serving food.
7. Food should be served attractively, in small portions.
8. Food should be easy to eat from a tray.
9. Remove tray when meal is finished.
10. Provide refreshing drinks at the patients bedside — homemade lemonade, aerated drinks, fruit juices. These must be kept covered.

A Light Diet

Table 26.1

Suitable Foods	Foods to avoid
Fresh fruit	Fried foods
Clear soup, broths	Highly spiced foods, *e.g.* curry
Chicken – roast, boiled, cold	Greasy foods, *e.g.* puff pastry
White fish – steamed, baked	Reheats
Eggs – boiled, poached scrambled	Convenience foods
Lean meat – grilled, boiled, baked or steamed	Foods which are difficult to eat, *e.g.* chicken on the bone, unpeeled
Salads	potatoes
Egg custard	Fat meat; pork
Milk puddings	Suet puddings
Egg flip; milk shakes; yoghurt	
Mousses; stewed fruit	
Jelly; ice cream (especially for children)	Rich creamy cakes and desserts
Sponge cake	Strong flavours, *e.g.* garlic
Light cooking methods *e.g.* boiling, steaming, baking.	

Presentation

Meals help to relieve the monotony of being confined to bed. Make every effort to serve food attractively as it is very easy to put an invalid off his food. Serve meals punctually, at regular intervals. The tray should be neatly laid, with all the necessities. Glasses, cutlery and china should be spotless. Use a clean napkin and tray cloth. A tray cloth is a good investment for long term patients.

A Day's Menu for a Convalescent

> *Breakfast*
>
> *Strained orange juice*
>
> *Poached egg on toast*
> *Toast and honey*
> *Tea*
>
> *Main Meal*
>
> *Chicken broth*
>
> *Steamed cod with onion sauce*
> *Boiled potatoes*
> *Carrots*
>
> *Apple Snow*
>
> *Evening Meal*
>
> *Chicken salad, with pineapple*
> *Brown bread (if allowed)*
>
> *Sponge cake*
> *Tea*

Some nourishing drinks suitable for invalids

Lemon Drink

Ingredients

1 lemon
250 ml water
25 g sugar

Method

1. Wash lemon.
2. Peel lemon rind thinly and infuse (place over very low heat) in a saucepan for about 10 minutes.
3. Stir in sugar, and squeezed lemon juice.
4. Strain into a warmed glass and serve at once.

Variation

Orange Squash: Use 1 orange + 1 lemon.

Iced Fruit Drink
(using liquidiser)

Ingredients

1 lemon or orange	*500 ml water*
2 tablespoons sugar	*A few icecubes*

Method

1. Wash lemon, cut in 4 and place in liquidiser.
2. Add other ingredients and blend for 10 seconds.
3. Strain into chilled jug.

Egg Flip

Ingredients

250 ml milk	*2 teaspoon brandy*
1 egg	*2 tablespoons sugar (or glucose)*

Method

A. Hot:
Beat egg in bowl, heat milk to just under boiling point. Pour onto beaten egg, stir in sugar and brandy. Strain into warmed glass.

B. Cold:
Place ingredients in liquidiser and blend at top speed for 10 seconds. Strain into glass. Sprinkle with nutmeg.

Beef Tea

(A type of clear soup)

Ingredients

100 g lean beef
300 ml water
A little salt and pepper (if permitted)

Method

1. Trim fat from meat, wipe with damp kitchen paper and mince finely.
2. Put into bowl with water and seasoning and steep for 1 hour, stirring now and then.
3. Place bowl over saucepan of cold water, cover and bring slowly to the boil. Simmer for about 2 hours, stirring now and then.
4. Strain into hot glass or soup bowl. Serve with fingers of toast.

Milk Shakes

Ingredients (for 1 or 2)

250 ml milk
1 scoop vanilla ice cream
1 tablespoon caster sugar

Flavourings:

Choose one of the following:

1 banana
75 g strawberries or raspberries
2 tablesps. blackcurrant drink
1 teasp. coffee essence

Method

1. Peel and mash fruit if necessary.
2. Whisk all ingredients in a bowl, or liquidise until frothy.
3. Strain into a tall glass.
4. Garnish with orange or lemon slices.

Breakfast Wake-me-up

Ingredients (for 2)

150 ml chilled orange juice
1 egg
150 ml plain yoghurt
1 teaspoon sugar

Method

1. Blend or whisk ingredients together.
2. Serve in tall glass.

Over to you . . .

1. List five basic rules to be remembered when planning meals for a person who has had a digestive upset. Plan a suitable dinner menu for this patient.
2. Your grandmother who lives with you is bedridden. Plan two days meals which will ensure she gets sufficient nourishment without overtaxing her digestive system.
3. People who are sick in bed are inclined to go off their food. List the points to be remembered when setting trays for invalids in order to ensure that meals served looks as attractive as possible. Draw a diagram of a tray set for lunch.

27 *All About Simple Preserving*

The reason fruit and vegetables have such a short life is that the chemicals in them called enzymes, which help them to grow and ripen, continue to cause changes, which make them decay and die. This is the natural cycle of life.

If we want to preserve fruit, we must break the cycle and destroy the enzymes so that they can no longer cause decay.

Micro-organisms (small living cells), which are present in the air, also help to cause decay. These organisms — moulds, yeasts and bacteria — land on the food and make it go bad.

In order to survive, micro-organisms and enzymes need:

Warmth
Air
Moisture

We can preserve food by taking away:

1. **Warmth** . . . . **Freezing**
2. **Air** . . . . **Canning, bottling, jam**
3. **Moisture** . . . . . **Drying**

Jam Making

Fruit can be preserved, when it is plentiful, by making it into jam. The fruit and sugar are boiled, in order to destroy the organisms and enzymes. The sugar in jam also helps to preserve it — every pot of jam contains 65% sugar!

Advantages of Preserving at Home

1. Home made jams have a better flavour.
2. They have a higher food value — as only best quality, pure ingredients are used.

3. There are no additives, *e.g.* colouring.
4. Saves money — home made preserves are cheaper than bought.
5. Prevents waste — if you have fruit in the garden.
6. A wide selection can be made — adding variety to the menu.

Characteristics of good jam

A well made jam should be **well set**; have a **good bright colour**; a **fresh fruity flavour; no sugar crystals; be well sealed**; and **last** up to one year.

Ingredients

The two main ingredients in jam are **fruit** and **sugar**. If the jam is to set well, the fruit must have plenty of **pectin** and **acid**.

A. Pectin

Pectin is a substance which helps jam to set. It is present in large amounts in some fruit.

Table 27.1

High Pectin fruits	Medium Pectin fruits	Low Pectin fruits
Gooseberries Apples Plums Blackcurrants	Blackberries Raspberries Apricots	Strawberries Rhubarb Pears

When you are making jam, choose a fruit which has lots of pectin — if it has not, you will have to mix it with a high pectin fruit (*e.g.* rhubarb and apple jam) or add bought pectin (in liquid or powdered form).

Pectin is present in fruit which is **just ripe.** If you use fruit which is **overripe,** the pectin will have changed and the jam will not set.

B. Acid

Acid is necessary when making jam because:

  (i) It helps draw out the pectin and make the jam set.

  (ii) It improves colour and flavour.

  (iii) It prevents crystallising (sugar stays in crystals and the jam tastes crunchy and unpleasant).

Fruit low in acid, *e.g.* strawberries and blackberries, should have lemon juice (2 tablesp. per kilo), or citric acid ($\frac{1}{2}$ teasp. per kilo), added at the beginning.

C. Sugar

1. It is important to weigh the sugar carefully. If too little is used, the jam won't keep, and will go mouldy. If too much is used, the jam will harden and crystallise.

2. Be careful *how* you add the sugar. Warm sugar. Stew the fruit first to soften skins before adding sugar. Heat gently, sirring all the time, to dissolve the sugar.

3. **Do not boil** until sugar is dissolved.

Stages in Jam making

1. **Prepare containers:** Use a large aluminium saucepan for preserving. Check jam jars for flaws and chips. Wash and rinse thoroughly. Place in a low oven to dry and heat.

2. **Prepare fruit:** Use good quality, sound, dry fruit, which is ripe or slightly under-ripe. Wash fruit, peel, stone and cut up, according to type. Pick over soft fruits. Remove stalks, shake dry.

3. **Stew fruit to soften:** then **add sugar** and **stir until dissolved.**

4. **Boil rapidly:** until setting point is reached (see over). Stir now and then to prevent sticking. Remove scum towards the end of boiling.

5. **Test for setting:** Turn off heat. Pot at once.

6. **Cool:** Jam with large pieces of fruit, *e.g.* marmalade or strawberry jam, should be cooled for 10 minutes to prevent fruit rising in jars.

7. **Potting:** Stand warmed jars on a board or newspaper and using a heat-proof jug, pour the jam into jars, to within 5 mm from top (to allow for shrinkage). Wipe outside.

 Take great care during this process as hot jam is very dangerous. Never hold jam jar when filling.

8. **Covering:** Place a waxed disc on surface of jam, waxed side down. Damp one side of cellophane covers with a little water (in a saucer). Place dry side down on top of jar, stretch carefully and secure with rubber band.

9. **Storing:** Label with name and date. Store in a cool, dry, dark place.

To Test for Setting

1. **Wrinkle test:** When you think the jam is ready, put a teaspoon of jam on a cold plate. Let it cool for 1-2 minutes. Push jam with your finger — if it wrinkles it is ready.

Wrinkle

2. **Flake test:** Lift out some jam with a clean dry wooden spoon. Allow to cool slightly. Turn spoon and allow jam to run off. If it forms into wide flakes, it is ready. If it trickles off into a thin stream, it is not.

Flake

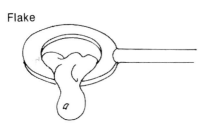

3. **Thermometer test:** Use a sugar thermometer — it will read 105°C (220°F) when it is ready to pot.

Thermometer

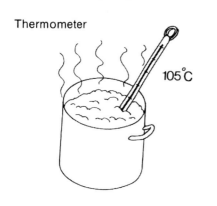

105°C

Raspberry Jam

Ingredients

2 kg raspberries
2 kg sugar

Method

1. Only wash fruit if very dirty. Pick over and remove stalks.
2. Warm fruit gently in saucepan until juices begin to flow.
3. Add sugar (warm first if wished) and stir over a gentle heat until sugar is dissolved.
4. Boil rapidly for about 10 mins until setting point is reached.
5. Skim, pot and cover.

Blackberry and Apple Jam

Ingredients

2 kg Blackberries
1 kg apples
250 ml water
1 tablesp. lemon juice
3 kg sugar

Method

1. Wash, peel, core and slice apples.
2. Wash blackberries in colander. Shake dry and pick over.
3. Stew apples gently in the water until soft.
4. Add blackberries and continue simmering until both fruits are soft.
5. Add sugar and stir over a low heat until dissolved.
6. Boil rapidly for 10-15 minutes, stirring now and then until setting point is reached.
7. Skim, pot and cover.

Marmalade

Ingredients

1 kg Seville oranges
2.5 litres water
2 kg sugar
2 lemons

Method

1. Wash oranges and lemons well, and dry.
2. Peel, removing some of the very thick pith.
3. Cut rinds into fine shreds.
4. Chop flesh — reserving pips.
5. Tie pips in muslin bag.
6. Put chopped flesh, rinds, pips (in bag) and water into a bowl and steep overnight.
7. Place in greased saucepan, bring to the boil and simmer, until rinds are soft and one third of the water has evaporated. Remove bag of pips, squeezing to extract pectin.
8. Add warmed sugar, stir until dissolved.
9. Boil rapidly until settling point is reached. Test.
10. Skim, stand for 10 minutes, then pot, cover and label.

Rhubarb and Ginger Jam

Ingredients

2 kg rhubarb
2 kg sugar
Juice of 4 lemons
$\frac{1}{2}$ tsp. ground ginger

Method

1. Wipe rhubarb, top and tail, and slice. Put in a bowl with sugar in layers and allow to stand overnight.
2. Put rhubarb into greased saucepan, add ginger and heat slowly, stirring all the time, until sugar is dissolved.
3. Bring to the boil and boil rapidly until setting point is reached (20-30 minutes) Test for setting.
4. Skim, pot, cover and label.

Over to you . . .

1. List five important points to be remembered when making jam in order to ensure a good set.

2. Name five garden fruits from which jam is often made. Find out two recipes for jam making — other than those in your book — which make use of cheap garden produce. Write them into your copybook.

3. What causes food to go bad? List three ways of preserving food in order to prevent it decaying. Write a note on **pectin**. What is its function?

4. Jam must be properly stored if it is to remain in good condition. List five points to remember when storing preserves. What are the results of badly stored jam?

5. List briefly the steps to be followed when making jam. Why must special care be taken when adding the sugar?

2

Hygiene

28 *All About Good Health*

Not everyone is blessed with perfect health, but our chances of staying as healthy as possible are helped by:

1. A good diet.
2. Fresh air and exercise.
3. Enough rest and sleep.
4. Clean, healthy surroundings in which to live, work and sleep.
5. Avoiding habits which may lead to ill health.
6. Personal hygiene.

1. A Good Diet

Food is necessary for:

(a) growth and repair of body cells;
(b) heat and energy;
(c) protection from disease.

A balanced diet is one of the best defences against disease. Several diseases can be traced to a bad diet. Fibre in our diet is important, as it helps move food quickly through our intestine, preventing bowel disorders, such as constipation.

2. Fresh Air

Fresh air ensures a supply of oxygen to the body, it gives us a good appetite and helps us to sleep. Our homes should be well ventilated to make sure that we breathe fresh air both indoors and out.

Sunlight: is good for us because the sun works on our skin to produce Vitamin D. When sunbathing, always take care to expose your skin gradually to sunlight, to avoid the danger of sunburn.

Exercise: it is a mistake to abandon exercise altogether when you leave school. Exercise is good for the body — breathing, circulation and all body systems work more efficiently when stimulated by exercise. It keeps muscles in trim and helps avoid overweight, by burning up extra kilocalories. Exercise is especially important for those who spend most of their time sitting, *e.g.* students and office workers.

Try walking to school or work instead of taking the bus; cycle instead of driving. Once or twice a week go swimming or play tennis. Don't overdo it at the start — a little and often is the best policy.

3. Rest and Sleep

'All work and no play, makes Jack a dull boy.'

Each person needs regular periods of rest and relaxation to help him unwind. A person with an active job might find it relaxing just to sit and read a book. Someone with a sedentary (sitting down) job might relax by doing some gardening. Failure to relax can cause stress and nervous tension.

Sleep is our main form of rest — during sleep the body systems slow down and worn out cells are replaced. The amount of sleep each person needs varies — young people need more than adults for instance. The important thing is to get sufficient for your needs. If you constantly feel tired, try to get more sleep. An odd late night does no harm, but too many affect concentration and efficiency at work and school, and lower the resistance of the body to disease. When you are constantly tired you catch infections more easily, and you feel lethargic and depressed.

4. Clean Surroundings

It is easy for people from comfortable homes to keep their surroundings clean and healthy. Those who are less well off may find it harder to keep their homes hygienic, especially if they live in cramped accommodation with inadequate washing and toilet facilities. However, it is important for all of us to try our best, because careless hygiene will almost certainly lead to illness. Babies and elderly people are particularly at risk from diseases caused by lack of cleanliness.

5. Avoid Unhealthy Habits

None of us is perfect, but it is wise to avoid habits which might lead to illness or an early death. Cigarette smoking, unnecessary use of drugs and drinking too much alcohol are such habits. The connection between cigarette smoking and lung cancer is well known, but many are unaware that it also increases the chances of heart disease and chronic bronchitis. Women who smoke during pregnancy produce smaller, less healthy babies.

Do not get into the habit of taking pills for every ache and pain. It would be better to find out *why* you feel unwell. Perhaps it is because you have had too many late nights, or not enough fresh air and exercise.

6. Personal Hygiene

This involves following habits of cleanliness which will help us stay healthy. In order to look and feel well, and in order to avoid spreading germs, we should obey four basic rules:

1. Have a good wash first thing in the morning and last thing at night.
2. Wash hands after using the lavatory.
3. Wash hands before handling food, *i.e.* cooking or eating it.
4. Change clothes, especially underclothes, frequently.

Immunisation

People can be protected against many serious illnesses by being vaccinated against them. Children can be vaccinated free, at their local health centre, against T.B., polio, diptheria, whooping cough and many other diseases. When they go to school, treatment and medical checks are continued free of charge. It is important for parents to avail of these services in order to give their children the best possible chance of good health.

Over to you . . .

1. Name 3 diseases against which it is possible to have children immunised. Where is such immunisation available?

2. Do you think jogging is a healthy activity? List its advantages and disadvantages. Give reasons. What are aerobics?

3. Why is sunlight good for us? List some precautions to be taken when sunbathing at the beginning of a hot spell or when on holiday abroad.

4. Write a paragraph on the importance of (a) kitchen; (b) personal hygiene. List five important points to be observed in order to prevent the spread of germs.

5. **Project**
   Find out all you can about the dangers of cigarette smoking. Write the results into your copybook.

29   *All About Personal Hygiene*

The Skin

The Skin:

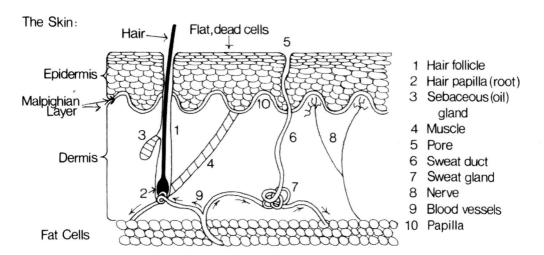

Hair → Flat, dead cells 5

Epidermis

Malpighian Layer →

3 1

Dermis

4

2   9

Fat Cells

10

6   8

7

1 Hair follicle
2 Hair papilla (root)
3 Sebaceous (oil) gland
4 Muscle
5 Pore
6 Sweat duct
7 Sweat gland
8 Nerve
9 Blood vessels
10 Papilla

Our whole body is covered with a waterproof protective layer which we call **skin.**

The skin is made up of two thin layers:
(a) The Epidermis — on the outside.
(b) The Dermis — on the inside.

The Epidermis

This is the part of the skin we see. It has no nerves or blood vessels. Its surface is made up of **flat, dead cells** which are constantly being rubbed away as flakes of dust. The lowest layer of the epidermis is called the **Malpighian layer.** Here new cells are made to replace those worn away from the skin surface and those damaged by accidents and burns. This layer also contains the **pigment** or colouring matter of our skin.

The Dermis

This is the deepest layer of the skin. It contains **bloodvessels** which bring oxygen and nourishment to the skin cells. It contains **nerves** which enable us to feel pain, pressure, heat and cold. Nerves are more plentiful in areas sensitive to feeling, such as the fingertips. The top of the dermis is raised into little 'bumps' called **papillae.**

The dermis is connected to the muscle and bone underneath by **connective tissue.** Also in the deepest part of the dermis are layers of **fat cells** which help to insulate the body.

The dermis contains millions of tiny **glands.** These are of two kinds — **sweat glands** and **oil glands.** Sweat glands are coiled up tubes which remove excess water, salts and impurities from the tiny bloodvessels around them. These waste products pass upwards through the epidermis in **ducts,** which open onto the surface of the skin as **pores.**

Sweat

Sweat (or perspiration) is the name of the liquid removed from the body as just described. Heat is taken from the body to evaporate (dry up) the sweat and so the body is cooled. The impurities from sweat remain on the skin after the liquid is evaporated and must be washed off regularly. About 1 litre of sweat is produced and evaporated by the average adult in 24 hours.

A rise in temperature increases sweating, so we perspire more in a warm room, or on a hot day. When sweating is increased, we see beads of sweat on the body, *e.g.* the forehead, as the body cannot evaporate it fast enough. This happens during fever, for example, or after active sports or strenuous work.

> Sweat contains water, salts and urea (a waste protein product).

Hairs

Hairs are made from cells of the epidermis. A hair begins as a knob (**papilla**) at the base of a narrow shaft known as a **hair follicle,** which lies deep in the dermis. As new cells are formed in the papilla, the other cells are pushed upwards, forming the hair.

Oil glands or Sebaceous glands

These are small glands attached to the hair follicles. These produce an oily substance (**sebum**), which keeps the hair and skin soft and makes the skin waterproof. If too much sebum is made, it clogs up the hair follicles and may cause infections (causing 'spots' or 'pimples').

Functions of the Skin

1. It protects the body against harmful substances, such as bacteria.
2. It prevents loss of body fluids.
3. It removes waste — by perspiration.
4. It is an organ of touch.
5. It helps regulate body temperature — by perspiration.
6. It manufactures vitamin D — from sunlight.

Reasons for Washing

The sebum produced by the oil glands remains as a sticky film on the surface of the skin. Also present are the solids from evaporated sweat, such as salts and urea, and loose dead cells of the epidermis. Bacteria on the surface of the skin begin to decompose these substances, causing an offensive smell (body odour).

During the day we regularly handle objects which carry germs — money, door handles, animals, *etc.* Unless we are careful, the bacteria we pick up on our hands will pass onto our food and into our mouths, causing infection and illness.

It is very important to wash our skin frequently in order to remove these substances and prevent infection and body odour. If not, the pores become blocked, preventing the removal of waste, and blackheads and pimples result.

Unwashed skin:
1. Prevents sweat glands working.
2. Causes a stale offensive smell.
3. Encourages growth of bacteria.

Skin Hygiene

1. **Wash hands frequently,** particularly after using the lavatory and before handling food.
2. Have a **good wash daily,** to remove bacteria, sweat and dirt from the skin. The easiest way to do this is to have a

shower or bath every day. If this is not possible, see that you have a thorough body wash.

3. **Warm water, soap** and **friction** are necessary to remove grease and dirt, but water which is **too hot** causes open pores. Rinse off soap after washing and dry well.

4. Pay particular attention to **underarms, feet and groin** as these are areas which tend to perspire more frequently and from which it is difficult for the sweat to evaporate.

5. **Underarm hair should be removed** to reduce the odour of perspiration. Use either a razor or a depilatory (hair removing) cream.

6. **Deodorants** are useful, as they help prevent an **unpleasant smell. Antiperspirants** are more efficient, as they **prevent perspiration** in the area to which they are applied. Test for sensitivity first on the lower arm. Sticks and roll-on products are more efficient and economical than aerosols.

7. **Change underwear frequently.** If you perspire freely, avoid wearing non-absorbant fabrics, *e.g.* nylon, next to the skin. Cotton is more comfortable, as it is highly absorbant.

8. **After games** or strenuous activity have a **cold shower** to wash off perspiration and close pores.

Warm water, soap and friction

Problem Skin

Problems may be caused by:
1. Dry skin.
2. Greasy skin.
3. Acne.

Dry skin: Use gentle skin care products, specially prepared for dry skin. Wear a moisturiser during the day and use a little dry skin cream before you go to bed.

Oily skin: This skin is usually quite shiny and is prone to blemishes. Watch your diet — avoid too many rich or greasy foods. Wash skin thoroughly with soap and water. Use a toning lotion for oily skin (this dries up the oil).

Acne: Its main cause is a change in hormone levels which occurs in adolescence. This affects the sebaceous glands, so that they produce too much oil. Bacteria on the skin surface react with the oily film, clogging pores and causing blackheads. Infected hair follicles swell up, causing pimples.

To avoid spreading acne:

(a) Keep skin absolutely clean — wash frequently with soap and water.
(b) Never scratch, rub or squeeze pimples.
(c) Avoid greasy food — eat lots of fruit and vegetables.
(d) If using medicated lotions and other preparations, follow instructions exactly.
(e) Avoid using greasy creams and makeup.
(f) Use an antiseptic soap.
(g) Drink lots of water.
(h) If severe, consult a doctor.

Skin Care

There are three steps to skin care:
1. Cleanse.
2. Tone.
3. Nourish.
Always wash hands before handling skin.

Cleanse: Remove makeup with cleansing cream or milk. Massage cream gently into skin to soften makeup. Remove gently with a clean tissue or cotton wool, using upward strokes.

Tone: Cleansing opens the pores, the purpose of toning is to close them. The skin can be toned by sprinkling with cold water or by using a toning lotion suited to your skin type. Apply toner with a moistened pad of cotton wool, dabbing gently all over the face. Blot off with a clean tissue.

Nourish: Apply a little skin food or nourishing cream and gently rub it in, working from base of neck upwards. Tissue off before you go to bed.

Guidelines

1. Use this routine twice a day — morning and night.
2. Apply creams sparingly.
3. Massage gently with fingertips to avoid stretching skin.
4. Work from base of throat upwards, to avoid causing wrinkles. Always include your neck in any beauty treatment.

Neglect of your skin causes:	A good wash removes:
Pimples Blackheads Chapped skin Dry skin Premature wrinkles	Grease and sweat Dirt and dead skin Bacteria

Make-up

A young person should only wear the lighest of cosmetics, avoiding heavy creams. Put on make-up very carefully. Foundation and powder should be as near as possible to the colour of your skin.

1. Cleanse, tone and apply moisturiser to face and neck.
2. Apply a light touch of tinted foundation to face and neck — blend well in.
3. Dust on translucent facepowder with clean cotton wool.
4. Apply a little blusher high on the cheek bones.
5. Apply eye shadow — light shades on upper half (under brow) a darker shade on lid.
6. Apply a little mascara.
7. Apply lipstick or gloss following the natural shape of the mouth.

Having a Bath?

1. Water should not be too hot.
2. Ventilate room.
3. Rub down briskly with towel.
4. Rub on body lotion.
5. Use talc sparingly.

Going Swimming?

Follow these rules:

1. Never bathe straight after a meal.
2. Go to the lavatory before you swim.
3. Never swim alone.
4. Protect feet from verrucas.
5. Don't stay in too long.
6. Have a shower afterwards.
7. Wear swimming cap, especially in pools.

For Clear Skin

1. Eat well, particularly protein foods and protective foods, such as fruit and vegetables. Avoid greasy food.
2. Get plenty of sleep.
3. Get some fresh air and exercise daily.
4. Keep skin clean — always remove make-up before going to bed.
5. Protect it from the weather by using a moisturiser.
6. Avoid alcohol and cigarettes.

Care of Hands

1. Wash frequently — using a nailbrush for nails.
2. Apply handcream at least once a day.
3. Use rubber gloves for washing up and protective gloves or barrier creams, if necessary, for other jobs.
4. Dry hands well, particularly before going into fresh air, *e.g.* out to the clothes-line. Otherwise they will get chapped.
5. Manicure once a week.

Care of Feet

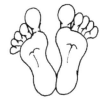

1. Wash once a day in warm, *not* hot, water.
2. Dry thoroughly, particularly between the toes.
3. Use talcum powder sparingly — it may become stale and clog pores.
4. Shoes and stockings should fit well — badly fitting shoes and socks cause corns and bunions.
5. Stockings should be changed daily. At least once during the day, change your shoes to rest your feet.
6. Avoid badly designed footwear or fashion footwear which gives little support to your feet.

Nails

Nails are made from hard epidermal cells. They are directly attached to the dermis. The base of the nail contains very active cells, which multiply, causing nails to grow. The area around this — the quick — contains many nerves and injury to this area can cause acute pain.

Care of Nails

1. Keep them absolutely clean, short and well manicured.
2. Use a nailbrush to clean nails.
3. Avoid biting nails.

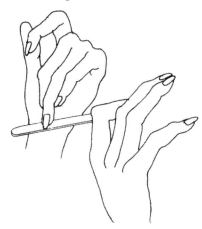

4. Manicure once a week:
   (a) File nails from edge to centre, using an emery board and rounding the tops.
   (b) Push back cuticle with orange stick wrapped in cotton wool; get into the habit of pushing back the cuticle each time you wash your hands.
   (c) Clean nails with orange stick or nail file.
   (d) Rub in a little handcream.
5. Toe nails should be cut straight across, to avoid the danger of ingrowing toe nails.

Hair

Care of Hair

1. Brush hair thoroughly every morning and night, from nape to crown, to brush out dust and stimulate circulation in the scalp.
2. Use a good quality brush — bristle is best.

3. Shampoo hair at least once a week — using a shampoo suited to your hair type *e.g.* greasy or dry. If you must wash your hair very often — use a gentle shampoo.
4. Keep brush, comb and other items used in hair care absolutely clean.
5. Never use other people's brushes, combs, *etc.* — hair infections can pass readily from one person to another.
6. Treat hair with care — avoid over use of bleach, perming and colouring lotions, hair sprays, *etc.* If you wish to cut, perm or colour your hair, consult a qualified hairdresser.
7. Too much heat damages hair — use warm, rather than hot, water. Never place the hair dryer too near hair when drying.

Problem Hair

As with skin, a good diet helps keep the hair in top condition.

Greasy hair: is caused by overproduction of sebum. Brush hair thoroughly and shampoo frequently, using a specially formulated shampoo for greasy hair.

Dry, flyaway hair: often caused by bad circulation in scalp and inactive oil glands. Massage hair thoroughly when washing. Apply a little warm olive/almond oil to scalp a half hour before washing and wrap in a hot towel. Wash in the usual way.

Dandruff: occurs in people with both dry and greasy hair. It consists of flakes of skin trapped among the hair roots. Dandruff attracts bacteria and is aggravated by dust and soap — for this reason hair should be brushed thoroughly, washed frequently and rinsed *very* well. Medicated shampoos have little effect on dandruff — special preparations are available from the chemist which are more successful at clearing it. If dandruff persists, see your doctor.

Conditioners

These form a protective coating on the outside of the hair, reducing tangling, making it easier to comb and more soft and shiny. Conditioners are essential to those with coloured or permed hair. They are applied after washing and rinsing, combed in, left for a few minutes, then rinsed out.

Lice

These are small insects which live in human hair, passing easily from one person to another. They are greyish in colour and lay their eggs (called nits) in the base of the hair; these develop into lice in a couple of weeks. If you find you have head lice, be scrupulous about hygiene. Use a special *fine comb* to comb hair each night and ask your chemist or doctor about a suitable preparation. Keep away from others during the infection.

To Shampoo the Hair

1. Brush hair thoroughly.
2. Wet hair completely, using a shower spray and warm water.
3. Apply a little shampoo to hair, following directions supplied.
4. Rub in well with fingertips, massaging scalp at the same time, until a lather is produced. Rinse well.
5. Apply a little more shampoo and repeat.

6. Rinse very thoroughly — until hair squeaks (a sign that it is really clean).
7. Apply conditioner, if wished, following directions supplied. Rinse all traces from hair.
8. Dry gently with a towel to absorb most of the moisture.
9. Comb carefully, being careful not to tug any tangles — this causes split ends. Never use a brush to comb out wet hair.
10. Blow dry or allow to dry naturally. Never hold a hot dryer too close to the hair.

To wash a Brush and Comb

Wash your brush and comb everytime you wash your hair.

1. Comb out hair and fluff from brush.
2. Wash brush, using warm 'sudsy' water. Run fingers between bristles to get the base really clean.
3. Use a nail brush to clean the comb.
4. Rinse well in warm water.
5. Give a final rinse in cold water, to which a little disinfectant has been added.
6. Shake both well, dry in towel, then lay on their sides to dry completely, or hang out of doors.

Care of Eyes, Ears and Nose

1. **Eyes:** Be sure to get enough sleep. Eat lots of foods containing Vitamin A, which is good for the eyes. Do close work, *e.g.* reading or sewing, in a **good light.** Use eye make-up with care, removing completely before going to bed.

2. **Nose:** The nose filters dust and bacteria. Do not blow too hard or put anything into the nose as you may damage the delicate membrane lining the nose. Wash hankies frequently and boil them regularly to destroy the bacteria. Paper tissues are more hygienic.

3. **Ears:** Wash daily when washing face. Never put anything into the ears, as the delicate eardrum may be damaged. To remove excess wax, pour in a few drops of warmed oil and wipe gently with cotton wool.

Re foreign bodies in eyes, ears, nose, *see First Aid, p. 236.*

Over to you . . .

1. Copy into your copybook the diagram of the skin at the beginning of this chapter. Make sure to draw it large enough — and to label all parts.

2. Write a page on the care of your skin. Visit the beauty counter in your local chemist/department store and find out the skin-care products which would suit your skin type. List these, together with the price of each, at the end of your exercise.

3. List the advantages and disadvantages of wearing make-up.

4. Why is it essential to cleanse the skin regularly? Do you think a daily bath is a good idea? Why? List the problems which result from the lack of cleanliness.

5. Make a list of all the items you would need in order to be clean and fresh. Find out the cost of each and write this in also.

30 *All About The Teeth*

Healthy teeth are necessary for speaking and eating, as well as for comfort and appearance — a pleasant smile is an asset to anyone. Bad teeth look ugly and cause pain, discomfort and bad breath.

Structure

The Tooth:

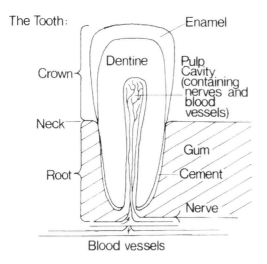

Each tooth consists of:

1. *The Crown* — the part you can see.
2. *The Root* — which is embedded in the gum.
3. *The Neck* — between the two, where the crown meets the gum.

A tooth is composed of a hard, bone-like substance called **dentine.** The dentine is protected on the outside by **enamel,** an extremely hard substance, while the root is protected by a layer of **cement,** which helps hold the tooth in position in the gum.

There is a space called the **pulp cavity** in the centre of each tooth. This contains **nerves** and **bloodvessels,** which supply nutrients, particularly calcium, to the teeth.

In our lifetime we grow two sets of teeth:

1. **Temporary or first teeth:** (20 in number), which start appearing at around 6 months and are complete by about the age of two. They fall out between the ages of 6 and 12.
2. **Permanent teeth:** (32 in number) replace the temporary teeth.

One half set of teeth

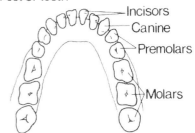

Lower jaw

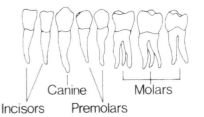

Teeth vary in shape — each shape suits the job it has to do. There are:

8 incisors— flat, sharp, biting teeth in the front.

4 canines— strong, pointed teeth, used to tear food.

8 premolars—flat-topped for grinding food.

12 molars— large, flat-topped teeth with ridges, which make it possible to chew our food.

By the age of twelve years, there are 28 teeth; the last four molars, called the **wisdom teeth,** come a few years later.

Tooth Decay

Tooth decay (dental caries) usually happens when the enamel is damaged. Bacteria act on the food waste (lodged between the teeth when we do not wash them), forming acids which destroy the dentine. It is when they come in contact with the nerves in the pulp cavity that they cause toothache. Bacteria can get into the bloodstream, causing general ill health. Bacteria may also collect to form an abcess in the root.

How a tooth decays:

Gum diseases, *e.g.* pyorrhoea (bleeding gums), are caused by food acids or incorrect brushing. Plaque (see below) gathers beneath the gum, detaching it from the teeth and eventually the teeth fall out.
Watch out for: Swollen gums,
bleeding gums,
bad breath.

These are a sign that something is wrong.

Plaque: After eating food, particularly sweet foods, our teeth are covered with a sticky layer. Bacteria present in the mouth act on this layer, forming a substance called plaque, which clings to the teeth (you can feel it when you run your tongue over the surface of the teeth). The food turns to acid which, if not washed off, dissolves the enamel coating on the teeth, leaving the dentine open to decay.

Care of the Teeth

1. **Eat the right foods:** *e.g.* Foods rich in calcium, phosphorus and Vitamins A and D, *e.g.* milk, cheese, eggs, fruit and vegetables.
2. **Avoid the wrong foods:** Primitive people who eat no sweet foods never suffer from tooth decay. Avoid refined carbohydrate foods, particularly sugar, sweets and soft drinks, as these rot the teeth.
3. **Do not eat between meals:** If you must eat sweets, eat them at the end of a meal and brush your teeth afterwards.
4. **Chew raw crunchy foods:** *e.g.* apples, celery, raw carrots and nuts, to exercise teeth and help keep them clean.
5. **Brush teeth after every meal:** or *at least* twice a day — after breakfast and before going to bed. Never go to bed without brushing your teeth. If you do, the bacteria will have the whole night to work on your teeth.
   On occasions when it is not possible to brush teeth after meals, rinse out the mouth with water.
6. **Replace toothbrush regularly.**
7. **Do not use your teeth for** jobs such as opening bottles, cutting thread, *etc.* This damages the enamel.
8. **Never pick teeth with metal objects** (such as pins). Use a toothpick or dental floss.
9. **Visit the dentist every six months:** so that decay is checked before it goes too far. Do not wait until your teeth ache.

Fluoride

This is a mineral which occurs naturally in some drinking water. As it reduces incidences of tooth decay, most local authorities put small amounts of it into our drinking water.

Fluoride in toothpaste helps to strengthen the teeth, reducing tooth decay. Fluoride can also be painted onto teeth by the dentist — this helps prevent decay for about 6 months.

Brushing Teeth

How to clean your teeth

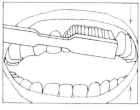

Clean upper teeth from gum downwards, clean lower teeth from gum upwards

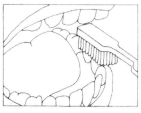

Clean biting surfaces of teeth

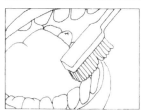

Clean backs of teeth

1. **Regular brushing** is important. Ideally it should be done after every meal.
2. Use a fluoride toothpaste — it helps prevent decay.
3. A good **brushing action** is even more important than toothpaste: brush (a) from gums to biting edge of teeth; (b) brush the back of the teeth and the top grinding edges; (c) finally, gently massage gums, using a circular motion (to improve circulation). Incorrect brushing can weaken gum edge and cause infection.

4. Rinse thoroughly with fresh water two or three times.
5. Use a **good quality brush** of medium firmness — neither stiff nor too soft. Nylon is better than bristle, as it is non-absorbant and therefore less likely to harbour bacteria.
6. **Replace brush regularly** (approximately every 3 months).
7. Rinse mouth with antiseptic to avoid bad breath.
8. Rinse brush after use and allow to dry upright. Now and then sterilise brush in a solution of disinfectant.
9. Never let anyone use your toothbrush.
10. Use dental floss once a day to remove plaque — pull taut and slide up and down between teeth and around base of teeth.

Teaching children to care for their teeth

* See that children eat the right kinds of food — milk, cheese, fruit and vegetables.
* Try not to let children develop a taste for sugar — avoid giving them biscuits, sweets and fizzy drinks. Never bribe them with sweets.
* Get them to wash their teeth properly and regularly from an early age.
* Bring them to the dentist while they are young (to help them feel at ease there).
* It is important to keep first teeth healthy, as decay and infection can pass into a growing permanent tooth.

An apple a day?

It is now thought that the idea of finishing a packed meal with an apple is not such a good idea after all. The acid in the apple will encourage plaque. Instead, rinse the mouth with cold water.

31   All About First Aid

Preventing Accidents

To Children

1. Fix children securely into prams, high chairs, baby buggys, *etc.* with a safety harness.
2. Keep dangerous objects out of the reach of children — matches, lighters, knives, pins, beads and plastic bags.
3. Store medicines, dangerous cleaning agents, weedkillers, cosmetics, *etc.* out of reach of children, ideally in a locked cupboard.
4. Never allow children play unsupervised, especially near water — ponds, pools, septic tanks, *etc.* A child can drown in a few centimetres of water.
5. Use a guard rail around the cooker, turn saucepan handles towards the back.

Fires

6. Place a fire guard around *all* fires. Buy flameproof nightwear only.
7. Never place a mirror over a fireplace.
8. Have a fire extinguisher (which works) in the centre of the house and a fire blanket in the kitchen.
9. Do not leave lighted cigarettes unattended. and *Never* smoke in bed; better still — never smoke!
10. Close downstairs doors at night, to prevent spread of fire.

Falls

11. Avoid overpolishing floors. Do not polish under rugs.
12. Have worn floor coverings mended or secured — particularly those on stairs.
13. Avoid leaving objects, *e.g.* toys, lying about on the floor, particularly the stairs.
14. Use a non-slip floor covering in bathroom and kitchen. Wipe up spills at once.
15. Light stairs and steps well, with a light switch top and bottom.
16. Use proper steps or a step ladder to reach inaccessible places or for 'do-it-yourself' work.

Poisoning

17. *Never* put poisons in harmless bottles, *e.g.* lemonade. Keep in original container, clearly marked 'poison'.
18. Make sure rooms containing gas appliances are well-ventilated, particularly bathrooms with gas geysers. Keep the door or window open.

Electricity

19. Water and electricity must *never* mix — never touch electric appliances with wet hands. Unplug or switch off electrical appliances before repairing, handling or filling — especially kettles, washing machines, dishwashers.
20. Never take electric appliances into the bathroom. Bathroom switches should be outside the room with only a pull cord inside.
21. Unplug T.V. and other appliances before going to bed.
22. Make sure electric appliances are properly earthed. Use modern three-pin shuttered sockets.
23. Do not buy cheap, shoddy electrical equipment.
24. Never use faulty appliances. Have faulty wiring seen to; replace frayed flexes.

Simple First Aid

First aid is the ability to deal promptly and correctly with simple accidents and emergencies and, in more serious cases, to be able to make the patient as comfortable as possible, without worsening the condition until medical help arrives. In serious cases, ring, or have someone else ring, 999 for an ambulance.

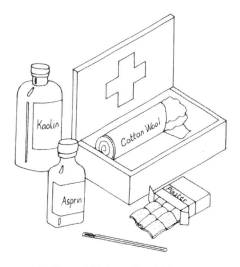

The First Aid Box

Every home should have a first aid box which is well stocked and easily available, but out of reach of children. As the kitchen is the site of most accidents in the home, keep the first aid box here, or in a utility room nearby. Your medicine cupboard, which may hold dangerous drugs, *etc.,* should also be within easy reach. Keep it in a cool dry place, locked, or out of the reach of children. Special childproof medicine cupboards are available.

Keep your first aid box and medicine cupboard really clean and tidy. Tidy out regularly. Wipe bottle tops with clean cotton wool before replacing lids. Avoid overstocking a medicine cupboard. Keep pills, drugs, laxitives, *etc.* to a minimum. Only use them if they are really necessary — children who see their parents solve every little discomfort with a pill are also likely to turn to drugs to solve their problems.

Use up medicines and prescriptions promptly. Be sure to finish the treatment, *e.g.* antibiotics prescribed, even though your illness might seem to be over; if you stop before the treatment is finished, it may return in a more severe form. Return unfinished medicines and pills to the chemist for safe disposal.

A First Aid box should have:

A box of assorted plasters
   or a roll of strip dressings
Sterile bandages — wide and narrow
Sterile cotton wool
Sterile dressings
Gauze for burns
A small scissors
Safety pins
Tweezers (for splinters)
Thermometer
Bottle of antiseptic
Antiseptic ointment
Anti-histamine ointment
A crepe bandage

In your Medicine Cupboard you might also have:

A small bowl
An eye bath
Medicine spoon
Calamine lotion
Kaolin (for diarrhoea)
Indigestion tablets
Bottle of soluble aspirin
Preparations to suit family illnesses
   (*e.g.* eye ointment, cough bottle)

> Keep medicines in a cool dark place — out of reach of children.

Antiseptics, *e.g.* Iodine, *T.C.P.,* prevent the growth of bacteria.

Disinfectants kill bacteria. Various strengths are available; some are for household use, *e.g. Jeypine.* Very strong disinfectants are available for heavy jobs, like disinfecting outside drains, *e.g. Jeyes Fluid.*

The Thermometer

1. Keep your thermometer clean, sterilised and ready for use.
2. After use, shake down; rinse under a **cold tap;** soak in disinfectant solution; dry with cotton wool and store in its container.
3. Never put a thermometer in hot liquid (even if you want to convince your mum you are too ill for school!) as it will burst.

To take a temperature:

1. Make sure mercury is well below 37°C (98.4°F).
2. Place bulb of thermometer:
   (a) Under the tongue, and keep mouth closed.
   (b) In the armpit.
   (c) In the groin, crossing legs to hold it in position. This method is most suitable for children.
3. Leave for 3 minutes, making sure patient lies still and does not open mouth or dislodge the thermometer, as this would give a false reading.
4. Remove thermometer, taking care not to handle bulb. Twist to find the mercury line. The highest point shows the correct temperature.
5. Shake down, rinse and disinfect as above.

Before giving any first aid treatment:

1. Wash hands thoroughly.
2. Have everything as sterile as possible.
3. Reassure the patient — a few kind words help to calm a patient.
4. Use a little antiseptic in water when washing injuries.
5. Stop any bleeding
6. Place patient in a comfortable position, preferably lying down.
7. Work quickly and gently, without fuss or panic.
8. Guard against shock by keeping the patient cool and moving him as little as possible.

Simple Treatments

Cuts/Scratches/Grazes

1. Stop bleeding by applying pressure; press open cuts closed.
2. If wound is dirty, wash with cotton wool, using warm water containing antiseptic. Wash outwards from cut, easing out any grit if necessary.
3. Dry with cotton wool and cover with elastoplast.
4. If bleeding is very severe, especially if blood comes in spurts, apply strong pressure on bleeding point with a pad of clean folded cloth, pressing hard on cut. Do *not* use a tourniquet. Seek medical aid at once — an anti-tetanus injection or stitches may be necessary.

Burns/Scalds

Burns are caused by dry heat, *e.g.* fire, hot saucepans.
Scalds are caused by moist heat, *e.g.* water, steam or fat.

The heat involved sterilises the burn/scald, so avoid handling the area. The main object is to exclude air and so prevent pain and blistering.

Minor burns and scalds

1. Submerge the burn in clean water and leave until pain subsides.
2. Dry gently with a clean towel.
3. Do not apply fat or ointment of any kind.
4. Cover with a paraffin gauze square and/or clean dry dressing.

Major burns and scalds

1. If clothes catch fire, push patient to the ground, throw the nearest large garment, *e.g.* a coat, or a blanket or rug, over him and roll him up in it. Beat out flames, with a towel or rug.
2. Do not attempt to pull off burnt clothing. It is sterile and you might pull off skin with it. Cut away garment if necessary.
3. Submerge burnt part in water; if the body is affected, place patient in a bath of tepid water or wrap burnt part in clean dry cloth, *e.g.* a sheet to exclude air.
4. Put nothing on the burn.
5. Treat for shock and seek medical help.

Insect Bites and Stings

1. Remove sting with tweezers, sterilised with boiling water.
2. Apply anti-histamine cream **or** bathe with a breadsoda solution (for bee stings) or vinegar/lemon juice for wasp stings.

Remember: *Breadsoda for bees —*
'winegar' for wasps!

Animal Bites

1. Wash well with water containing antiseptic.
2. Dry with cotton wool, apply ointment.
3. Apply an elastoplast.
4. Attend a doctor for an anti-tetanus injection (or anti-rabies if abroad).

Splinters

1. Remove splinter, if possible, with sterilised tweezers.
2. If it does not come out, sterilise a needle and gently loosen skin around splinter. Then withdraw with tweezers.
3. Dap with antiseptic and apply a plaster or dressing.

Foreign Bodies

In Eye

1. Avoid rubbing the eye.
2. Lift top lid over bottom lid (to allow lower lashes to dislodge dust).
3. If dust is in lower lid, pull gently down and carefully remove with the corner of a clean cloth.
4. Bathe eye with tepid sterile water.
5. If irritation persists, see a doctor.

In Ear

1. Do not probe.
2. If you suspect it is an insect, shine a torch into the ear. The light should attract it. A little warmed oil may help dislodge blockage.
3. If not successful see a doctor.

In Nose

1. Make patient sneeze (give him pepper!) and blow nose gently.
2. Do not probe. If it does not dislodge, see a doctor.

Bruising and Black Eyes!

1. To reduce swelling apply ice or a cold compress (a cloth wrung out of cold water, folded and applied to eye).
2. Repeat until pain subsides.
3. If bruising is exceptionally severe, or eye is damaged, see a doctor.

Nose Bleed

1. Put patient sitting down, with head tilted forward, to prevent him swallowing blood.
2. Squeeze bridge of nose and/or apply a cold compress or ice.
3. Instruct patient to breathe through mouth and avoid blowing nose for some time.
4. If bleeding occurs frequently, or is unusually prolonged or heavy, see a doctor.

Sprains

1. Place joint under cold running water or place a cold compress on the swelling.
2. Put patient lying down with joint raised.
3. Apply a crepe bandage firmly, but not tightly, for support.

Aches and Pains

Headache

1. If you have been indoors a lot, try a brisk walk in the fresh air.
2. Otherwise lie down in a quiet darkened room. Keep warm.
3. If this does not work, take a mild painkiller, *e.g.* aspirin (as directed), to ease pain and induce sleep.

Earache

1. Keep ear warm — cover with a hat or scarf if possible.
2. Lie down in a quiet dark room — a hot water bottle held against the ear often helps (wrap it in a towel first).
3. Apply a few drops of warm *(not hot)* oil, *e.g.* olive oil, to the ear, using a teaspoon or dropper. Plug ear with cotton wool.
4. If this does not work, take a mild pain killer, *e.g.* aspirin.
5. If pain persists, temperature rises, or if there is a discharge from the ear, see a doctor.

Toothache

1. Avoid eating sweet or very cold foods. Clean teeth.
2. Pack cavity with cotton wool, dipped in oil of cloves.
3. Give a mild sedative — put patient lying down and keep warm.
4. If pain persists, see dentist as soon as possible (emergency cases get preferential treatment).

Tummyache (indigestion)

This is a dull pain or discomfort in the centre of the chest.

1. Have a drink of water and suck an indigestion tablet.
2. Avoid eating for a few hours — eat only light meals for a day or so.
3. If pain persists, or is a regular occurance after meals, see a doctor.

Menstrual Cramp

1. Drink plenty of liquids.
2. Do some exercises (*e.g.* touching toes) to stretch muscles and ease cramp. Yes, it's the last thing you want to do — but it works!
3. Take a warm bath and have an early night. Some people find a hot water bottle helps relieve cramp.
4. If very severe, take a sedative. Don't get into the habit of taking to your bed once a month — if you suffer from real pain, see a doctor.

Coughs/Colds/Sore Throats/'Flu

1. At the first signs, go to bed for a day or two.
2. If this is not possible, go to bed early for a couple of nights.
3. Take soluble aspirin every four hours and drinks lots of liquids.

4. There is some evidence that large doses of Vitamin C, taken at the first sign of a cold, will stop it developing.
5. Hot lemon juice and honey relieves coughs and sore throats.
6. Avoid spreading such infections by coughing and sneezing carelessly. Smoking aggravates such complaints.

Vomiting

1. Patient should be put lying flat and kept warm. Put him to bed if this is possible.
2. Avoid eating for 24 hours, but take a little boiled and cooled water, or carbonated drinks.
3. Do not take sedatives. If vomiting persists, or is accompanied by fever or pain, call a doctor.

Diarrhoea

1. Avoid solid food for 24 hours.
2. Drink plenty of water and carbonated drinks but **no milk.**
3. Take a tablespoon of kaolin mixture as directed on bottle.
4. If diarrhoea persists for more than a couple of days, see a doctor.

Constipation

1. This is usually caused by a bad diet, too low in fibre.
2. Eat lots of raw fruit, vegetables, brown bread and other high fibre foods.
3. Drink plenty of liquids, *e.g.* fruit juices.
4. Avoid laxatives — while they may solve the immediate problem, they make the bowel lazy and in the long term only aggravate the problem.
5. If constipation persists for longer than a few days, after the above treatment, see a doctor.

Choking

A person who is choking won't be able to call out. His skin will begin to go grey and you will hear a choking noise. *Act quickly.*

1. Slap patient sharply between the shoulder blades — four or five times if necessary. If it is a child, hold it upside down, or over your knee, with its head down, and slap in the same way.
2. Alternatively stand behind patient bringing both arms around patient. Grasp hands and jerk sharply inwards at base of rib cage.
3. Loosen clothing around neck and chest to assist entry of air.
4. If above methods do not work, try to remove the obstruction with your fingers.
5. If this fails, rush patient to casulty or a doctor and/or apply the kiss of life, *p. 241.*

Convulsions

1. Lay patient on floor with head to one side. Keep him away from any furniture, *etc.* which might injure him.
2. Place rolled handkerchief between the teeth to prevent patient biting his tongue.
3. When spasm is over allow patient to lie down quietly.

Poisoning

1. In any case of poisoning or suspected poisoning, including drug taking or overdose, bring patient **directly to hospital.**
2. Try to find out from the patient what he has taken and, if possible, bring samples of the poison or of the bottle containing it.
3. Keep any samples of vomit — these may help doctors to trace the type of poison.
4. If patient is conscious, give lots of drinks, especially milk.
5. If you suspect that the poison is corrosive, *e.g.* a strong acid or alkali, *do not* induce vomiting.
6. If it is not, induce vomiting by giving patient salted water to drink.
7. Patient should be kept lying in the recovery position (see below) to avoid inhaling vomit.

Gas Poisoning

1. If you have to enter a gas filled room, take a deep breath, then cover your nose and mouth with a damp cloth. Quickly open all windows and doors.
2. Bring patient into fresh air, have someone ring the doctor/ambulance.

3. Loosen clothing around neck and chest, lie patient in the recovery position. Cover with a blanket.
4. If necessary, apply artificial respiration.

Fainting

This is caused by a shortage of blood to the brain.

Prevention

1. If a patient feels faint, bring him/her to an open window or into fresh air.
2. Loosen clothing around neck, chest and waist.
3. Sit patient down with the head between the knees.
4. Give him or her a drink of water.

Treatment

1. Bring patient into fresh air (try to stop people crowding around).
2. Place lying flat with feet slightly raised.
3. Loosen clothing around neck and chest.
4. Cover with a coat or blanket.
5. Apply a cold cloth to his face.
6. Only when attack has passed, give patient a cup of tea.
7. Allow patient to rest. Do not move him/her too soon.

Electric Shock

1. Switch off current at once *or* if this is not possible . . .
2. Try to push or pull patient away from electricity without touching them directly. Use a wooden (not metal) pole, or put on rubber gloves and stand on a good insulating material, such as newspaper.

3. Treat for shock (see below) and apply first aid to any burns.
4. If necessary, apply artificial respiration and send for medical help.

Shock

Not to be confused with electric shock (above). Shock is a physical reaction likely to follow any accident. The patient looks pale, feels cold and shivers, even on a warm day. He may feel dizzy, weak and sick and the pusle will be rapid (about 90).

Treatment

1. Lie patient down, with feet up. Cover with a light coat or sheet — but do not make him/her too warm.
2. Loosen clothing around neck, chest and waist.
3. Unless shock is very mild, do not give anything to drink, especially alcohol.

Serious Accidents

Often more harm is done by mishandling a patient after an accident than by the accident itself.

1. If you think there may be internal injuries or bleeding, or there are head injuries — DO NOT MOVE PATIENT — you may kill him.
2. Get someone to dial 999 for an ambulance.
3. Cover patient with a blanket. Apply pressure to any bleeding and try to reassure him.
4. Do *not* give anything to eat or drink (he must be fasting if he needs an anaesthetic in hospital).

Artificial Respiration

Study this well — one day knowledge of mouth to mouth resuscitation or 'the kiss of life' may help you save a life.

1. In the case of a drowning accident, firstly place patient with head down to drain out water.
2. If breathing has stopped, lie patient on his/her back and loosen clothing around neck, chest and waist.
3. Remove any foreign material from mouth, *e.g.* false teeth.
4. Kneel beside patient, place one hand on the top of his/her head and one hand under the chin, then tilt head back fully to clear the air passages.

Lift up chin

5. Pinch patient's nostrils.
6. Take a deep breath and place your mouth over the slightly open mouth of patient, sealing it.

7. Blow hard (like blowing up a balloon). In the case of a child, blow gently. Check that the lungs inflate (you will see the chest rising).

Chest rises, then falls

8. Remove your mouth and let the patient's lungs deflate while you take your next breath.
9. If chest does not rise and fall, the air passages may be blocked. Turn patient on his side and slap sharply between shoulder blades.
10. Continue to apply kiss of life until help arrives or patient recovers.
11. Place patient in recovery position.

Recovery Position

Never place an unconscious patient on his back — he may die from choking on his tongue or vomit, or by inhaling blood.

Place patient on his side, making sure there is nothing in the mouth which might block the breathing passages.

Head should be to one side, with arm and leg of same side raised, *see diagram.*

32   *All About Introducing Your Body*

The basic unit of all living things is the **cell.** Our body consists of millions of these tiny cells. Most cells are so small that they cannot be seen without a microscope.

In the body, similar cells are grouped together to form **tissues.** Various types of tissues group together to form **organs.** An organ is a part of the body which works as a unit, *e.g.* the heart, the liver, the skin. A **system** consists of groups of organs which work together to do a particular job. For example:

System	Organs
Circulatory	*Heart, arteries, veins.*
Respiratory	*Lungs, trachea, bronchi.*
Digestive	*Stomach, intestines, liver.*

The Skeleton

The **skeleton** is the bony structure which gives the body shape and firmness. It also helps to protect delicate internal organs. The skeleton is made up of head, trunk and limbs.

The trunk is divided into two halves by a strong wall of muscle, called the **diaphragm.** The upper half is called the **thorax** (this contains the heart and lungs) and the lower half, called the **abdomen,** contains the liver, kidneys, stomach and other digestive organs.

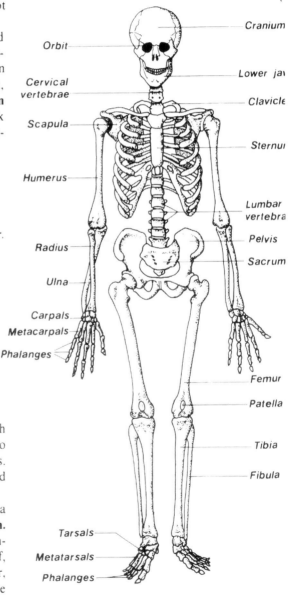

Cranium

Orbit

Lower jaw

Cervical vertebrae

Clavicle

Scapula

Sternum

Humerus

Lumbar vertebra

Radius

Pelvis

Sacrum

Ulna

Carpals

Metacarpals

Phalanges

Femur

Patella

Tibia

Fibula

Tarsals

Metatarsals

Phalanges

The Circulatory System

The circulatory system consists of the **heart, bloodvessels** and the **blood** which flows through them. The purpose of this system is to transport substances from one part of the body to another.

The Heart

The heart acts as a pump which drives blood to all parts of the body. Its regular contractions continue without stopping for our whole lifetime.

Position: The heart is situated in the centre of the thorax to the front, between the two lungs. It is behind the sternum (breastbone) and above the diaphragm.

Size and shape: The heart is about the size of its owner's fist. Its average weight is 275 g. It is pear shaped with its pointed end facing downwards, slightly to the left.

Structure:

1. The heart is a hollow muscular organ, containing four chambers.
2. A solid wall called the **septum** divides the right side (containing impure blood) from the left side (which contains only pure blood).
3. Each side is divided into an upper and a lower chamber. The two upper chambers are called **auricles,** the two lower chambers are called **ventricles.**
4. The auricles receive incoming blood and pass it to the ventricles below, through valves which prevent the blood flowing backwards.
5. The **tricuspid valve** lies between the right auricle and right venticle; the **bicuspid** or **mitral valve** between the left auricle and left ventricle.
6. The ventricles have thicker, more muscular walls than the auricles. Their job is to pump the blood out of the heart — the right ventricle to the lungs, the left ventricle to the rest of the body.

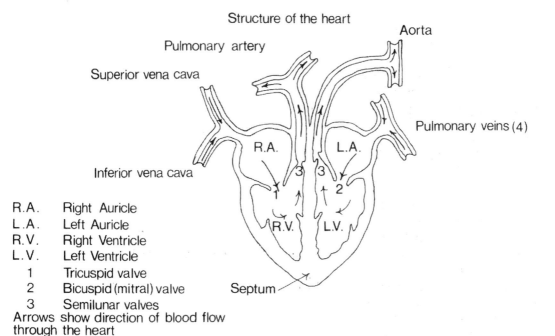

Structure of the heart

R.A.   Right Auricle
L.A.   Left Auricle
R.V.   Right Ventricle
L.V.   Left Ventricle
1   Tricuspid valve
2   Bicuspid (mitral) valve
3   Semilunar valves
Arrows show direction of blood flow through the heart

7. The heart is covered by a smooth membrane called **pericardium** and the inside is lined with a membrane called **endocardium.**

The blood vessels of the heart:

1. The *superior* and *inferior vena cavae* bring impure blood from the rest of the body to the right auricle — the superior vena cava from the upper parts of the body, the inferior vena cava from the lower parts.
2. The *pulmonary artery* brings impure blood to the lungs from the right ventricle. Its opening is guarded by a *semi-lunar valve* to prevent a backward flow.
3. The four *pulmonary veins* return pure blood from the lungs to the left auricle — two from the right lung and two from the left.

4. The *aorta* — the largest blood vessel in the body carries pure blood from the left ventricle all around the body. This too has a semi-lunar valve to prevent the blood flowing backwards into the ventricle.

Circulation

Every cell of the body needs a continual supply of oxygen and food — the blood distributes these to the cells and collects waste products for removal by the kidneys. There are in fact two circulations which are taking place at the same time:

1. Pulmonary circulation — from the right side of the heart to the lungs and back.
2. General (systemic) circulation — from the left side of the heart, all around the body and back.

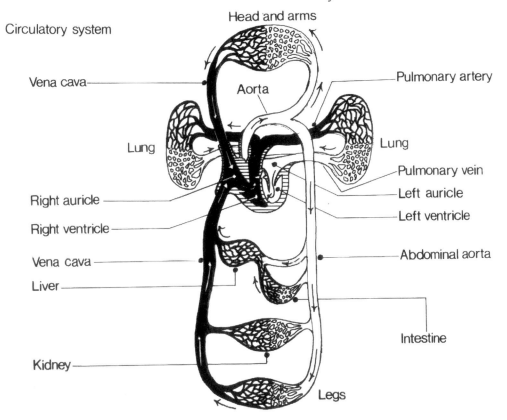

Circulatory system

Pulmonary Circulation

To explain circulation in more detail we will begin with the blood entering the right auricle of the heart:

1. The right auricle (containing impure blood) contracts, forcing its blood through the tricuspid valve, into the right ventricle.

2. The right ventricle contracts, forcing blood into the pulmonary artery, which brings blood to the lungs.

3. In the lungs the blood is purified — carbon dioxide is given off and oxygen taken in.

4. The blood, now bright red in colour, returns to the left auricle, through the four pulmonary veins.

General Circulation

5. The left auricle contracts, forcing blood through the bi-cuspid valve into the left ventricle.

6. This contracts, forcing blood into the aorta, which carries blood out of the heart.

7. The aorta forms branches, which get smaller and smaller as they move further from the heart, bringing blood to every organ and cell.

8. These capillaries release their oxygen and nutrients to the cells and take up CO_2 and waste matter in exchange, which makes the blood darker in colour.

9. The capillaries unite to form veins, which join together and become larger, until they eventually form the superior vena cava (from the upper part of the body) or the inferior vena cava (from the lower part of the body). These flow into the right auricle and so the journey begins once again.

Summary of Circulation

Right auricle
Right ventricle
Pulmonary artery   **Pulmonary**
Lungs   **Circulation**
Pulmonary veins
Left auricle
Left ventricle

Aorta, all around body breaking into capillaries, then back through veins to the superior vena cava or inferior vena cava to the right auricle.

Blood Vessels

Blood passes around the body in tubes called bloodvessels. These vary in structure according to their function.

An artery

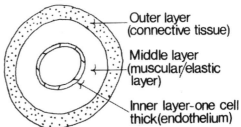

— Outer layer (connective tissue)

Middle layer (muscular/elastic layer)

Inner layer-one cell thick (endothelium)

Arteries: carry blood away from the heart. The blood in arteries (except the pulmonary artery) is bright red in colour, due to the presence of oxygen. They have thick elastic walls, consisting of three layers — an outer wall of **connective tissue,** a middle wall of **muscular and elastic tissue** and a thin lining of **endothelium.** Their elastic walls allow them to expand with each surge of blood being pumped from the heart. It is this rhythmic pressure of blood which causes the **pulse** *(see p. 247).*

Arteries branch into smaller vessels, called **arterioles.** As they get further from the heart, their outer layers get thinner and eventually there is only a single layer of endothelium left — forming tiny vessels known as **capillaries.**

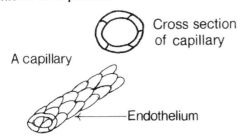

Cross section of capillary

A capillary

Endothelium

Capillaries: are very narrow hair-like tubes. Their walls consist of **endothelial cells.** They are so thin that substances such as gases and nutrients can pass easily through them. Oxygen and nutrients pass into the cells where the nutrients are oxidised (burned up). The wastes caused by oxidation, *e.g.* carbon dioxide, are collected by the capillaries. Capillaries form a very fine network between arterioles and veins.

A vein-same three layers but thinner

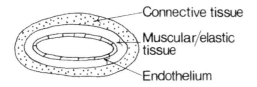

Connective tissue

Muscular/elastic tissue

Endothelium

Veins: carry blood towards the heart. The blood in veins (except the pulmonary veins) is **dark red** in colour, due to the presence of carbon dioxide and other impurities. The pressure of blood in veins is less strong than in arteries, so their walls are much thinner. The veins in the limbs have **valves** to prevent blood flowing backwards. Normal muscular movements, *e.g.* walking and exercise, assist the blood flow back to the heart. Faulty valves lead to swellings in the veins, causing varicose veins.

Valves in veins

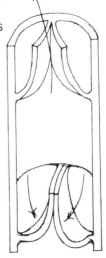

Summary

Table 32.1

	Arteries	Veins	Capilleries
1.	Thick elastic walls	Thinner walls with valves	Very thin walls
2.	Stay open when empty	Collapse when empty	Collapse when empty
3.	Blood under high pressure/flows in spurts	Blood under low pressure/flows smoothly	Blood under high pressure (due to narrowness of vessels)
4.	Oxygenated blood (bright red in colour) except pulmonary artery	De-oxygenated blood (dark red in colour) except pulmonary veins	Oxygenated blood at first changing to dark de-oxygenated blood
5.	Carry blood from the heart	Carry blood to the heart	Connect arteries to veins

Heart Beat

If you listen to your heart beating you will notice it has a double beat; this is because heart beat consists of two stages:

1. Both auricles contract — blood flows into ventricles.
2. Both ventricles contract — blood flows out of heart.

And then there is a rest.

The heart beats about 70 times every minute. Heart beat varies with age, activity and illness. Drugs can affect it also. The rate of heartbeat can be measured by taking the **pulse.**

The pulse: The surge of blood as it is pumped from the heart can be felt where an artery passes over a bone near the body surface. This is called the pulse.

To take a pulse — place the first two fingers (not the thumb) on the thumb side of the wrist, about 3 cm down. Feel around until the strongest pulse is felt, and count the beats per minute.

The Blood

The average adult has about five litres of blood circulating in his/her body. The main function of this blood is to transport oxygen and nutrients to the tissues and carry away waste.

Composition

The blood is made up of a liquid called **plasma,** containing three types of cell:

Red cells
White cells
Platelets

Blood cells

Red

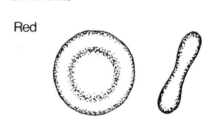

White

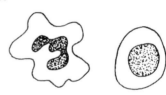

Platelets

Table 32.2

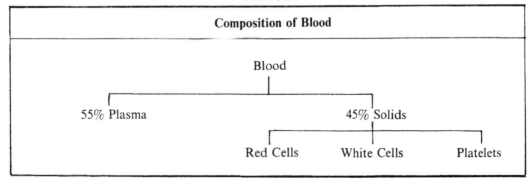

Composition of Blood			
Blood			
55% Plasma	45% Solids		
	Red Cells	White Cells	Platelets

There are 500 red cells to every white cell and platelet.

1. **Red cells:** These are tiny concave discs. They have no nuclei. They are very flexible, in order to be able to squeeze easily through the small capillaries. Red cells contain a very special chemical called **haemoglobin** which gives the blood its red colour. Haemoglobin takes up oxygen in the lungs and carries it to every cell of the body. *Anaemia* is caused by a shortage of haemoglobin. Red cells are made in the bone marrow and last only a few months.

2. **White cells:** These are larger than red cells. They vary in size and shape and are constantly moving about. Their main function is to fight infection — when bacteria or viruses enter the body *e.g.* through a cut, the white cells squeeze out of the capillaries and attack the invading germs. White cells are always found on the site of infection or injury. They also make antibodies which fight disease. White cells only last a few days.

3. **Platelets:** Very tiny cells which help the blood to clot.

How the blood clots

When we cut ourselves, before long a jelly-like clot forms over the wound. It is essential that this happens, otherwise we would bleed to death. Here is how it works:

The blood plasma contains a substance called **fibrinogen.** When a blood vessel is damaged (*i.e.* when we cut ourselves) the fibrinogen changes to **fibrin,** a stringy substance. As the blood flows out of the wound, blood cells and platelets become entangled in the fibrin, forming a **clot.** This clot dries to form a **scab** which protects the wound it heals underneath.

Table 32.2

Functions of the Blood	Parts of the Blood Involved
1. Transports oxygen from lungs to tissues.	Red cells
2. Fights infection.	White cells/Antibodies
3. Transports waste materials, *e.g.* CO_2.	Plasma
4. Transports nutrients.	Plasma
5. Temperature control (transports heat).	Plasma
6. Distributes hormones and enzymes.	Plasma
7. Protects body, by clotting.	Fibrinogen (Platelets)

33   *All About The Respiratory System*

The body needs a constant supply of oxygen in order to function. It gets this oxygen from the air — fresh air contains about 4% more oxygen than stale air.

Composition of Air

Table 33.1

Fresh (inspired air)	Stale (expired) air
Nitrogen 79%	79%
Oxygen 20.96%	16.96%
Carbon dioxide 0.04%	4.04%
Water vapour — varies	very moist
Temperature — varies	37%

Oxygen is taken into the body through the air passages and lungs. The whole system involved in taking in oxygen and getting rid of carbon dioxide — a poisonous gas produced by body cells — is called the **respiratory system.**

The Respiratory Tract

Take a deep breath. Air is now passing through a series of passages to the lungs. Together these are known as the respiratory tract.

1. **Nose/Mouth:** Air is warmed and filtered by fine hairs when passing through the nose — this is why it is better to breathe through the nose than through the mouth.
2. **Pharynx:** A wide space at the back of the nose and mouth. At the base of the Pharnyx is a little 'lid' — the **epiglottis,** which closes over the trachea when swallowing, to prevent food going down the 'wrong way'.

Respiratory tract

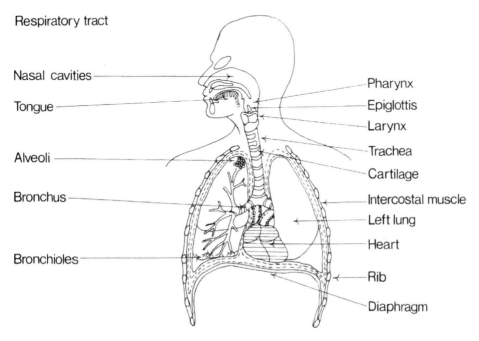

Nasal cavities

Tongue

Alveoli

Bronchus

Bronchioles

Pharynx

Epiglottis

Larynx

Trachea

Cartilage

Intercostal muscle

Left lung

Heart

Rib

Diaphragm

3. **Larynax (voice box):** Situated at the top of the trachea. Stretched across it are the **vocal cords** which vibrate to produce sound.
4. **Trachea (windpipe):** This is a tube about 10 cm long, which is held open by C-shaped rings of cartilage. It is lined with tiny hair-like cilia, which help remove foreign bodies by causing coughing.
5. **Bronchii:** The trachea divides into branches (the bronchii), one entering each lung. These branch into smaller tubes (bronchioles) as they pass further into the lung tissue.

The Lungs

Position

The lungs almost fill the thorax, with the heart lying between them. The base of each lung rests on the diaphragm. The lungs are protected by the sternum and ribs in the front and by the backbone behind.

Shape

The lungs are cone shaped — the broad end faces downwards, the pointed end upwards. The left lung falls into two lobes, the right into three.

Structure

The lungs are made up of millions of tiny air cells (alveoli). A network of bloodvessels, nerves and bronchioles weave in and out through the lung tissue — which is light and spongy in texture. The bronchii enter the lungs at the root — they break into smaller and smaller branches (bronchioles) until they end as tiny swellings, the air cells. The walls of these cells are extremely thin, to allow for the exchange of gases which takes place there.

The natural colour of the lungs is a deep pink, but smoking and polluted air can darken and damage the lung tissue. Each lung is covered with a smooth membrane called pleura. Inflammation of the pleura is known as pleurisy.

Blood Circulation in the Lungs

On leaving the heart, the pulmonary arteries break into two branches, one going to each lung. Soon after entering the lung they divide up into smaller branches (arterioles), until they finally break into capilleries which surround the air cells. Here oxygen is exchanged for carbon dioxide *(see below)*.

Alveoli surrounded by capilleries

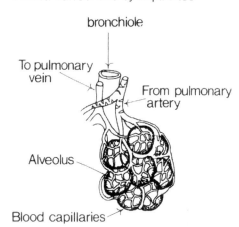

bronchiole

To pulmonary vein

From pulmonary artery

Alveolus

Blood capillaries

The capillaries, now containing bright red oxygenated blood, unite to form veins, which join up to form the two pulmonary veins, which leave each lung and return to the left auricle.

The Exchange of Gases

The walls of both air cells and capilleries are extremely thin so that gases can pass easily through them. When we breathe in air, the air-cells are filled with oxygen-rich air. The capilleries surrounding the air cells contain less oxygen than the air cells themselves, so the oxygen passes from the air cells to the capilleries, where it combines with the haemoglobin in the red cells.

The blood contains more carbon dioxide than the air cells, so the carbon dioxide passes from the capilleries into the air cells. This impure air is then breathed out through the respiratory passages.

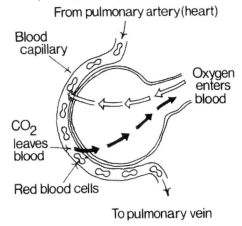

From pulmonary artery (heart)

Blood capillary

Oxygen enters blood

CO_2 leaves blood

Red blood cells

To pulmonary vein

Muscular Control in Breathing

The supply and removal of air from the air cells is brought about by the muscular movement of the thorax (which in turn is controlled by the brain). Breathing occurs in two stages:

Rate of Breathing

The average adult breathes about 16–20 times a minute (children breathe at a higher rate). When we are very active, *e.g.* playing sports, our bodies need more oxygen, so our rate of breathing increases. Illness and fever can also increase it, as can excitement. During sleep, the body needs less oxygen, so the respiration rate decreases.

Artificial Respiration

When, due to shock or accident, breathing appears to stop, we can save a person's life by doing his or her breathing for him/her. This involves either applying pressure to the rib cage or inflating the lungs (by blowing into the air passages). This latter method is known as mouth to mouth resuscitation or *the kiss of life* and is explained on *p. 241*.

Table 33.2

Inspiration (breathing in)	Expiration (breathing out)
1. Muscles of diaphragm contract and flatten. 2. Intercostal muscles contract and lift up rib cage. 3. The volume of the thorax is now increased so air rushes in to fill it. 4. Lungs expand and fill up with air.	1. Muscles of diaphragm relax and diaphragm returns to arched position. 2. Intercostal muscles relax and rib cage lowers. 3. This reduces the volume of the thorax, causing air to be forced out. 4. Rib cage presses in on lungs squeezing out the air.

Air drawn in

Ribs rise

Lungs expand

Diaphragm lowers

Air forced out

Ribs fall

Lungs return to normal

Diaphragm relaxes and rises

32   *All About The Digestive System*

The food we eat is made up of large molecules, which must be broken down into simple substances before they can be absorbed into the blood and eventually used by our cells. The process of breaking down food in this way is known as digestion. **Proteins** must be broken down into **amino acids; carbohydrates** into simple **sugars** (such as **glucose**) and **fats** into **fatty acids** and **glycerol.**

Table 34.1

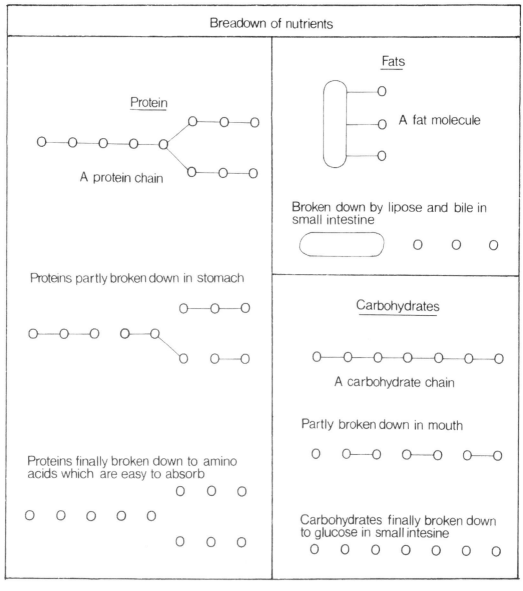

Breadown of nutrients

Protein

A protein chain

Proteins partly broken down in stomach

Proteins finally broken down to amino acids which are easy to absorb

Fats

A fat molecule

Broken down by lipose and bile in small intestine

Carbohydrates

A carbohydrate chain

Partly broken down in mouth

Carbohydrates finally broken down to glucose in small intesine

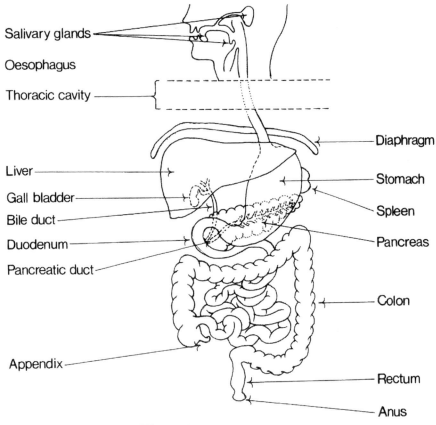

Salivary glands

Oesophagus

Thoracic cavity

Diaphragm

Liver

Stomach

Gall bladder

Spleen

Bile duct

Duodenum

Pancreas

Pancreatic duct

Colon

Appendix

Rectum

Anus

The Alimentary Canal

This is a continuous tube through which our food passes from the mouth to the anus. It is divided into sections (underlined below), each of which has a special function.

Brief summary of Digestion

In the **mouth** food is broken down by the teeth and then passes down the **oesophagus** to the **stomach** where many changes take place. The food then passes into the **small intestine** where further digestion takes place. It is here that most digested food is absorbed.

Undigested food and waste materials pass through the **large intestine,** then out of the body through the anus.

The Mouth

Food is broken up by the **teeth** and mixed with saliva, which makes it easier to swallow. **Saliva** is produced by three pairs of glands near the mouth. It contains an enzyme **ptyalin,** which changes cooked starch to **maltose.**

The Oesophagus or Gullet

This is a tube about 25 cm long, made of muscle, which brings food from the mouth to the stomach. Its muscles help move the food down the tube, by contracting and relaxing. This wave-like movement continues in the stomach and intestines. It is known as **peristalsis.**

The Stomach

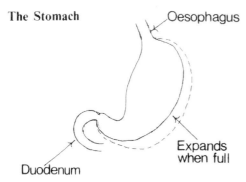

Position: The stomach lies in the top left of the abdomen, beneath the diaphragm. It is beside the liver, above the pancreas and it touches the large intestine and the spleen.

Shape: The stomach is shaped like a pouch, with the oesophagus entering at the top end. An opening at the lower end leads into the duodenum.

Structure: The walls of the stomach are in three layers (a) an outer membrane — called **peritoneum;** (b) a **muscular** layer; (c) an inner lining, the **mucous membrane.** This is folded up in tiny pleats when the stomach is empty. Between the folds are thousands of glands which secrete an important digestive juice — **gastric juice.** Gastric juice contains:
1. Hydrochloric acid.
2. Enzymes — pepsin and rennin.

Digestion in the stomach

1. The stomach churns the food about with the gastic juice until it is well mixed into a creamy liquid, called chyme.
2. The heat of the stomach melts fats and frees them for digestion later.
3. The enzyme **pepsin** acts on proteins and converts them into simpler substances, called peptones.
4. **Rennin** curdles milk.
5. Little absorption occurs in the stomach (alcohol, glucose and certain drugs may be absorbed however).

The length of time food remains in the stomach varies from 1 – 4 hours (fats and proteins stay longer than carbohydrates).

The food gradually leaves the stomach, passing into the first part of the small intestine, which is called the **duodenum.**

The Small Intestine

Position: This is a very long coiled tube (6 metres approx.), which stretches from the stomach to the large intestine. It lies coiled up in the centre of the abdomen, held in place by membranes.

Structure: The walls of the small intestine have the same three layers as the stomach:
(a) An outer layer of peritoneum.
(b) A middle layer of muscle.
(c) An inner mucus membrane, which is deeply folded and contains thousands of glands which secrete intestinal juice. The surface of this inner layer is covered with tiny hair-like projections, called **villi,** which give it a velvet-like appearance and increase the surface area for absorption. Inside each villus is a tiny arteriole, a vein and a lacteal (a vessel containing a milky fluid, called lymph, into which digested fats are absorbed).

A section of the small intestine

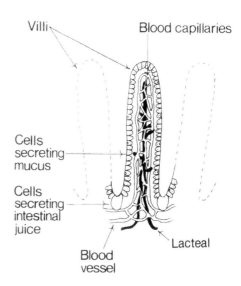

The same wave-like muscle movement which occurs in the oesophagus (peristalsis) moves the food along the small intestine.

Digestion in the Small Intestine

Three digestive juices work on food in the small intestine:

1. *Bile* — made in the liver. A small duct brings it from the liver to the duodenum. Bile breaks up fat into droplets (emulsifies them), so that they are easier to digest.
2. *Pancreatic juice* — this flows through a duct from the pancreas (a gland beneath the stomach) to the duodenum.
3. *Intestinal juice* — from the glands in the walls of the intestine.

Pancreatic juice contains three enzymes —

1. *Trypsin* — continues the digestion of proteins, to peptides and amino acids.
2. *Amylase* — changes starches to maltose.
3. *Lipase* — works with bile to split fats into fatty acids and glycerol.

Intestinal juice contains several enzymes. Among them are:

Eripsin — which finishes protein digestion, by converting proteins and peptides to amino acids.
Sucrase — converts sucrose (sugar) into glucose.
Maltase — converts maltose (from digested starch) into glucose.
Lactase — converts lactose (milk sugar) into glucose.

Absorption

Absorption is the process by which digested food passes through the walls of the digestive organs and eventually into the bloodstream.

Most absorption takes place in the intestine. Having been broken down into their simplest forms, nutrients are now soluble and pass easily through the thin walls of the mucus lining.

(a) **Amino acids and glucose** pass into the capilleries of the villi. These unite to form veins and eventually form the portal vein which carries the digested food to the liver.

(b) **Fatty acids and glycerol** pass into the lacteals in the villi, and re-form into fat droplets. The lacteals empty into lymph vessels, which pass up through the body and empty the digested fats into the bloodstream at the neck.

The Large Intestine

The large intestine, also called the colon or bowel, is about 2 m long. Its walls have the same three layers as the stomach and small intestine:

(a) Peritoneum.
(b) Muscular layer.
(c) Mucus membrane.

The large intestine begins at the **caecum,** where the small intestine joins it, passes up the right side of the abdomen, across the top and down the left side. The last few centimeters are called the **rectum.**

Functions of the Large Intestine

1. Absorption of water.
2. Any remaining nutrients are also absorbed.
3. Elimination of waste.
4. Manufacture of some B vitamins.

When food enters the large intestine, most of the nutrients have been absorbed and it is quite liquid. As it passes along, water is reabsorbed by the capillaries.

The waste food, now called **faeces** contains large numbers of bacteria. It is moved through the intestine by peristaltic action, until finally it is eliminated from the body.

The Importance of Fibre

In the first chapters we discussed how important fibre or roughage was in our diet. The muscular action of peristalsis needs bulky food if it is to take place efficiently. Smooth or liquid foods supply little bulk, so the food moves very sluggishly through the intestine.

Fibre (roughage) helps push the food along because its very roughness stimulates the peristaltic action of the muscles of the intestines. This ensures that food does not stay too long in the intestine, where it can harden and cause constipation and other bowel disorders.

Summary of Digestion

Table 34.2

Digestive gland	Digestive juice	Enzyme	Reaction
Salivary glands (mouth)	Saliva	*Ptyalin*	Starch to maltose
Gastric glands (stomach)	Gastric juice	*Pepsin* *Rennin*	Proteins to peptones Curdles milk
Liver	Bile	—	Emulsifies fats
Pancreas	Pancreatic juice	*Trypsin* *Amylase* *Lipase*	Proteins to peptides Starch to maltose Fats to fatty acids + glycerol
Intestinal glands	Intestinal juice	*Eripsin*	Peptides, *etc.* to amino acids
Small intestine		*Sucrase* *Lactase* *Maltase*	Sucrose to glucose Lactose to glucose Maltose to glucose

3

"About the House"

35 *All About Water*

A supply of pure water is essential to life. We need water for drinking, cooking, washing ourselves and our clothes; we need it to keep our homes clean and to flush away waste down the drains. In most houses, we get clean water simply by turning a tap.

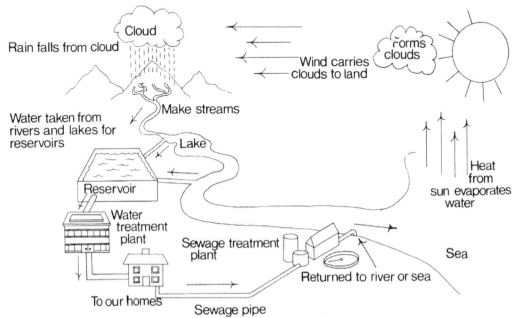

Where does Water come from?

All water begins as **rain.** It falls to earth and either flows over hard rocky surfaces to form **streams** or seeps through soft ground (picking up mineral elements on the way) and comes up as **springs** which flow into lakes and rivers.

Sometimes underground water is collected by sinking **wells.** Water from **shallow wells** is likely to be contaminated by soil and fertilisers from the fields above. **Deep wells** are better. These are drilled through rock, to a lower level of **non porous rock** and are likely to produce pure water.

Since any of these sources of water may be polluted, the local authorities test it and treat it to make sure it is safe to drink. They collect the water in large reservoirs, situated in high ground, and after treatment, pipe it to smaller service reservoirs, from where it

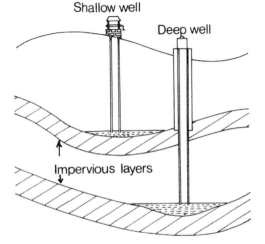

is piped to our homes in large **mains.**
Leading into each house is a smaller service
pipe, which fills the storage tank in the attic.

What is Water?

We have already seen *(Chapter 1)* that water
is a mixture of two gases — hydrogen and
oxygen. It dissolves things easily and for this
reason it is difficult to find *really* pure water,
i.e. water which contains nothing but H_2O.

One would expect rain water to be pure,
but, as it falls, it collects impurities such as
carbon dioxide (which we breathe out),
dust, and sometimes dangerous chemicals,
such as sulphur dioxide from polluted air.

Polluted Water

We hear a lot about pollution nowadays.
Rivers and lakes near farmland and towns
often become contaminated — animals may
pollute the water, sewage or slurry may
drain into rivers or streams, pesticides and
fertilisers used on the farm, or dangerous
chemicals from factories, may find their way
into the water. Impurities in water may be:
(i) suspended or (ii) dissolved.

Suspended impurities may be fairly harmless
(such as sand, grit, twigs, *etc.*) or more
serious decaying substances of animal or
vegetable origin (such as sewage) which carry disease-bearing bacteria.
Dissolved impurities include chlorides (mainly salt); lime salts, which make water hard
(see p. 261), lead salts, from lead pipes and
storage tanks; dissolved animal or vegetable
matter (*e.g.* sewage).

Water for Drinking

The water we drink should be pure, without
any harmful substances dissolved in it.
Hygienically pure water (water fit for
drinking) should be:
1. Colourless (bluish in large quantities).
2. Odourless.
3. Tasteless, but palatable.
4. Well aerated, sparkling.
5. Not acid or alkaline.
6. Free from any harmful impurities.

Purifying Water

Harmful impurities must be removed before
we drink it. The local authorities 'treat' the
water supply to make it safe. They remove
impurities by:
1. **Storage:** While the water lies in the
   reservoir, solids settle to the bottom,
   sunlight and air help to destroy
   dangerous micro-organisms and oxygen
   producing plants help to purify the
   water.
2. **Filtering:** When water leaves the storage
   reservoir it passes through filter beds,
   seeping slowly through layers of fine and
   coarse sand and gravel, which remove
   many of the impurities. It is then piped
   to the service reservoir.

A filter bed

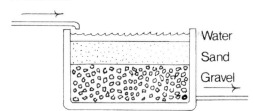

3. **Chlorine:** The amount of chlorine
   used must be carefully calculated.
   There must be enough to kill bacteria
   without leaving a 'swimming pool'
   taste in the water.

Other methods of removing imputities:
1. **Boiling:** It would obviously be impossible to boil whole reservoirs of water.
   This is the method you would use if
   you suspected the water was not pure
   when camping fo instance. Boiling (for
   at least 5 minutes) destroys dangerous
   bacteria and makes the water safe to
   drink. However, since boiling forces

the air out of the water, the liquid tastes insipid.

2. **Distillation:** This is a method of making pure H_2O. Water is boiled and the steam is passed through a coil of tubing which cools and condenses it back into water. Distilled water is used for medical and scientific purposes and for filling steam irons and car batteries.

Water for Washing

Hard or soft water?

Do you live in an area, or perhaps you have visited one, where the inside of the kettle has a hard furry deposit around it, or where, after you wash, a 'tide mark' of scum is left around the handbasin or bath? These are signs that the water in that region is hard, *i.e.* not good for washing.

What is Hard Water?

Hard water is water which does not make a lather easily when you use soap — modern detergents are not so easily affected, as they have a water softener included in their ingredients. Hard water contains mineral salts which were absorbed as it passed through the ground. These minerals are:

1. Calcium and magnesium bicarbonates.
2. Calcium and magnesium sulphates.

These prevent the soap from dissolving and combine with the soap to form a scum.

Disadvantages of Hard Water

1. Difficult to make a lather — wastes soap and detergent.
2. Hard on skin and leaves hair dull.
3. Scum clings to clothes and wash basins, *etc.*
4. Kettles 'fur' up — and take longer to heat. This wastes fuel.
5. Central heating boilers and pipes fur up and become blocked.
6. Not so good for cooking.

There are two types of hardness:

1. **Temporary hardness:** caused by calcium and magnesium *bicarbonates*. This can be removed (a) at home (by boiling); (b) at water treatment plants (by adding lime).
2. **Permanent hardness:** caused by calcium and magnesium *sulphates*.

This cannot be softened by boiling but (a) washing water can be softened by adding washing soda or borax to the water; (b) bath water can be softened by adding bath salts.

Removing 'fur' from a kettle

Fill the kettle, adding 2 tablespoons vinegar to every pint of water. Allow it to stand for at least four hours. Empty out and the deposit will crumble away. Re-fill kettle, bring to the boil; empty and rinse a few times before use.

Heating Water

(Day Vocational Syllabus only)

A good supply of hot water is essential for health and hygiene. Water can be heated by

(a) A back boiler, behind a fireplace.
(b) An instantaneous heater (*e.g.* gas geyser.
(c) An immersion heater.
(d) A central heating system.

Immersion heater: This is a long element enclosed in a metal cover. It is fitted into a cylinder (usually in the hot press). It contains a thermostat, which switches off when water reaches the correct temperature. A dual immersion heater is more economical, containing a long and a short element — the short one heats small amounts of water; the long element heats large amounts of water, *e.g.* for baths.

36   *All About Ventilation*

Air

Air is a mixture of gases — nitrogen, oxygen and carbon dioxide. A constant supply of fresh air is essential for good health.

Composition

Table 36.1

	Fresh Air	Stale Air
Nitrogen	79%	79%
Oxygen	20.96%	16.96%
Carbon dioxide	0.04%	4.04%

Carbon dioxide is released into the air by the breathing of animals and man, by the burning of fuel and by decay and fermentation. The normal level of carbon dioxide in the air is 0.04% — if it rises above this, it becomes a danger to our health.

Air Pollution

The air around us, particularly in cities, is contaminated with impurities:

1. **Suspended impurities:** such as dust; soot; bacteria and other micro-organisms; scales of skin; lead particles.

2. **Gas impurities:** carbon dioxide; carbon monoxide (from car exhausts); industrial gases.

Ventilation

Ventilation means exchanging stale air in a room or building for fresh air. This should be done without causing a draught or lowering the temperature too much.

Why we Need to Ventilate

When a room is occupied:
1. Carbon dioxide increases.
2. Oxygen level is reduced.
3. Bacteria multiply and reach dangerous levels of concentration.
4. There is a rise in temperature (from body heat).
5. A stale smell develops from un-evaporated perspiration.
6. Breathing causes increased humidity.
7. Cigarette smoke may pollute the air.

Kitchens and bathrooms have a very high level of humidity (water vapour), due to steam. This causes **condensation** (wetness on walls and windows), which damages paintwork and causes rusting of equipment.

Effects of bad Ventilation

1. Lack of concentration.
2. Drowsiness, headache, weakness, even fainting.
3. Clamminess, increased perspiration.
4. Increased risk of infection, due to high concentration of bacteria.
5. Condensation.
6. Long term effects for those frequently exposed to inadequate ventilation — respiratory problems, bronchitis, T.B.

Good Ventilation

A good system of ventilation will:
1. Introduce fresh air, remove stale air.
2. Cause gentle circulation currents without draughts.
3. Make sure air is directed upwards; this helps air circulation.

4. Ensure moderate humidity — air should not be too damp or too dry.
5. Ensure air entry/exit points are above head level.
6. Supply a complete air change every hour.

> *Note:* Remember stale air gets warm and *rises,* so outlets for stale air should be near the top of the room.

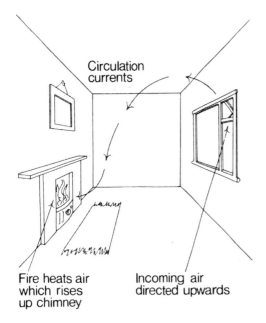

Circulation currents

Fire heats air which rises up chimney

Incoming air directed upwards

Natural methods of Ventilation

These depend on the normal diffusion of gases which take place between warm and cooler air.

1. **Open fire:** Air is heated in front of the fire. It rises up the chimney and cool air is drawn into the room to replace it.
2. **Windows and Doors:** (doors to a lesser extent because open doors can be very draughty):
   (a) *Casement windows:* similar to a door. Most have a horizontal top window, which is efficient at removing stale air.

Casement window

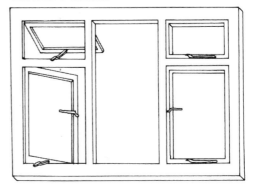

(b) *Louvred windows:* one, two or more panels of glass, mounted horizontally (looking a little like a Venetian blind). A lever opens the glass panes, so that the incoming air is directed upwards.

Louvered window

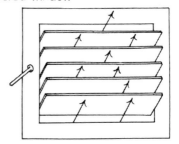

(c) *Sash:* top can be lowered so that stale air leaves through the top of the window while fresh air enters between the panes in the centre, and is directed upwards.

Sash window

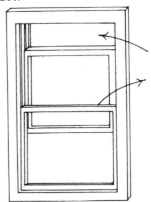

Coopers Ventilator

This may be made of metal, or, more usually, of plastic or glass. The latter is fixed into a circular hole, cut out of a window. It consists of two discs, with holes in each, which can be arranged to correspond so that air enters, or does not (so that it remains closed). It may be opened or closed, by pulling a cord or turning a centre knob.

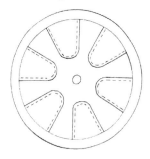

Airbricks

These are set high in the outside wall of the house, and open into a room which has no other system of ventilation, except perhaps a window. They usually have a metal grill on the outside.

Mechanical or Artificial ventilation

Extractor fan

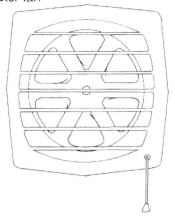

1. **Extractor fans:** ideal for kitchens and bathrooms. These can be fitted into a window or a wall. They consist of propellers, driven by electricity, which rotate at speed, so that stale air is drawn out of the room. They operate by a pull cord and usually have shutters which can be closed when the fan is not in use.

It is important to position fans correctly for maximum efficiency. They should be reasonably near the cooker and sink, and as far as possible from the door opening into the house.

2. **Cooker hoods:** work on the same principle, except there is a hood which helps to collect fumes and a filter to absorb grease.

3. **Air conditioning:** is a system which ventilates by filtering the air. It controls temperature, humidity and circulates the air constantly. It is usually part of a warm air central heating system.

All About Lighting

Good lighting in a home makes it more attractive and pleasant to live in. It can create interesting decorative effects as well, but the main reasons why lighting is important are:

1. So we can see what we are doing — cooking, washing, writing, *etc.*
2. To prevent eyestrain.
3. To prevent accidents.

The best type of light is natural daylight. **Natural lighting** in a home depends on the position and size of the windows and, to a lesser extent, the doors. **Artificial light,** can be provided by oil lamps, gas burners and candles (very romantic!), but the simplest, safest and easiest form to use is electric light.

There are two types of lamp (bulb):

(i) **Filament type:** which gives a warm light and comes in different sizes and varieties, *e.g.* plain and pearl.

Filament lamp

Fluorescent lamp

(ii) **Fluorescent:** a long tube which gives a white shadowless light. These tubes are more expensive but last 3 times as long, give three times more light per watt and are cheaper to run. They are ideal for bathrooms and kitchens.

Good lighting should be **adequate** and **safe**, with **no glare, no shadows, and no flickering.**

Rules for Good lighting

1. Make sure you have enough light for the job *i.e.* a bulb with a sufficiently high wattage and/or a sufficient number of fittings.
2. A good light should not cause glare, *i.e.* dazzle your eyes. Shades and pearlised bulbs are used to prevent glare.
3. Have extra lighting for close work, *e.g.* sewing, reading or studying.
4. Buy safe, reliable fittings and shades.
5. Good lighting should not cause shadows — unless these are for decorative effects and there is sufficient light elsewhere.
6. All dangerous places — steps, stairs and places where you do dangerous jobs, *e.g.* a kitchen or workshop — should be well lit.

Light fittings

Lights can be fitted to ceilings or walls; they can be portable, standard (tall floor lamps) or table lamps.

Shades are used to cover the bulb and avoid glare. They can help direct light or spread it around. They can absorb or reflect light or diffuse it through a translucent shade (a shade which allows light through, but is not transparent).

Lighting can be
 (a) **General** — a translucent fitting allows light rays to spread in all directions.
 (b) **Direct** — all light thrown in one direction, *e.g.* desk lamps, spotlights.
 (c) **Indirect** — the light is thrown onto a pale coloured wall or ceiling which reflects it back into the room.

Lighting Room by Room

Once you see that the light you choose is safe and adequate, lighting a home is very much a matter of individual taste. Here are some suggestions:

1. **Living room:**
   Central diffused 100w fitting — switch at door.
   Two table lamps (100w) for reading and closework.

2. **Dining room or eating area:**
   Background wall lights (60w).
   'Rise and fall' fitting over dining table (100w).
   Serving area — a spot light or wall lights.

3. **Kitchen:**
   One or two — 1 metre flourescent fittings (100w — depending on size and shape of kitchen). These should be mounted on the ceiling.
   Optional — strip lighting under wall cupboards or spotlights to highlight work or eating areas.

4. **Hall, Stairs and Landing:**
   1 light (75w) with attractive fitting in hall.
   1 light (100w) shining on steps of stairs; this should have a two-way switch.
   If necessary, another (75w) light in landing (stair light might be sufficient).

5. **Bedrooms:**
   Central diffused light (100w).
   Bedside light for each occupant (75w).
   Strip light at dressing table.

6. **Children's rooms:**
   Emphasis on safe, secure fittings; avoid bedside lights until children are old enough not to tamper with them..
   A dimmer switch is a good idea (the room light can be turned down to a very low level).

7. **Bathroom:**
   Central diffused light (100w) fluorescent or filament.
   Light over mirror, with pull-cord.
   All other switches *outside* bathroom.

Over to you . . .

1. Write a note on air pollution — use an encyclopaedia, to get extra details.

2. Name three methods of ventilation frequently used in modern homes. Describe in detail how *one* works.

3. Write a note on the importance of ventilation. Why must fresh air inlets be high on the walls of a room?

4. How can you ensure a maximum amount of natural lighting in a home? Finish this sentence: Good lighting should be ....

5. List the effects of bad lighting. Describe the method of lighting you would choose in each of the following cases: (a) for needlework; (b) in a large kitchen; (c) at your front and back door.

6. Explain the following terms: (a) diffused; (b) 'rise and fall' fitting; (c) dimmer switch; (d) indirect lighting; (e) fluorescent lamp.

37   *All About Heating*

A warm home is important for the health and comfort of the family. Money spent on heating should be one of the top priorities in the family budget. It is better to be warm and comfortable, than to sit around freezing in an expensively furnished home. On the other hand, there is no point in wasting heat, so take note of the economy tips at the end of this chapter.

Heat Transfer

Heat travels in three ways:

Conduction — Convection — Radiation

Heat transfer

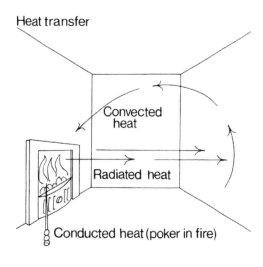

Conducted Heat

The heat travels from the heat source along an object from one part to the next. A poker in a fire is a good example of conduction. The fire heats the part of the poker in the flame, this heats the next part, and so on, until the handle gets so hot, you can't hold it. Conduction is a very slow method of heating

so it is not much used in home heating. Most methods of heating are based on Convection or Radiation.

Convected Heat

This works on the principle that **hot air rises.** Air is heated, gets lighter, rises and is replaced by cooler air. This sets up convection currents which circulate around the room, warming both the air and the people in it.

Radiated Heat

Rays of heat travel from the heater to the first solid object they touch, *e.g.* furniture, or people. They do not heat the air, or the backs of the people, so if you sit facing a fire, your front will get toasted while your back stays cold!

When rays of heat are allowed more space to travel, they heat the furniture or a wall and the heat rises, setting up convection currents which warm the whole room.

A Good Conductor?

A material which allows heat to travel easily is known as a good conductor — metals are good conductors (think of that hot poker).

Materials which do not pass heat along, but which retain it, are known as bad conductors — wood, paper, fibre glass and fabrics (such as wool) are bad conductors. These materials are very important when insulating houses as they don't conduct the heat outside, but keep it in the house.

Home Heating

A home can be heated by:
1. Individual heaters — fixed in each room (or portable heaters).
2. Background heating — to take the chill out of the air, *e.g.* storage heaters.
3. Full central heating.

The type of heating depends on the lifestyle of the family. If a person is at home all day with small chldren, 24 hour heating will be needed — perhaps a **boiler grate** with radiators. In a family where everyone is out all day, **individual heaters,** which heat up quickly when people return from work or school, would be sufficient.

Central heating is probably the ideal, but it is very expensive to install and run, particularly in these days of soaring fuel costs.

Amount of Heat

The average winter temperature in this country is about 6°C. The temperature we should try to have in our homes is at least 15°C (a little warmer in the sitting room — at least 18°C). Old people and young children need even higher temperatures.

Fuel

Fuel is something which gives off heat when burned. **Coal, gas** and **oil** are fuels. **Electricity is not.** Electricity is a source of direct **energy.** As it does not have to be burned to produce heat, it is cleaner and more efficient than fuel. All fuels are dangerous and inflammable — so treat them very carefully and follow the instructions on heaters.

Solid Fuel

Solid fuel includes smokeless fuels (coke, anthracite), coal, briquettes, turf and wood. They are listed here in order of efficiency, *i.e.* you get more heat from coke than coal, but coal gives more heat than wood.

Solid fuels are used in open fires, solid fuel cookers, room heaters and central heating boilers.

Solid Fuel Fires

1. Open Fires

Most people still prefer an open fire to any other form of heating (particularly those who do not have to clean and fuel it!). A modern fireplace is more efficiently designed than in the past — it throws out more heat and there is less waste of heat up the chimney.

Two features which increase efficiency:
(a) **A back boiler** — which heats water, often enough to supply 2-3 radiators.
(b) **Convector grate** — air enters at the front of the fireplace and circulates through a duct at the back of the fire, where it is heated and passes out through a grid above or beside the fire.

Advantages of an Open Fire

1. Pleasant to look at — homely and comfortable.
2. Helps ventilate room — does not dry air.
3. Burns many types of fuel including turf and wood.
4. Running costs are fairly cheap.
5. A back boiler can be installed to heat water and heat other rooms.

Disadvantages of an Open Fire

1. Dirty to handle, *e.g.* ashes, coal, *etc.*
2. Makes room dirty — it needs cleaning and repainting more often.

3. Requires a lot of work — cleaning out, setting, fuelling, *etc.*
4. Inefficient — much of the heat goes up the chimney.
5. Fuel storage required.
6. Delivery has to be arranged.
7. Not easily controlled — slow to build up heat.
8. Pollutes the air.

To Clean and Set a Fire

Use dry materials and arrange fuel loosely for maximum air circulation:

1. Protect yourself and your surroundings, *e.g.* wear an apron and rubber gloves.
2. Gently rake the ashes from the grate. Save all cinders.
3. Collect ashes with shovel and place in metal box or bucket.
4. Crumple or twist newspaper tightly and place in grate.
5. Arrange sticks in a criss-cross or wigwam shape, or use a fire lighter.
6. Place cinders and a few lumps of coal on top and light.

For economy:

1. Build up a good fire, then place a shovel of damp slack (powdered coal) on the back. This will retain heat and save fuel.
2. Avoid poking or riddling ashes too often.
3. Once fire is burning well, regulate air flow to slow down burning.

For safety:

1. Use a reliable fireguard, particularly if there are children or old people about. It should be fixed securely to the fire surround or wall.
2. Have chimney or flue cleaned regularly.

Solid Fuel Room Heaters

These are more efficient and economical than open fires but are expensive to buy. They work by convection and radiation. They consist of a metal box, with a door at the front. A flue connects it to the chimney. They burn smokeless fuels, although some burn all fuels. Many have a back boiler, which may be large enough to heat several radiators as well.

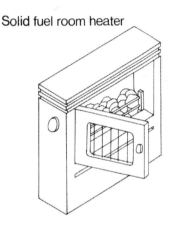

Solid fuel room heater

Compared to Open Fires — Advantages

1. More economical — they use less fuel.
2. Greater heat output and less waste of heat.
3. Can heat water and radiators.
4. Less fuelling and emptying.
5. They burn continuously — can be left in all night.

Compared to Open Fires — Disadvantages

1. Not as attractive to sit at.
2. Although less dirty, there is still a lot of dust, *etc.*
3. Involve much the same work, fuelling and emptying.
4. Fuel has to be delivered and stored.
5. Ventilation reduced.

Gas

Town gas, which is usually made from coal, is piped to some of the larger cities. Natural gas, from under the sea bed, is now replacing it, however. Bottled gas (butane) is a liquid form of gas. It is sold in strong metal cylinders. Empty clinders are returned when buying a new one. Bottled gas is useful in areas where there is no gas supply and also for boats and caravans.

Radiant-convector heater

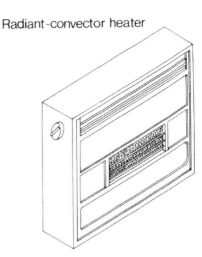

Gas Heaters

Gas heaters may be fixed or portable.

1. *Convector heaters:* Air is warmed by gas jets in the heater. The hot air rises and leaves by a grille at the top. Cool air is drawn in at the base.

Convector heater

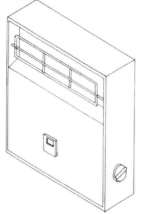

2. *Radiant/convector heaters:* Gas jets heat a fireclay grille, which becomes red hot. Air is drawn in at the base, heated at the back of the fire and passes out through grills at the top.
Both types of heater may be fitted into a fireplace using the existing flue or onto an external wall with a small flue exit.

3. *Portable heaters (e.g. Superser):* These run on bottled gas — the cylinder fits into the heater casing. They are an efficient way of heating a large room — but the room *must* be well ventilated. *Never* use flueless or portable gas heaters in a bedroom.

Advantages of Gas Heaters

i. They heat a room quickly and efficiently.
2. Easy to control, simple to use.
3. Attractively designed.
4. Some heat water, and radiators.
5. Gas is piped direct (except for bottled gas), so there is no problem with delivery or storage.

Disadvantages of Gas Heaters

1. Some heat loss up the flue.
2. Must have good ventilation — or dangerous fumes can build up.
3. Gas can have an unpleasant smell and also dries the air.
4. Cylinders look ugly, unless concealed.
5. Dangerous, unless expertly installed and serviced.

Oil

Oil is mainly used to fuel central heating systems. Paraffin oil is used in portable room heaters. Oil is dangerous, if not handled carefully.

Oil Heaters

(a) *Radiant Oil Heaters:* A wick dips into the oil and soaks it up — this gives off radiant heat when burned. Hot air also rises from this heater and circulates around the room.

Radiant heater

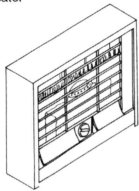

(b) *Convector Oil Heaters:* These work on the same principles. Cold air enters at the base, is heated by the burning wick and leaves through a grille at the top — giving rise to convection currents.

Convector heater

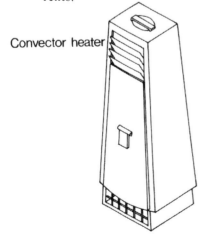

Safety: Oil heaters can be very dangerous and often cause fires.

1. Never move when lit.
2. Avoid standing heaters near furniture, curtains, or in a draught.
3. Avoid using when children are about.
4. Buy a reliable make, which conforms to basic safety standards:
   (a) It should have a secure guard.
   (b) It should not be easily knocked over.
   (c) Flame should cut out if it falls over.

Advantages of Oil Heaters

1. Cheap to buy and run.
2. Efficient — no waste of heat.
3. Portable — *when unlit.*
4. Easy to control — they heat a room quickly.
5. No fuel bills — you buy it as you need it.

Disadvantages of Oil Heaters

1. Dangerous — risk of fire *(see above).*
2. Need to be refilled often — a messy job.
3. Unpleasant fumes — unless kept very clean.
4. Not very attractive.
5. Cause condensation — need good ventilation.

Electricity

Electricity is a very efficient form of heating. A wide variety of heating appliances is available — radiant and convector heaters, fan heaters, storage heaters, and central heating systems.

Radiant Heaters (usually called electric fires).

A single or double electric bar, with a shiny back, which reflects heat outwards. Coal effect fires are also available.

Radiant heater

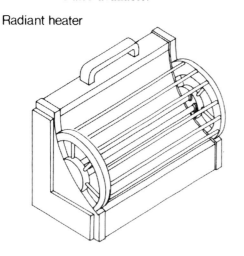

Convector Heaters

These consist of a metal case with electric elements near the base. These heat the air, which rises and comes out the top of the heater. Cool air enters at the bottom.

Fan Heaters

These are a type of small convector heater, with a fan to blow out the heated air. They heat up a room quickly but are inclined to be noisy.

Fan heater

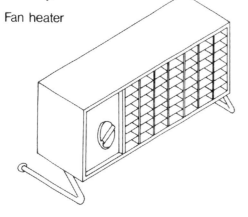

Oil Filled Radiators

These contain oil, which is heated by electric elements. The heat is radiated into the room. They are very efficient and streamlined but expensive on electricity.

Storage Heaters

A storage heater consists of a metal casing, filled with fireclay blocks. An electric element passes in and out through them and heats them up at 'off peak' times, *i.e.* when electricity is cheaper. They store the heat and give it out slowly during the day, giving an even background heat.

Storage heater

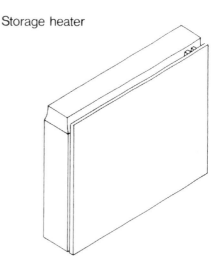

Advantages of Electric Heaters

1. Simple and quick — they turn on and off at the flick of a switch.
2. Clean — no fumes, ashes or smell.
3. Very efficient — no wasted heat.
4. Most are easy to carry and can be plugged-in in any room.
5. Most have modern features, such as time switches, thermostats, *etc.* making them easier to control.
6. Wide variety of models.
7. No delivery or storage problems.

Disadvantages of Electric Heaters

1. Expensive — especially when turned on for a long time.
2. They dry up the air and do not assist ventilation.
3. They do not heat the water.
4. No heat during power cuts.

Heating Economy

1. Insulate house.
2. Switch off when not needed.
3. Keep doors closed — windows should be opened just sufficiently to ventilate.
4. Turn down thermostats as weather gets warmer — an extra sweater is a cheaper way of keeping warm.
5. Slack down open fires — let the fire die down some time before going to bed.
6. Buy coal in bulk — it is cheaper.

Insulation

Most homes lose large amounts of heat through the roof, walls and windows. Insulating a house is like putting on an overcoat — it keeps the house warmer by cutting down the heat loss. Insulation saves money, no matter what form of heat you use. All insulating materials make use of bad conductors of heat.

Reducing Heat Loss

If you insulate well, you could cut your heat loss by 75%. The first method mentioned below is the cheapest, the second costs a bit more, and so on.

1. *Hot water cylinder:* Lagging the cylinder with a thick lagging jacket will save money on water heating bills.

Lagged cylinder

2. *Draughts:* Fit foam, plastic or metal draught excluders around doors and windows. Fill cracks in floor boards with filler. Use thick carpets and underlays. Block up fireplaces if they are not being used.

Draughtproofing

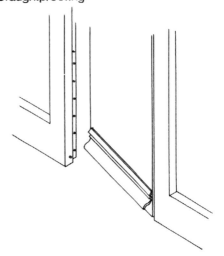

3. *Attic:* A 10 cm layer of fibreglass blanket or loose-fill insulation will pay for itself in three years — by the saving you make on fuel.
   N.B. Do not insulate under water tank or it may freeze up in winter.

Attic insulation

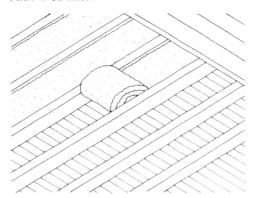

4. *Walls:* Modern houses are constructed with cavity walls. These have a 5 cm air space which provides some insulation (air also is a bad conductor of heat). It is possible to pump plastic foam into existing cavity walls to improve insulation, but this is an expensive job. It is important to employ a reliable company. Check also the type of insulation used — some contain substances which might damage health.

5. *Windows:* Heat loss through windows can be reduced by using heavy, lined curtains. Double glazing cuts heat loss through windows by 50% but it is very expensive unless windows have to be replaced anyway.

Double glazing

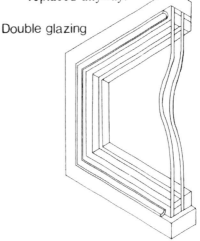

Walls   Polystyrene insulation

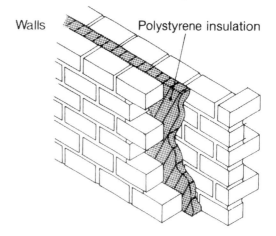

Over to you . . .

1. Explain the difference between (a) radiated heat and (b) convected heat. Name two heaters which use (a) and two which use (b). Explain how *one* of the heaters mentioned works.

2. Compare a solid fuel open fire with an electric storage heater.

3. Write a note on the importance of insulation. Name four useful methods of insulating a house. Find out how much it would cost to insulate the average house with *two* of them.

38 All About Kitchens

The Kitchen

The busiest room in a home is the kitchen. It is here that meal preparation, cooking, washing up, laundry and a great deal of the day-to-day cleaning is done. Much of the work done in a kitchen is carried out in this order:

Storage—Preparation—Cooking—Serving

Try to arrange large pieces of equipment with this in mind and store smaller equipment, such as saucepans, bowls, cutlery, *etc.*, near the area where they are most used.

Laundry equipment should be near the sink or in a separate alcove or utility room. Everything in a kitchen should be **safe** and **easy to clean.**

A Kitchen should be:
1. **Well lit,** day and night, for safety and comfort.
2. **Well ventilated,** *e.g.* have an extractor fan.
3. There should be plenty of **storage space.**
4. Make sure there are lots of **electrical sockets,** at *least* 6.

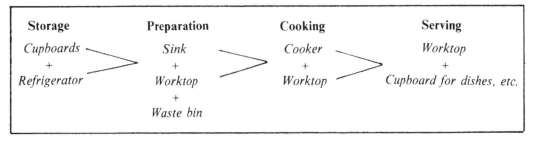

* *Kitchen surfaces should be easy to clean* *

Table 38.1

Item	Suggested Materials
Work surfaces	Laminated plastic *(Formica)*
Floor	Vinyl — easy to clean, non-slip
Walls	Ceramic tiles, gloss or emulsion paint
Cupboards	Vinyl wall covering Strong laminated plastic fronts. Lighter laminated plastic linings.
Windows	Avoid curtains near cooker, use a washable roller blind instead

Now we will look at some of the most important pieces of equipment in any kitchen.

When buying a large piece of equipment, *e.g.* a cooker or a washing machine, ask yourself the following questions:

1. **How much** can I afford?
2. What **size** do I need? — this depends on the size of the family and the amount of cooking done.
3. How much **space** have I got for it? *e.g.* height, width, *etc.*
4. Is it **safe?**
5. Will there be a good **after-sales service** if it breaks down?

Read consumer magazines in the library, *e.g. Which.* Visit different electrical shops and compare models and prices. Study the various brochures before deciding which to buy; some companies will arrange a loan (H.P.).

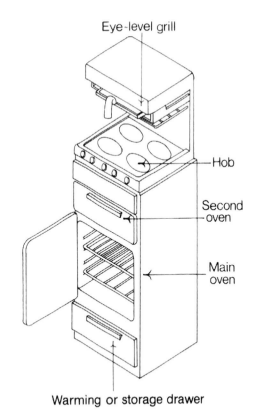

Warming or storage drawer

All About Cookers

Position

The position of the cooker depends on where the electric connection is situated. Never place it at the end of a line of units, or in a corner. Arrange to have a worktop on each side, on which you can rest saucepans, jugs, *etc.* when cooking.

Description

Most cookers consist of:

An oven
A hob
A grill

The Hob — The average family cooker has **four hot plates** or burners on **the hob.** Some are thermostatically controlled to prevent food boiling over or burning. Under the hob, there may be a **spill tray** which can be removed for easy cleaning.

The Grill — may be at eye level (good for tall people) or under the hob, at waist level (better for small people). Some continental cookers have the grill in the oven (this is a bad idea as the oven cannot be used when the grill is in use). Many grill compartments can also be used as a small oven — a good economy point.

The Oven — The modern oven is large enough for most family cooking. The heat is controlled by a thermostat, which keeps the oven at the temperature set on the dial. Its walls are well insulated to keep the heat in. It has two or three shelves, which can be moved to several positions.

The inside walls may be finished with tough vitreous enamel. Some have removable wall panels for easy cleaning. Many modern ovens have 'non-stick' or 'self-cleaning' linings.

Many ovens have a separate glass door, so the cooking can be checked without letting in cold air. A light inside the oven helps make it easier to see. The door of the oven may be side hinged or drop down. The drop down door is handy to place food on when you are removing if from the oven, but makes it more difficult to reach in when you are cleaning it.

The outside of the cooker has an enamel finish which is easy to clean, but care must be taken not to scratch it by using harsh abrasives.

Modern Features

Split-level Cookers: The hob and oven are 'split' — the hob is set into a worktop; the oven is fixed into a special cupboard unit (usually at eye level).

Advantages:

1. You can have the oven and hob exactly where you want them.
2. They are easy to clean as each is sealed into a unit.
3. It is possible to have a gas hob and electric oven or the other way round if you prefer.

Disadvantages

1. More expensive to buy and install.
2. Wastes worktop space.

Double Ovens: As already mentioned, the grill compartment in some ovens is well insulated and can be used as a small oven, when you are cooking only one or two items. This is a significant economy point.

Automatic Ovens: These have **auto-timers** or clocks attached to the oven, which can be pre-set to switch on and off at a given time. These are ideal for a family who are out at work all day. Dinners can be prepared the

night before, kept in the refrigerator overnight, then placed in the oven before going to work. The clock is set to turn on several hours later and to switch off when cooking is completed. This means there is a hot dinner ready for the family when they get home.

Autotimer

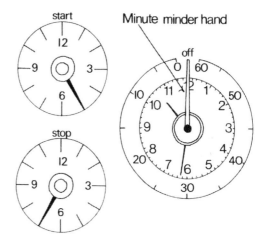

An Automatic Timer

The autotimer has a clock, a starting button and a dial/button which registers the number of hours the dish takes to cook.

Here is how it works:

Let's say you are going to work at 8 a.m. You have a casserole ready, which you want to start cooking at 4 p.m. so that it is ready to eat at 6 p.m.

1. Make sure the clock is at the correct time — 8 a.m.
2. Set the starting button to start at 4 p.m.
3. Set the timing button to 2 hours cooking time — this means it will switch itself off should you be delayed.
4. Set oven switch to correct temperature for casserole and make sure main cooker switch is on.
5. Don't forget to put in the casserole — you might like to cook a few baked potatoes at the same time.

Rules

1. Choose foods which need approximately the same temperature and time.
2. Add 10–15 minutes to the cooking time to allow for the heating up of oven.
3. Cover dishes — to prevent drying out.
4. Make sure food is absolutely fresh. Remove food from the refrigerator at the last minute to avoid the danger of bacteria multiplying during the long wait in the oven. In very hot weather it might be safer to avoid cooking meat dishes by autotimer.

Suitable Foods

Casseroles, braised dishes, meat loaf, curry, baked fish, roast meat, chicken, milk puddings, baked custard, swiss apple — are all suitable. Most baking recipes, *e.g.* cakes and breads, should go into a preheated oven and are therefore unsuitable for autotimer cooking.

Economical Use of Ovens

1. Make full use of oven space — plan cooking so that whole meals are cooked in the oven. *Never* turn on the oven for one item, this is unnecessarily extravagent.
2. Turn off gas cookers when cooking is finished. Electric ovens can be turned off ten minutes before the end of cooking, as they retain heat well.
3. Do not get into the habit of cooking things with the rings/burners turned on too high — this wastes fuel, causes 'boiling over', overcooks or burns many foods, and stains the hob.
4. Use small burners (or inside of dual ring) for small saucepans. And turn on half the grill for small amounts, if this is possible.
5. Use rising heat (heating-up time) for starting milk puddings and casseroles.
6. Use a pressure cooker, steamer or sectioned saucepan to save fuel.

Gas Cookers

Gas ovens may be worked by natural gas, coal gas or bottled gas. Natural gas is more efficient, cleaner and less dangerous than coal gas.

Most modern gas cookers have **push button ignition,** otherwise they will have a **pilot light** which, when lit, will automatically light burners, grill or oven, when any of these are switched on. Make sure to find out which type you are using before you light it — you may have to use a **gas lighter** or a match. Never turn on a gas switch until you are ready to light it — escaping gas can cause gas poisoning and explosions.

Modern gas ovens generally have a back burner with a **flame failure device,** which switches off the gas if the flame goes out. The gas flame heats the air in the oven, which rises and circulates around the oven in convection currents. A **flue** removes fumes from the back of the cooker.

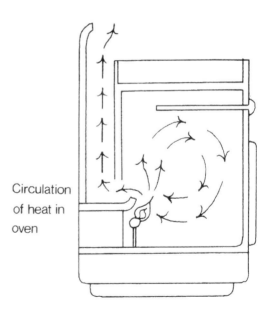

Circulation of heat in oven

The oven is thermostatically controlled — the temperature in the centre of the oven corresponds to the temperature set on the dial *e.g.* Gas Mark 5. The top of the oven will be slightly hotter, the lower shelves slightly cooler. Many gas grills have a **rotisserie** attachment.

Shelf position

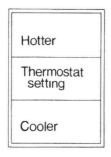

Hotter

Thermostat setting

Cooler

Advantages of Gas Cookers

1. They are quick — supplying instant heat.
2. They are easy to control, as the flame is visible, and adjusts at once when you change the dial.
3. Cookers are easy to clean.
4. Most have plate warming facilities over hob.
5. Because of variation in oven temperature, dishes which require different temperatures can be cooked at the same time.

Disadvantages

1. They are less clean than electricity.
2. Some give off fumes.
3. They do not heat water, warm radiators, *etc.*

Care of Gas Cookers

1. Light burners and cooker according to directions supplied.
2. Make sure to light burners immediately they are turned on.
3. Place cooker out of draughts which might cause flame to blow out.
4. Adjust burner to suit size of saucepan. Do not allow flame burn up the sides of saucepans — this causes blackening.
5. Keep cooker clean — wipe up spills at once.

6. Avoid scratching hob with saucepans and abrasive cleaners — use a paste cleaner.

Electric Cookers

These are quick, clean and easy to use, with many modern features.

Hob

(a) *High-speed coiled rings* — these are quick to heat up; slower solid rings are less common now.
(b) *Dual rings* — the centre of the ring is on a separate element and can be switched on alone, for small saucepans. The whole ring can be used for larger saucepans.
(c) *Simmerstat* —a thermostatically controlled ring which makes sure milk does not boil over or fat overheat.
(d) *Ceramic hob* — the rings are concealed behind a sheet of heatproof glass, easy to clean, but expensive.
(e) *Spill tray* — which can be removed for easy cleaning.

Grill

(a) The grill may double as a second oven.
(b) *Dual element grill* — half the grill can be turned on alone, when grilling small amounts.

Oven

The oven is heated by **elements** which may be fixed to the sides, back or base of the oven, beneath enamelled lining panels. The oven is heated by convection currents — the elements heat the air which rises and circulates. A **thermostat** controls oven temperature and an **indicator light** on the oven switch tells when the oven has reached the correct temperature.

Modern Features:

(a) *Fan-oven* — a fan blows hot air, heated by an element at the back of the oven. This helps to create convection currents which give an even temperature all over the oven. This means the oven can be filled to capacity with foods which require the same temperature.

(b) *Self-cleaning ovens:* These can be set to a very high temperature which burns off the spilled food.

(c) *Rotisserie* — a rotating spit which roasts evenly, without any need for basting.

(d) *Glass door* — so cooking can be checked without letting in any cold air.

Care of Electric Cookers

1. Keep hob, grill and oven clean — never let them get too dirty or stained.

2. Use flat heavy based saucepans — a cheap saucepan will buckle and waste heat.

3. Protect oven against spills — wipe them up quickly when they occur.

4. Do not drag untensils across hob — this scratches enamel.

5. Avoid harsh cleaners — use hot soapy water and a paste cleaner for stubborn stains. Only use **Brillo** and caustic cleaners (in oven only) when absolutely necessary.

Caustic Cleaners (oven cleaners)

These are very powerful alkaline cleaners which dissolve away difficult stains and burned-in oven dirt. Use very carefully, according to directions. Protect your clothes, wear rubber gloves, and rinse off well. Never allow them to come into contact with the outside enamelling of a cooker.

Cleaning a Cooker

N.B. **Turn off electric current/pilot light before beginning to clean.**

After every use, while still warm.

1. Wipe over hob with a cloth wrung out of hot soapy water. Use a non-scratch cleaner for stubborn stains.

2. Wipe over drip-tray.

3. Wash grill-pan, if used, using a brush for grid. Rinse and dry.

4. Wipe out oven and shelves, paying particular attention to any spills — use a *Brillo,* if necessary. Rinse and dry.

Major clean (do not wait until it gets too dirty):

1. If very soiled, spray or rub on caustic oven cleaner a few hours beforehand (or according to directions).

2. Remove all loose parts — saucepan supports, burners, shelves, oven linings, grill pan, spill-tray, *etc.* and wash well in hot soapy water, using *Brillo* for stubborn stains. Rinse and dry.

3. Wash out inside of cooker — avoid wetting the element.

4. Wash outside of cooker, from top down, with a cloth wrung out of hot soapy water. Pay particular attention to switches and corners. Rinse and dry.

5. Polish up chrome, *etc.* with a dry cloth.

Solid Fuel Cookers

A solid fuel cooker is no longer the old fashioned 'range' of the past. These cookers are now smart, streamlined and highly efficient. They are available in several colours. They burn several types of fuel — coal, coke, anthracite and even oil. A solid fuel cooker consists of:

1. A Hob
2. An Oven
3. A Firebox

Solid fuel cooker

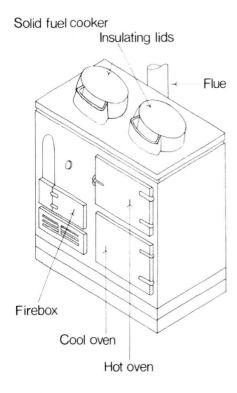

The best (but most expensive) is the **heat storage cooker** — a well insulated cast iron cooker. Warm air from the fire circulates around the back of the oven and under the hot plates, before going up the chimney. This type needs less attention, *i.e.* fuelling and emptying, than the traditional model and less heat is lost up the chimney.

Hob
This has two large hot plates, a very hot one, over the fire, for fast cooking and a cooler one for simmering. One or two insulated lids help retain heat by covering the hot plates when they are not being used.

Oven

There are usually two ovens — a hot oven and a cooler one, which is used for slow cooking, such as casseroles and fruit cakes.

The oven temperature is not as easy to regulate as that of a gas or electric cooker as it is controlled by dampers. These are used to create a greater draught, which makes the fire burn more quickly and raises the temperature of the oven.

Fire Box

This contains the fire. Ashes fall into the ash-pan beneath, which must be emptied regularly. The fire must be refuelled a few times each day and the ashes riddled to allow air to circulate more freely.

Care

1. Use recommended fuel. Smokeless fuels are cleaner, more efficient and produce less ash, but they are more expensive.
2. Clean flues regularly, depending on use. This is necessary to remove soot and other deposits which would prevent circulation of air.
3. Rake firebox and refuel regularly. Empty ashpan daily.
4. Use heavy flat based saucepans for maximum efficiency.
5. Cover hob when not in use.
6. Keep hot plate and oven clean — wipe up spills at once.

Cleaning

1. Brush out oven and hot plate to remove dirt and ash.
2. Rub over hob with greased paper.
3. Wipe enamelled front with a cloth wrung out of hot soapy water. Rinse and dry.
4. Polish up chrome and metal with a dry duster or clean according to metal type.
5. Clean flues regularly, and chimney about twice a year.

Advantages of Solid-fuel Cookers

Gas and electric cookers can only be used for cooking, whereas a solid-fuel cooker can also:

1. Heat the kitchen.
2. Heat water for washing and baths.
3. Heat radiators in other rooms.
4. Burn rubbish.
5. They are always available for cooking.
6. They are cheap to run and ideal for large numbers.

Disadvantages of Solid-fuel Cookers

1. Expensive to buy and install.
2. Need regular attention — emptying ash and refuelling.
3. Fuel storage space is needed.
4. Flues need regular cleaning.
5. They are slow to heat up and not as easy to regulate as gas or electric cookers.

All About Refrigerators

A refrigerator is a cold, well insulated cupboard which keeps perishible food cold and fresh and protects it from dust and flies. Food stored in a fridge keeps longer, because the bacteria which make food go bad cannot work so well in a very cold place. The temperature in a refrigerator should be between 2°C and 7°C.

If you have not got a refrigerator, keep food cool in a cold pantry larder or in a food safe (a metal cupboard which should be hung *outside* the house in a shady spot, near the kitchen door). This allows free circulation of air.

Description

A refrigerator is made from enamel covered steel. The door contains moulded shelves for bottles, eggs, cheese, *etc.* There are 3–4 plastic coated shelves and a storage drawer

for salad/vegetables. Most have an adjustable thermostatic control, a magnetic door seal and a light.

A frozen food storage compartment (usually at the top of the refrigerator) is useful for storing frozen food and making ice cubes.

Advantages of a Refrigerator

Although you may think a refrigerator is a luxury, it will soon pay for itself by:

1. Preventing waste.
2. Making it possible to use more leftovers.

It also:

3. Keeps food cool and fresh.
4. Cuts down on shopping trips.
5. Allows you to store frozen food.
6. Helps you make cold sweets and better pastry.

How it Works

A special liquid circulates at the back of the refrigerator. As it evaporates (dries up), it takes heat from the surrounding area, *i.e.* the inside of the refrigerator — thus cooling the air and the food in the refrigerator. A refrigerator can be fuelled by gas or electricity.

Defrosting

In use, ice builds up around the evaporator (frozen food compartment). This ice must be removed or the refrigerator will be unable to work properly. It will also use more electricity, trying to keep the temperature down.

Many modern fridges have push-button defrosting, which switches the refrigerator back on when defrosting is completed. Automatic models need never be defrosted — they defrost automatically several times a day, so there is never a build up of ice.

To Defrost and Clean

1. Switch to defrost or switch off and pull out plug (you can speed up defrosting by putting a bowl of boiling water in the icebox).
2. Remove contents of frozen food compartment and wrap well in insulating material such as newspaper.
3. Empty ice cube tray and drip tray. Wash and dry.
4. Using 500 ml warm water to 1 tablespoon breadsoda, wring out a clean cloth and wipe out inside of refrigerator, doors, shelves, *etc.* Rinse and dry.
5. If shelves or other removable parts have been neglected, remove, wash in hot soapy water, rinse well and dry before replacing.
6. Wipe out frozen food compartment; replace refilled ice cube tray.
7. Wash outside of cabinet with warm soapy water, rinse and dry. An occasional rub with all-purpose polish will help keep it in good condition.
8. Rub up chrome fittings with a soft duster.
9. Switch on and replace frozen food.

Using a Refrigerator

1. Position: A refrigerator should *not* be placed near a source of heat, *e.g.* a boiler, cooker or heater.
2. Allow circulation of air behind refrigerator.
3. Always keep fridge door closed, especially during 'power cuts'.
4. Arrange food so that air can circulate — do not pack too closely.
5. Never put warm foods in a refrigerator — this raises the temperature of other foods.
6. All foods should be clean before storing — wash fruit and vegetables. Place meat *etc.*, on a plate, to avoid dripping.
7. Check foods daily, using up leftovers.
8. Cover all foods, especially strong smelling foods, to prevent drying out and mingling smells and tastes. Suitable covering materials include cling film; aluminium foil; plastic bags; plastic storage boxes.
9. Defrost regularly (unless automatic).
10. When refrigerator is not in use, unplug, clean well and leave door open to allow air to circulate.

The Star System

Most refrigerators have a frozen food storage compartment in which you can make ice cubes, ice cream and store frozen food. Some are set at a lower temperature than others.

These frozen food stores are not suitable for freezing fresh food — this should be done in a freezer which has a four star marking (**** *i.e.* a temperature between –18°C and –25°C).

Star symbols

✳	One star: (—6°C)	frozen food keeps for one week
✳ ✳	Two stars: (—12°C)	frozen food keeps for one month
✳ ✳ ✳	Three stars: (—18°C)	frozen food keeps for three months
✳ ✳ ✳ ✳	Freezer Four stars: (—18°C - —25°C)	fresh food can be frozen and frozen food can be stored for up to one year

Storing food in a refrigerator

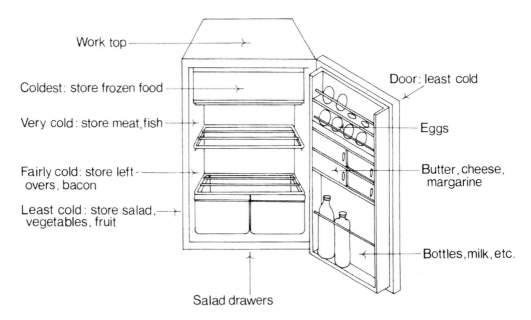

Work top

Coldest: store frozen food

Very cold: store meat, fish

Fairly cold: store left-overs, bacon

Least cold: store salad, vegetables, fruit

Door: least cold

Eggs

Butter, cheese, margarine

Bottles, milk, etc.

Salad drawers

Placing food: The coldest part of a refrigerator is the shelf next to the frozen food compartment. The vegetable drawer and door shelves are the least cold. Store food in this order:

N.B. Never store bananas, apples or root vegetables in a refrigerator.

The Sink

Sinks should be placed under a window:
  (a) For good light.
  (b) To provide ventilation for steam to escape.
  (c) To give a pleasant outlook.

A water proof splashback, *e.g.* ceramic tiles, will protect the wall behind the sink.

Description

Most modern sinks are made from stainless steel — this is hardwearing, easy to clean and stain-resistant. Stainless steel sinks are usually moulded in one piece with a single or double draining board. They have curved corners to make them easier to clean. Every sink should have work space on one side, usually the left, to stack dirty dishes, with a draining board on the other side to drain them.

Most modern sinks are fitted over unit cupboard bases, which provide storage space for cleaning agents, basins, *etc.*

Taps: are usually made from stainless steel. They should be high enough to allow a large saucepan or bucket to be lifted out when full. A swivel tap is handy as it can be moved out of the way.

'S' trap

Beneath the sink is an 'S' trap, which is fitted with a nut, which can be removed to clear the sink when it is blocked. The 'S' trap always holds water — to prevent unpleasant smells and germs reaching the sink from the outside drain.

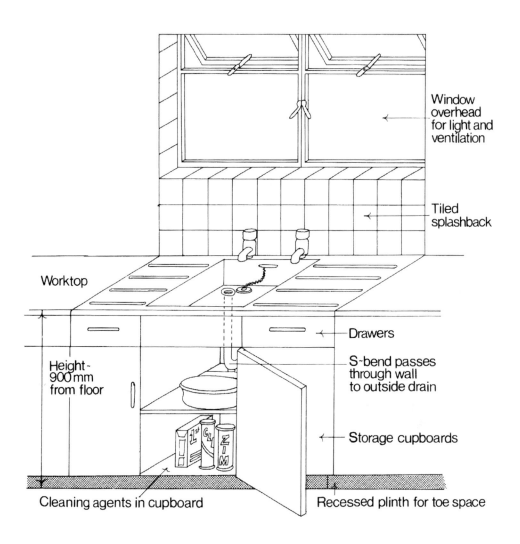

Window overhead for light and ventilation

Tiled splashback

Worktop

Drawers

S-bend passes through wall to outside drain

Height ~ 900 mm from floor

Storage cupboards

Cleaning agents in cupboard

Recessed plinth for toe space

The kitchen sink

Care of Sink

1. Keep the sink spotlessly clean — wipe down after use.
2. Avoid emptying greasy water, tea leaves or other unsuitable substances down the drain.
3. Use a sink basket for scraps and tea leaves, *etc.*
4. Stainless steel sinks are easy to clean — there is no need for harsh abrasives. Use hot soapy water and a little cream cleanser for stubborn stains.
5. Rinse with cold water after cleaning, to fill 'S' trap with fresh water.
6. Disinfect drains regularly.

Cleaning

1. Wipe down after use — give sink a thorough clean daily, after the main meal.
2. Empty sink basket and wash it.
3. Wash draining board, sink and taps with hot soapy water. Clean around overflow with a brush and dry off with a cloth wrung out of clean hot water.
4. Wooden draining boards must be thoroughly scrubbed with the grain of the wood, using abrasive powder, *e.g. Vim.* Pay attention to grooves and corners. Rinse and wipe dry.
5. Wipe over surrounding area — tiled splashback, cupboard fronts, *etc.*, with a damp cloth. Polish taps with a dry cloth.
6. Once a week, pour washing soda solution down waste pipe.
7. Disinfect sink area twice a week.

A Blocked Waste Pipe

If your sink gets blocked now and then, it is usually a sign that unsuitable things are being emptied into it. When trying to unblock a sink, try the simplest method (1) first, and gradually try the other methods until it is freed.

1. Plunger: Run 3–4 cm water into sink. Seal overflow with a folded dish cloth and place cup of plunger over waste outlet. Press plunger firmly up and down several times.

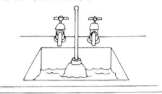

2. Put a lump of washing soda, or a measure of drain cleaner over sink grating. Pour boiling water over washing soda or cold water over drain cleaner, as directed.

3. Try loosening blockage with a long wire.
4. Finally, place a basin under 'S' trap and carefully unscrew nut. Use a wire to loosen blockage from the top, then flush sink with boiling water. Replace nut, flush with cold water, empty basin and wash out.

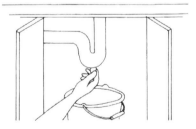

Waste Disposal Unit

This is a powerful grinder fitted under the sink in place of the 'S' trap. It is driven by an electric motor. Waste food — peelings, meat scraps, *etc.* — are pulped and flushed away down the drain.

39   *All About Home and Hygiene*

Germs

One of the main causes of disease is bacteria — often called 'germs'. These are tiny one-celled creatures which are found everywhere — in the air, soil, water, in animals and in man. Not all bacteria are harmful, but those which are, can cause serious disease and even death.

They are very tiny — thousands of them could fit on one full stop! They multiply very quickly — one germ can become almost a million overnight, if it has the right conditions.

In order to live bacteria need:

Warmth — Moisture — Food

For this reason, they like to settle in a kitchen, as this is often warm, with lots of moisture and food about. If we are careless about hygiene, bacteria can infect our food and cause food-poisoning.

Cold temperatures **slow down** the growth of bacteria (this is why we put food in a refrigerator). Very cold temperatures **stop** growth of bacteria, *e.g.* in a deep freeze. But remember **cold does not kill bacteria** — when you thaw frozen food, any bacteria in it will start multiplying again.

Bacteria like dark dirty unhygienic conditions. They hate fresh air and cleanliness. Bacteria can be destroyed by:

Heat (high temperatures) ⎫
Soap and Water ⎬ **Cleanliness**
Disinfectants and Antiseptics ⎭

Food Hygiene

If a kitchen is not kept really clean and if those working with food are careless about personal hygiene, there is a strong possibility of **food poisoning.** Food poisoning is caused when bacteria are present in our food in large numbers. They particularly like moist foods — meat, fish, poultry, gravy, stock, milk and cream. Food can become infected with bacteria:

(a) By human beings who are careless about personal hygiene.
(b) By flies.
(c) By vermin, *e.g.* rats and mice.
(d) By pets.
(e) By dust and dirty utensils.

Hygiene in the Kitchen

1. Keep work surfaces, store cupboards, equipment and utensils clean.
2. Wash equipment, *etc.* with **hot** soapy water; rinse and dry.
3. Pay particular attention to kitchen cloths *(p. 292).*
4. Keep room well ventilated — to remove moisture.
5. Sweep floor after cooking or preparing meals.
6. Wash floor at least once weekly, using disinfectant.
7. Dispose carefully of all kitchen waste. Empty bin daily.
8. Never allow pets in the kitchen.

Hygiene and Food

1. Keep long hair tied back.
2. Do not cough or sneeze over food.
3. Wash hands before handling food.
4. Never lick fingers or handle face or hair when cooking.
5. Cover cuts with a clean plaster. Replace when soiled.
6. Buy perishables in small quantities and use up quickly.
7. Store them in a cool place — ideally the refrigerator.
8. Keep all food covered.
9. Certain foods, such as meat, fish and poultry should be cooked thoroughly to destroy any bacteria.
10. Pay particular attention to reheated food. Cooked food, *e.g.* meat, should be cooled quickly and stored in the refrigerator.

Flies

Flies often cause food poisoning. They land on dirt and pick up bacteria on their hairy legs. They may fly in the kitchen window and land on uncovered food. They deposit saliva on the food in order to soften it, and stamp it in with their dirty feet. Having made the food unsafe to eat, they fly off to deposit more germs elsewhere.

Removing Refuse

Most household refuse contains bacteria and must be disposed of hygienically. If not, it causes unpleasant smells and attracts flies, rats and other vermin.

Methods of Disposing of Waste

1. **Compost heap** — place garden refuse, fruit and vegetable peelings here, to rot down into garden compost.
2. **Wastepaper collection** — save newspapers for charity. They will be recycled to produce more paper.
3. **Bottle collections** — some charities collect bottles for recycling.
4. **Dumps** — in country areas you may have to dispose of your own refuse by emptying it into a pit and covering it with earth. These dumps should be as far as possible from the house, to avoid attracting flies and vermin.
5. **Burning** — if you have a suitable place, burning refuse is a hygienic way of disposing of it.
6. **Bin collections** — in most cities and large towns, a refuse truck collects refuse from householders and bring it to a dump, where it is burnt and then covered over with soil (to reclaim land).

Dustbins

These are made of metal or plastic and should be large enough to cope with weekly refuse. They should have a well-fitting lid.

Choosing a container:

1. *Galvanised metal: e.g.* zinc, is heavy and noisy. It lasts a long time and is heat resistant.
2. *Plastic bins:* are lighter and easier to carry. They are less noisy, but you cannot put hot ashes into them.
3. *Plastic bags:* must be securely tied. Even so they are easily torn by stray animals and often cause litter.

Care of a Dustbin

1. Don't have the bin too near the house, it will attract flies.
2. Keep lid firmly in position, to keep out animals and flies.
3. Line bottom of bin with newspapers, to keep it dry.
4. Wrap rubbish tightly in newspaper or plastic bags, to keep bin clean.
5. Scrub bin inside and outside regularly with hot soapy water. (Keep a lavatory brush specially for this job). Rinse, disinfect and allow to dry completely before putting in rubbish.

Kitchen-bins

These are usually made of plastic and should always have a lid. They may have a swing-top lid or a pedal lid, which can be lifted without the lid itself being touched — this is more hygienic and saves bending.

Care

1. Keep covered at all times.
2. Wrap wet rubbish in newspaper before disposing.
3. Line with plastic or strong paper bags to keep clean.
4. Empty bin daily.
5. Wash in hot soapy water and rinse and disinfect at least once a week.

Over to you . . .

1. Name four ways of destroying bacteria. In the case of each — state how you would use them to keep the following free from germs: (a) kitchen cloths; (b) kitchen floors; (c) handkerchiefs; (d) lavatory.

2. What are the main causes of food poisoning? List the *six* most important rules to remember if you are to avoid food poisoning.

3. Look at the list of ways of disposing of waste. In the case of each, say whether or not you think it is a good method and why.

4. List the points to remember when choosing a distbin. Write a note on the importance of keeping dustbins and kitchen bins clean and hygienic. How would you clean a dust bin and how often should this be done?

40   *All About Keeping Your Home Clean*

Cleaning Materials

The right cleaning equipment makes it much easier to do a job well. Keep all your cleaning equipment in one cupboard. Store everyday items in a small basket or plastic container. When you are cleaning the house, you can carry the basket around with you. This saves constant trips back to the cleaning cupboard.

Cleaning cupboard

Here are some basic pieces of cleaning equipment.

Sweeping Brush	Cleaning cloths
Hand brush	Polishing cloths
Dustpan	Scrubbing brush
Mop	Washing-up
Bucket	brush/mop
Lavatory brush	Carpet sweeper
Dusters	Vacuum cleaner

Cleaning Agents

A cleaning agent is something which removes dirt and stains. There is a wide variety to choose from. Many modern cleaners cut the 'elbow grease' out of cleaning, they are just rubbed on and wiped off. Aerosol cleaners are quick, but they are also more expensive.

Some cleaners are better than others — compare the results and see which work best for you. Compare sizes and prices to get best value for money. Most cleaning agents fall into the following groups:

1. **Water** — the most important cleaning agent of all is water. Steep dirty clothes and utensils in water to make them easier to clean. Cold water softens dirt and stains. Hot water is important for cleaning, as it dissolves grease. Very hot water kills bacteria.

2. **Soap** — a mixture of fat and alkali. It emulsifies (breaks down) grease and floats it away on the water. Soap often leaves a scum, particularly in hard water areas.

3. **Detergents** — strictly speaking a detergent is anything which removes dirt. The usual detergents used in a home are:
   (a) *Liquid detergents, e.g.* washing-up liquid;
   (b) *Clothes washing detergents, e.g. Tide.*
   (c) *Biological powders,* these have enzymes which are especially good for dissolving protein stains.

4. **Abrasives** — these are cleaning agents which remove dirt by friction (rubbing if off):
   (a) *Powered abrasives:* Some abrasives are in the form of powders, *e.g.*

Vim. Many are harsh, and scratch surfaces and equipment. Salt and sand are also abrasives you can use for cleaning.

(b) *Paste and cream abrasives:* These have fine particles of grit in them. They are smoother than powders and less likely to scratch, *e.g. Gumption* (paste); *Jif* (cream).

(c) *Scouring pads:* These are usually metal or plastic pads which scrape away the stains by friction, *e.g.* steelwool. Some have soap in them, *e.g. Brillo.*

5. **Acids** — *e.g.* lemon juice, vinegar, can remove some stains but must be rinsed off well to avoid damaging the material.

6. **Alkalis** — *e.g.* washing soda; many detergents, soaps, *etc.* contain washing soda. Washing soda may also be bought separately. It is very good for removing grease. Caustic cleaners are powerful alkalis used to clean ovens.

7. **Solvents** — *e.g.* white spirit, benzine; mainly used for removing stains *(p. 314).*

8. **Bleaches** — these remove stains from fabrics and ceramic surfaces. They also whiten, and may remove colour from some substances. Strong bleaches, such as chlorine, also act as disinfectants. Most bleaches are diluted before use — always follow directions on bottle.

9. **Polishes** —
(a) Metal polishes, *e.g. Brasso, Silvo* — these clean by friction.
(b) Floor polishes may be wax or liquid.
(c) Furniture polishes.*
(d) Window cleaners.*

*All-purpose polishes, *e.g. Mr. Sheen,* combine the two.

10. **Disinfectants** — the purpose of a disinfectant is to kill bacteria. It does not remove stains. Disinfectants may be used diluted or full strength, for general household hygiene in bathrooms and lavatories, in drains and in gullies. To sterilise brushes, cloths, work surfaces, equipment and floors — put a little disinfectant into the final rinsing water.

Rules for using Cleaning Agents

1. Use the mildest agent first; only use strong cleaners as a last resort. Try soaking things in water — it is amazing how many stains can be removed simply by steeping in cold water.
2. Many cleaning agents are dangerous, *e.g.* bleach. Store them out of reach of children.
3. Use according to directions.
4. Rinse away all traces of cleaning agent.
5. Protect skin and clothes. Many cleaning agents have a drying effect on the skin, others damage both skin and fabric. Use rubber gloves and wear an apron when working with cleaning agents.

Kitchen Cloths

Many different cloths are used to keep a house and kitchen clean. Make sure you have enough cloths for each job and that each cloth is kept for one purpose only. The average kitchen should have:

(a) 6 glass cloths (teatowels) for drying glass, delph, cutlery, *etc;*

(b) 3 dish cloths (or a packet of disposable cloths, *e.g. Jeycloths*). These are used for general cleaning — wiping down worktops and equipment; washing the sink and cooker.

(c) 2 floorcloths or 1 floor mop.

(d) 2 ovengloves.

(e) 2 handtowels.

(f) 1 meat cloth.

Caring for Cloths

Daily

1. Wash cleanest cloths first *e.g.* teatowels; finish with the dirtiest, *e.g.* floor cloth.
2. Steep meat cloth in cold water before washing.
3. Wash cloths in hot soapy water, rubbing well to remove stains. Rinse in hot water, then in cold (containing 1 tablespoon disinfectant).
5. Dry in the fresh air, if possible.
6. When dry, fold and store.

Weekly

1. Steep cloths for at least two hours, in warm water containing biological detergent.
2. Wash cloths in hot soapy water, cleanest ones first.
3. Rinse in warm water.
4. Place cloths in a saucepan of cold water containing 1 tablespoon detergent; bring to the boil and boil for 15 minutes.
5. Rinse in warm water and finally in cold.
6. Wring out, hang on clothes line to dry.
7. Fold and store.

Washing-Up

Few of us like washing up but it is a job which must be done, and done properly if we are to avoid the risk of food poisoning.

When cooking, have a sinkful of hot soapy water at hand, leaving utensils to steep as you finish with them. Wash up as you go along. (At school, however, if you share a sink, this may not be possible). Don't forget to rinse everything in hot/warm water, to remove soap from utensils.

Washing-up after a Meal

1. Tidy away any unused food, *e.g.* butter, pepper, salt and unused delph and cutlery.
2. Collect soiled delph and cutlery, pile onto a tray and bring to the sink. Stack neatly on draining board.
3. Shake and fold cloth or mats and wipe down table.
4. Make sure everything is ready for washing — lots of hot water, washing up liquid, dish mop, *etc.* Wear rubber gloves to protect your hands.
5. Scrape scraps into newspaper; burn or put in bin. Empty teapot. Place leftovers in clean dishes, cover and place in refrigerator.
6. Steep any dishes/utensils which may be difficult to clean — starchy, milky foods in cold water; greasy pans in hot soapy water.
7. Wash cleanest things first, *e.g.* glasses, in *warm* soapy water; rinse and drain.
8. Add hot water and wash in this order: cups, saucers; sideplates; soup and pudding plates; dinner plates; vegetable dishes; saucepans; frying pan/roasting tin. Use abrasives for stubborn stains. Change water if it gets too dirty.

9. Rinse everything, drain and dry. (A draining rack is more hygienic than a teatowel).
10. Wipe over cooker and worktops; wash out sink and draining boards.
11. Wash and rinse cloths, dry off sink, flush with cold water.
12. Sweep floor and wash, if necessary.

General Cleaning

Before doing housework, make sure you are wearing old clothes or an apron. A headscarf will keep long hair back and keep dust out of your hair. Use rubber gloves to protect your hands for 'wet' jobs, old gloves for dirty jobs.

Washing Glass/China/Delph

A. Washing Glassware, *e.g.* drinking glasses.
1. Use a plastic basin and wash each item separately to avoid breakage.
2. Wash in *warm* (not hot) soapy water. Use a bottle brush for vases, and narrow items.
3. Rinse in warm water.
4. Drain, dry and polish with a dry glass cloth.
5. Do not stack glassware — store it upside down.

B. Washing Heat-resistant Glass, *e.g.* Pyrex.
1. Never use a damp cloth to remove hot dishes from oven — the sudden change in temperature can crack the glass.
2. Never place hot dishes on cold surfaces, *e.g.* worktops.
3. Wipe splashes from dishes before putting in oven.
4. Rub stained dishes with salt or other mild abrasive.
5. Wash and dry as above.

C. Washing Vases, to remove stains.
1. Put 1 tablespoon salt, 1 tablespoon vinegar and some tea leaves into vase; fill up with water and leave to steep for a few hours.

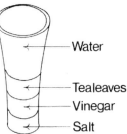

Water
Tealeaves
Vinegar
Salt

2. Shake well, using a bottle brush if necessary. Empty, wash, rinse and dry as above.

D. Washing Windows
1. Roll up blinds. Remove net curtains. Tie back large curtains.
2. Use one of the following:
   (a) warm soapy water and a chamois or window cloth;
   (b) window cleaning fluid and a non-fluff duster; or
   (c) newspapers moistened with paraffin.
3. Clean outside of window first, washing each pane from top down.
4. Polish up at once with newspaper or dry cloth.
5. Repeat on inside of window.

E. Washing Mirrors.
Avoid using too much liquid — it may penetrate the back of the mirror. Clean with window cleaning fluid or methylated spirit.

F. Washing China and Delph.
1. Wash in hot soapy water — cleanest things first.
2. Rinse in hot water.
3. Drain dry, or use a clean teatowel.

Milk Jugs
1. Steep in cold water, then wash as above.
2. Scald inside with boiling water and drain dry (a 'not-so-clean' teatowel will *put* germs on it).

Cleaning Wooden Surfaces

A. Plain wood, *e.g. pastry board:*

N.B. **Do not soak in water; do not use hot water**

1. Scrape scraps of pastry away lightly, with the back of a knife.
2. Wash in warm soapy water, using a brush to scrub (with the grain). Don't forget the sides of the board.

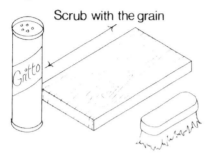

Scrub with the grain

3. Use abrasive powder, *e.g. Vim,* to scrub any stubborn stains.
4. Rinse well with warm water, then cold.
5. Dry with a cloth, wrung out of clean water.
6. Leave upright until dry, preferably in an airy place. Never store while damp — this would cause warping.

B. Painted Wood:
1. Dust.
2. Using a cloth wrung out of water containing detergent, *e.g. Flash,* wash from the top down.
3. Remove any stains with non-scratch cleaner.
4. Rinse well and shine up with a dry cloth.

C. Polished Wood:
1. Dust regularly and rub with a soft cloth.
2. Only if very soiled wipe over with a cloth wrung out of warm water containing a little vinegar.
3. Polish when dry with a little furniture polish. Use it sparingly as too much makes furniture sticky.
4. Rub well in with a duster, polish off with another — use plenty of 'elbow grease'!

Care of Polished Wood:
1. Avoid placing hot objects directly on its surface.
2. Avoid spilling liquids on it, especially perfume.
3. Do not use harsh cleaning agents.
4. Look out for woodworm and have it treated if necessary.

Metal Utensils

Choosing Pots and Pans

1. Heavier pans last longer and give more even heat than thin, lightweight pans.
2. Lids should fit well.
3. Handles should be heat resistant and easy to hold.
4. Pans used for electric cookers should have a heavy base.

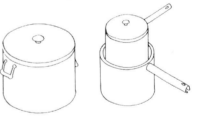

Washing Pots and Pans

1. Drain off grease and wipe with kitchen paper. Steep if necessary.
2. Wash in hot soapy water using an abrasive, *e.g. Brillo,* for stubborn stains. Pay particular attention to corners and inside rim of lids.
3. Rinse in hot water and dry well.
4. Store saucepans, *etc.* without lids, to allow circulation of air.

Note: Many metals will rust, if not dried properly — put them in a warm place, *e.g.* a low oven, to dry them out.

Frying Pan

1. Cool slightly before washing.
2. Drain grease into small bowl. Wipe out with kitchen paper.
3. Soak if necessary, in hot soapy water.
4. Wash in hot soapy water, using a brush. Avoid using abrasives unless absolutely necessary — they roughen the surface and cause sticking.
5. *Never* use abrasives on non-stick pans (see non-stick ware).
6. Avoid washing omellete pans — wipe out after use with kitchen paper and, if necessary, a damp cloth.

Special Points about Metals

Note: Many metals are unsuitable for the dishwater, *e.g.* tin, enamel, iron, non-stick pans.

1. **Aluminium:** used for saucepans, teapots, kettles, frying pans. Never use washing soda or strong alkaline cleaners.

2. **Stainless Steel:** used in draining boards, serving dishes, cutlery. Avoid overheating. Use non-scratch scouring cream to remove stains. Avoid draining dry — dry and polish straight after washing to avoid streaks.

3. **Tin:** used for baking tins, utensils. Use steel wool or *Brillo* to remove stubborn stains. Tin rusts easily — dry thoroughly and place in a warm place to complete drying. Very dirty tins should be steeped in warm water containing washing soda.

4. **Iron:** a very heavy metal used for pots and pans. It rusts easily — complete drying in a warm oven. If storing for some time, rub oil over the surface to prevent rusting.

5. **Enamalled cast iron:** used in casseroles, cooking pots. Most of the iron utensils we use today are made from cast iron. They are coated with an attractive enamel finish or may be lined with a non-stick finish. Never heat enamelled cast iron to high temperatures, especially when the saucepan is empty, as this may cause cracking of enamel. Avoid abrasives and handle carefully — it chips and scratches easily and if dropped, can break.

6. **Enamel:** a strong glassy substance, which can be applied to several metals, *e.g.* tin, steel. It is very easily chipped. It is used as a coating on cookers, saucepans, plates, *etc.* Take great care, when washing, to avoid chipping. Use a fine abrasive for stains — never use washing soda.

7. **Copper/Brass:** brass is a yellow metal, copper is darker. Clean by polishing with a metal polish, *e.g. Brasso.* Shine up with a soft cloth.
   To remove tarnish: rub with salt and lemon juice. A squeezed lemon, dipped in salt, works well. Rinse thoroughly. Dry and polish with a soft cloth.

8. **Lacquered brass:** some brass ornaments have a varnish or lacquer applied to prevent them from tarnishing. Find out when you buy brass whether or not it is lacquered. Never apply polish to lacquered brass — just rub with a soft cloth.

9. **Chromium (chrome):** used on the handles, trimmings of cookers, fridges, *etc.,* on kettles and on ornaments. Wash with soapy water, rinse and polish with a dry cloth. Avoid abrasives. A special chrome polish may be used — avoid other metal polishes.

10. **Silver:** most 'silver' today is simply coated in silver and marked *Electro plated nickel silver (E.P.N.S.).* This varies in quality, according to the thickness of the coating. Avoid harsh abrasives — use a silver cleaner to remove tarnish.

11. **Cutlery:**
    (a) After meals steep cutlery in a jug of soapy water.
    (b) *Knives:* Those with separate handles, *e.g.* bone or wood, should be treated with care. Avoid soaking in water.
    (c) *Forks:* Use a brush to wash well between prongs. Avoid washing forks with knives and spoons, as they may scratch them.
    (d) Wash cutlery in hot soapy water, rinse and dry well.
    (e) *To polish silver cutlery:* Soak in silver-dip cleaner or rub on silver polish. Polish off with a soft cloth. Wash well (to remove traces of polish), rinse, dry and polish. Remove egg stains from silver with salt.

To store silver cutlery: Avoid white tissue — it contains sulphur which tarnishes the silver. Wrap each piece separately in black tissue, or cloth; place in polythene bags and seal well to prevent air tarnishing silver.

12. **Non-stick Ware:** Many frying pans and saucepans are lined with a special slippery plastic *(PTFE)* which prevents food sticking. Non-stick surfaces must be treated with care to avoid scratching.

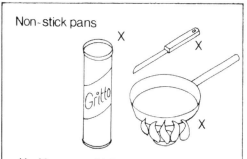

Non-stick pans

X   Never use high temperatures

X   Never use abrasives

X   Never use metal utensils

Care:
1. Before using for the first time — wash, rinse, dry then rub with oil.
2. *Never* use high temperatures — a moderate heat is sufficient.
3. *Never* use abrasive of any type.
4. Avoid stacking saucepans, *etc.* on top of non-stick ware.
5. Never use metal cooking implements — they scratch the surface. Special heat resistant plastic or wooden utensils should be used.
6. Non-stick cooking tins should be well greased before use; use a plastic spatula to loosen cakes.
7. Do not wash in a dishwasher.

Cleaning:
1. Wash each item separately in hot soapy water, using a soft cloth or nylon brush.
2. Rinse and dry thoroughly.
3. If badly discoloured, put one cup of water, a half cup of bleach and 2 tablespoons breadsoda into the pan. Boil for 5-10 minutes. Empty, wash, rinse and dry.

Care of Plastics

Many types of plastic are used in the kitchen — nylon, polythene, polethelyne and melamine. Many are unsuitable for cleaning in a dishwasher.
1. Wash in hot soapy water, rinse in hot water and dry.
2. Do not use abrasives — avoid using strong chemicals, *e.g.* bleach.

A. Laminated plastic, *e.g.* worktops
Cleaning: as above. Badly stained worktops can be cleaned with bread soda. Rinse well and dry.
Care: Never chop on worktops — use a wooden chopping board. Do not use abrasives — they are unneccessary and damage

surfaces. Plastics are damaged by dry heat — never leave hot tins, saucepans *etc.* directly on surface (use a pot stand).

B. Cupboards and Drawers
1. Tidy and clean out regularly — throw away any rubbish.
2. Remove everything — a shelf at a time; wipe jars, *etc.*
3. Wipe out inside with a cloth wrung out of hot soapy water; rinse and dry.
4. Wipe over outside — pay particular attention to handle.
5. Leave to air, then replace contents.

C. Teapot
Empty into sink basket and rinse out.
China/Delph: Wash in hot soapy water, using a brush, rinse and dry.
Chromium/Stainless Steel: as above — polish up with a dry cloth.

To remove tanin: Put 1-2 tablespoons vinegar in teapot. Fill up with boiling water. Leave to soak for a few hours, rinse a few times, wash, rinse and dry.

D. Bread Bin
1. Wipe out crumbs every day with a dry cloth.
2. Each week, wash well with a cloth wrung out of hot soapy water.
3. Rinse and dry well. Leave open for a while to air before returning bread.

E. Wooden Bowl
1. Avoid washing.
2. Wipe with a clean cloth (or kitchen paper). Rub a little oil into the wood now and then.

F. Sieve
1. Scrape out any food.
2. Wash well in warm soapy water, using a brush. Be particular about corners and edges.
3. Rinse by pouring warm water through sieve.
4. Dry thoroughly and leave to air before storing.

G. Mincer (or any gadgets which have to be assembled)

1. Unscrew or separate all loose parts.
2. Scrape off scraps.
3. Wash in hot soapy water using a brush.
4. Rinse in hot water. Dry thoroughly.
5. Store, when completely dry, in a box, *without* assembling.

H. Liquidiser
1. Empty all waste.
2. Half fill with warm water, replace on machine and switch on to clean.
3. Unplug and lift off goblet. Do not place base containing the motor in water.
4. Wash in warm soapy water using a small brush to clean underneath knives. Rinse well and dry.
5. Leave lid off for a while to allow it to dry out, then replace.

Brushes

Caring for Brushes
1. Remove any dust or fluff, by combing through brush head.
2. Wash in warm soapy water, washing handle and backing first, then swish bristles up and down until clean.

3. Rinse in warm water, then cold, containing disinfectant.
4. Shake well, out of doors, then hand up to dry.

Special Points about Brushes

1. Avoid leaving in water for any length of time — this softens the glue holding the bristles in place and rots wood and bristle.
2. Never rest brushes on their back when wet — water will run into bristle base and soften glue.
3. Avoid standing brushes on bristles — then will be damaged. Hang up when drying and storing.
4. *Lavatory brush* — store in special stand and disinfect regularly.

Mops

Mops consist of cotton threads, forming a 'head', which is securely fixed onto a broom handle. They can be used dry, for dusting and polishing floors, or wet, for washing floors. (These may have a specially designed bucket for squeezing out the water.)

Traditional floor mop
Use wet or dry

Dry Mops

1. Shake well after use.
2. Wash occasionally (see below).

Wet Mops:

1. Shake well. Wash in hot soapy water.
2. Rinse in several changes of warm water and give a final cold rinse.

3. Squeze well and hang to dry.
4. Never leave a damp mop hanging about for long periods. This encourages bacteria to grow in it.

Spong Floor Mops (Squeegee)

These have a replaceable flat sponge head which is fixed onto a hinged holder which can squeeze out water very effectively.

Squeegee mop with lever
to squeeze out water

1. Never try to squeeze mop when dry.
2. Wash after use in hot soapy water.
3. Rinse in several changes of warm water, with disinfectant in final rinse.
4. Squeeze well and hang dry.
5. When storing, place head upright or hang up.

Cleaning Routines

In a home there are some jobs which must be done every day and others, *e.g.* cleaning windows, walls, floors, washing curtains, which are done less often. You will get through all housework more quickly and efficiently if you **organise** your work in a logical way. There is no point, for example, in dusting a room before sweeping the floor — the sweeping raises dust which falls straight back on the clean furniture. **Disorganised work makes more work for you.**

General Rules for Cleaning

1. Protect yourself and your clothes — wear a headscarf to keep long hair safely back and keep dust out of your hair. Wear old clothes or an apron.
2. Use rubber gloves, or old gloves, for dirty jobs.
3. Protect surroundings, *e.g.* spread newspapers around the fire when cleaning it, or on the table when cleaning shoes, brass, silver, *etc.*
4. Do dirtiest jobs first, *e.g.* clean fire before dusting.
5. You generally clean from the top down, *e.g.* when cleaning a wall, a cooker or cupboard. This prevents dirty dribbles falling on freshly cleaned surfaces.
7. When cleaning a room, work in this order:
   Tidy
   Sweep/Vacuum
   Dust
   Wash
   Polish
6. Where possible, make use of modern labour saving cleaners and equipment, *e.g.* vacuum cleaners, washing machines, self-cleaning ovens. These save time and energy.

Cleaning a Kitchen

Daily

1. put away all food. Wipe out refrigerator if necessary.
2. Wash up dishes, saucepans, *etc.* Put away all utensils.
3. Empty waste bin, wipe out and re-line.
4. Wipe over all work surfaces and table.
5. Wipe over cooker — clean grill and over, if used.
6. Wash out sink, taps and draining board. Flush drain with cold water.
7. Sweep/mop over floor if necessary.

Weekly

1. Open windows to air room.
2. Tidy away food and utensils. Empty, wash and disinfect wastebin.
3. Clean cooker thoroughly, using *Brillo* for stubborn stains. Clean hob, grill and oven if necessary.
4. Defrost and wash out refrigerator.
5. Tidy and wipe out food cupboards. Clean other cupboards when necessary.
6. Wash over work surfaces, paintword and cupboard doors.
7. Clean windows and light fittings.
8. Sweep floor. Wash thoroughly, using disinfectant.

Cleaning a Living Room

Daily

1. Open window to air room.
2. Clean out fire (if there is one) and reset.
3. Empty waste basket, ashtrays, *etc.* Remove dead flowers and water flowers/plants.
4. Tidy room — collect newspapers, books, toys, *etc.* and tidy them away.
5. Sweep or vacuum floor — according to type.
6. Dust over furniture and shelves and painted surfaces.
7. Straighten cushions.

Weekly

1-7 As above.
8. Clean light fittings, polish furniture, mirrors, *etc.*
9. Clean windows if necessary.
10. Wash paintwork, *e.g.* doors, skirting boards, window sills.

Cleaning a Bedroom

Daily

1. When you get up, open windows to air room and turn back bedclothes.
2. Tidy up — hang up clothes, put away books, toys, *etc.*
3. Collect soiled clothes for the wash.
4. Make beds (each member of the family should make his/her own bed).
5. Dust or vacuum floor.
6. Dust surfaces and wipe over hand-basin, if there is one.

Weekly

1-6 As above.
7. Clean windows if necessary.
8. Wash paintwork; give handbasin and surrounds a thorough cleaning.
9. Polish furniture, mirrors,*etc.*
10. Change bed-linen once a week.

To Make a Bed

1. Pull down bedclothes over a chair to air for a short while.
2. Pull bed away from wall, if necessary.
3. Straighten underblanket and spread bottom sheet smoothly over top — wide hem to top of bed.
4. Lay top sheet right side down, smooth and tuck in ends and sides of both sheets, using mitred corners.
5. Lay blankets smoothly on top, one by one. Tuck in neatly all around, using mitred corners.
6. Fold top of blankets and topsheet down, leaving room for pillows.
7. Plump up pillows and replace — fold nightwear and replace.
8. Cover with bedspread.

Note: Fitted sheets and continental quilts (duvets) make bed-making easier.

Making a bed - mitred corner

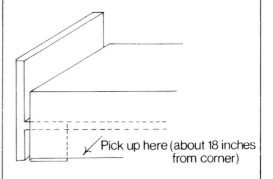

Pick up here (about 18 inches from corner)

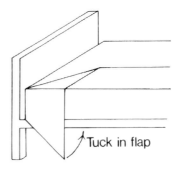

Tuck in flap

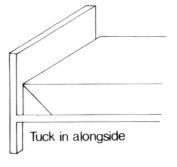

Tuck in alongside

Cleaning a Bathroom

Daily

1. Open windows to air room.
2. Tidy soap, flannels, *etc.* Rinse out tooth mug. Straighten towels.
3. Wipe over bath and wash handbasin.
4. Wipe over lavatory seat, brush lavatory bowl and rinse.
5. Dust paintwork and mop floor.
6. Check soap, lavatory paper, toothpaste and replace if necessary.

Weekly

1-2 As above.
3. Wash out handbasin, bath and tiled surrounds — using a non-scratch cream for any marks on bath. (Everyone should wipe out the bath straight after use).
4. Rinse, then polish up tiles and taps with a soft cloth.
5. Brush lavatory pan with lavatory brush — pay particular attention to under rim. Flush and apply lavatory cleaner, *e.g. Harpic,* or bleach, *e.g. Domestos.*

 N.B. Never use both together — they produce dangerous fumes.

6. Wash lavatory with hot soapy water, starting at the cistern and working down — don't forget the *outside* of the lavatory bowl. Pay particular attention to the lavatory seat and cover. Rinse, using disinfectant, and polish up cover if necessary. (Keep a cloth specially for cleaning the lavatory.)
7. Wash over paintwork, shelves, *etc.* with a damp cloth, wrung out of hot soapy water. Rinse and dry.
8. Sweep and wash, or vacuum, floor, according to type (use disinfectant in rinsing water).
9. Shake mats outside and replace.

> *Note:* Bathroom sets, *i.e.* bathmat and toilet mat, should be washed regularly and disinfected.
> Cistern and lavatory seat covers are unnecessary and unhygienic.

Over to you . . .

1. Make a list of basic cleaning equipment which you consider essential in a home. Find out the cost of as many items as possible.

2. List the basic cleaning agents you use at home and find out the current cost of each.

3. Describe briefly how you would clean the following:
   (a) a teapot stained with tannin;
   (b) a stained non-stick pan;
   (c) a liquidiser.

41 *All About Floor Coverings*

Covering floors can be the most expensive part of furnishing a home. Study different types of floor coverings before choosing and shop around for good quality and value.

Floor coverings have to put up with heavy wear — they should be

> Hard wearing
> Long lasting
> Stain resistant
> Easy to clean
> Non-slip (especially in kitchen
>   and bathroom)
> Attractive
> Comfortable

The choice of floor covering depends on the room in question and what it is used for. You might put:

A carpet — in the living room, hall and stairs, bedrooms.

Why? — it is warm, comfortable, quiet and hardwaring.

Vinyl tiles — in a kitchen, bathroom or dining room.

Why? — they are easy to clean, water resistant and cheap.

Carpets

How They are Made

Some carpets are **woven** into a backing and the pile (threads of wool/fibre) is cut. Axminster and Wilton weaves are of this type. Pile can be long (shaggy pile) or short.

Others have tufts or wool fibre stuck into a foam or plastic backing, these are called **tufted** carpets.

Carpet Fibres

1. **Wool** — is warm, hardwearing, doesn't soil or flatten easily but is expensive.
2. **Nylon** — hardwaring and easy to clean but produces static electricity which attracts dirt. Fairly cheap.
3. **Acrylic** — same as nylon; water resistant (good for bathrooms).
4. **Rayon** — cheap, soils easily, does not wear well.
5. **Hair/jute** — very hard wearing but not easy to clean; rough on the feet and quite slippy.
6. **Mixtures** — some carpets are a blend of 2 fibres, *e.g.* 80% wool/20% nylon. These combine the wearing qualities of wool, with the washability of nylon (adding nylon also makes them slightly cheaper).

Buying Carpets

1. Buy the best quality you can afford, especially for heavy-wear areas, *e.g.* hall, stairs, living room. Cheap carpets are bad value for money except for light wear areas, *e.g.* bedrooms.
2. Choose a carpet to suit your room. Remember dark colours and plain carpets show up dust and fluff; pale carpets, on the other hand, soil easily and are hard to keep clean. Patterned designs are most practical as they do not show up dirt and stains.
3. A carpet may be fitted up to the walls of a room, or you can buy a carpet 'square' — a large square or oblong carpet which will leave borders, alcoves, *e.g.* without carpet. Fitted carpets make a room look bigger and are easy to keep but they cannot be turned to give even wear. Carpet

squares and carpet tiles can be moved around to give even wear and are easy to take with you if you move house.

4. *Underlays:* An underlay makes a carpet more comfortable and helps it to wear better. Underlays are made from (i) felt; (ii) foam; (iii) a mixture of felt and foam. Some carpets have a built-in foam underlay and such carpets do not need a separate underlay.

Vinyls

Vinyl is a hardwearing plastic floor covering, suitable for kitchens, bathrooms, dining rooms and halls. If used in bedrooms or living rooms, lay some rugs on the floor to provide warmth.

Buying Vinyl

Vinyl can be bought in tile form (30 cm square) or by the metre (2, 3 or 4 metres wide). **Cushioned** vinyl has a foam backing, which makes it more comfortable, especially if you have to stand on it for long periods, *e.g.* in a kitchen. Vinyl comes in lots of patterns and colours.

Advantages

1. It is hardwearing and easy to clean.
2. It resists water and most kitchen stains.
3. It is cheap.
4. It is hygienic — for kitchens and bathrooms.
5. It is easy to put down.
6. It is quite comfortable, especially cushioned vinyl.

Care and Cleaning

1. Follow manufacturers instructions and use recommended cleaners.
2. Sweep and wash regularly to remove grit.
3. Wash with warm water, containing suitable detergent, *e.g. Flash.*
4 Never use abrasives.
5. Never use wax polishes — these soften the surface.
6. Avoid wearing pointed heels — these damage the surface.
7. If self-shine polishes, *e.g. Seel,* are used, remove build-up every six months with recommended solvent.

Vacuum Cleaner

Choose between
1. An upright model — best for lots of flat carpeting.
2. A cylinder model — ideal if you have lots of stairs.
3. A canister, *e.g. Nilfisk* — good on both carpet and polished floors.
Most come with several attachments.

Care

1. Never let dust bag get overfull; empty or replace regularly. Empty over newspaper, wrap up well and put in the bin.
2. Take care to avoid picking up pins and other metal objects as these break the fan belt and damage the machine.
3. Wipe over outside occasionally with a damp cloth and comb threads from brushes.
4. Have machine serviced regularly to keep it in good working order.

Carpet Sweepers

These are handy for quick carpet sweeping jobs.
1. Empty dustbox regularly.
2. Comb through brushes, to remove fluff and threads.
3. Wash brushes occasionally — dry thoroughly with old rags.
4. Wipe outside occasionally with a damp cloth.

42   *All About Caring For Our Clothes*

Washday is no longer a day of drudgery. Modern detergents remove dirt and stains easily and washing machines and launderettes take the hard work out of washing. The family wash can be done:

1. At the laundry
2. At the launderette.
3. By hand
4. By machine.

1. The Laundry

Advantages

1. Washing collected and delivered.
2. No work involved.
3. Very good for finishing table linen, etc.

Disadvantages

1. Very expensive.
2. Constant laundering wears out clothes and linen.
3. Items are often lost.

Conclusion

Few can afford the luxury of sending all their washing to the laundery. A working wife might find it useful, however, for large items, such as sheets and towels, especially in winter, when drying is difficult. You may need to have more linen and clothes as they will be at the laundery for about a week. Don't foregt to send a list — items can then be checked on return.

2. The Launderette

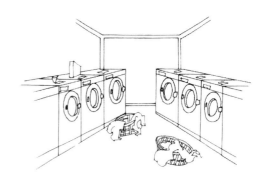

Advantages

1. No need to buy a washing machine or drier.
2. They usually work out cheaper than buying and running your own machines.
3. Clothes can be left damp or dried completely.
4. Assistant may see to your laundry (service wash) — this saves you waiting at the launderette.
5. Handy in emergencies, when washing machine has broken down.
6. Useful for large items, *e.g.* blankets, which would not fit in standard washing machines or driers.

Disadvantages

1. May be difficult to carry large bundles of washing to and from the launderette.
2. Waste of time waiting for clothes to be washed and dried.
3. Machines take large loads — so you may have to mix fabrics and colours to save expense. The results will not be good if you do this.

Conclusion

Very useful if you have not got a washing machine, although results are not usually as good. It is not as handy as popping the washing into a machine in your own kitchen. But, for some, the weekly visit to the launderette is an opportunity to meet and make friends and have a chat while watching the washing go round.

3. Washing by Hand

Advantages

1. Good for delicate fabrics which may be harmed by machine washing.
2. Good for colours which are not fast, *i.e.* the dye runs out of them.
2. Handy for small amounts of washing — more economical than turning on the machine for just a few items.

Disadvantages

1. Very tiring if you have to do a large family wash.
2. Harsh on hands — use rubber gloves.
3. Takes up more of your time than other methods.
4. Hard to get clothes (especially whites) as clean as when washing by machine, as a machine can wash at much higher temperatures.

Conclusion

It is very tiring to do a large wash by hand. It might be better (but more expensive) to wash a few items each day. Make hand washing easier by steeping clothes the night before. Hand washing is ideal for fabrics, *e.g.* woollens, which are not suitable for machine washing. A spin drier can be used to remove excess moisture.

4. Washing by Machine

Advantages

1. Automatic machines take all the work out of washing.
2. Large amounts (up to 6 kg) can be washed together.
3. Clothes are washed more thoroughly as higher temperatures and stronger detergents are used.
4. Washing machines have programmes to suit most fabrics, and most include spin drying.

Disadvantages

1. Machines are expensive to buy and service.
2. They are costly to run — cost of water heating, detergents, *etc.*
3. Failure to sort washing can result in a whole wash being discoloured by one item.

Conclusion

If you can afford one, a washing machine is a good investment. You will be less tired, with more free time. An automatic machine will wash, rinse and spin dry clothes — some even tumble clothes bone dry.

Types of Machine

(a) Single tub, with wringer.
(b) Twin tub — washing machine with separate spin-drier.
(c) Automatics.

Advantages of Twin-tub

1. Quicker than automatics.
2. You can wash several loads in one lot of hot water, starting with whites and cleanest clothes and finishing with dirtiest, *e.g.* dusters. This is very economical.
3. Spinning action is better than automatics.

Disadvantages

1. You have to be there to spin and rinse clothes.

Advantages of Automatics

1. They take the work out of washing, giving greater freedom since, once you set the programme and switch it on, the machine goes through the whole cycle automatically.
2. Water temperature, length of wash and length of spinning can be controlled according to the type of fabric washed. Most modern automatics have programmes to suit the 9 main wash-care labels, *p. 307.*

Buying a Washing Machine

1. Decide whether you want a single tub, twin tub or automatic machine — the automatic is handiest but costs more to buy and repair.
2. Check the wash load, *i.e.* how much dry washing the machine holds (usually between 3 and 6 kg). You will need the larger machine if you have a big family. Some automatics have an economical wash for small loads.
3. Most washing machines have heaters. Has it a hot and cold water fill? (A hot fill will take water from your immersion or other water heating system — this saves fuel but might use up all the bath water!)
4. Do you attach it to the taps at the sink? If so you will probably have to push it out and back every time — and it will prevent you using the sink while it is on. It is more efficient to plumb it in.
5. Is it safe — with an electrically safe guarantee?
6. Is there a good after sales service?
7. If automatic — does it have programmes to suit the types of wash you do?
8. How long are the programmes? — some take up to four hours.
9. Is it noisy? — some washing machines are too noisy because they are not level (adjust the leg on the base of the machine to steady it).

Automatics can be (a) front loading, (b) top loading.

Front loading — clothes are tumbled around in the water.

1. Can be fitted under a worktop (unless the soap dispenser is on the top of the machine).
2. Tumbling action more gentle — more suitable for delicate fabrics.
3. Low-lather detergents must be used.
4. Once it has started, it is usually not possible to open the door.

Top loading

1. Cannot be fitted under a worktop, unless it is on wheels and can be pulled out for use.
2. Clothes can be added and taken out during a wash.
3. You can use ordinary detergents which are cheaper.

Using an Automatic Machine

1. Follow instruction book exactly — especially rules about weight of load, amount of detergent, washing temperature and length of wash and spin.
2. Sort washing into groups, corresponding with washing programmes in machine, *e.g.* whites; cotton; easy-care, *etc.*
3. Put washing into machine — taking care not to add more than recommended weight.
4. Add prewash powder (if using), detergent and fabric conditioners, into appropriate compartments of soap dispenser.
5. Set programme dial to suitable wash programme and turn on — it will proceed without any further assistance.
6. If there is a rinse and hold setting, to prevent creasing you will have to turn the dial to drain and spin clothes.
7. Most machines have a safety lock which cannot be opened for a few minutes after the machine stops.

Wash Care Labels

In the past few years, so many new fabrics and finishes have come on the market that it would be difficult to know how to wash each one. For this reason, most clothes now have sewn-in labels, with instructions for washing and drying them. Some have symbols which indicate how to launder them, others have written instructions as well. Follow the instructions exactly — a carelessly washed garment may be damaged beyond repair.

The H.L.C.C. Code

This divides washing processes into 9 or 10 groups. These are numbered 1 – 9, with a separate label for handwashing. These labels are also printed on detergent packets and washing machine programmes are numbered to correspond with them. Check the label on each garment before washing.

White cotton and linen:

	MACHINE	HAND WASH
1 / 95	Very hot to boil	Hand-hot or boil
	Maximum wash	
	Spin or wring	

Colour-fast cotton, linen, and rayon:

	MACHINE	HAND WASH
2 / 60	Hot	Hand-hot
	Maximum wash	
	Spin or wring	

White nylon, polyester/cotton:

	MACHINE	HAND WASH
3 / 60	Hot	Hand-hot
	Medium wash	
	Cold rinse. Short spin or drip-dry	

Most synthetics and special finishes:

	MACHINE	HAND WASH
4 / 50	Hand-hot	Hand-hot
	Medium wash	
	Cold rinse. Short spin or drip-dry	

Cotton, linen, rayon – less colour-fast:

	MACHINE	HAND WASH
5 / 40	Warm	Warm
	Medium wash	
	Spin or wring	

Acrylics and wool mixtures:

	MACHINE	HAND WASH
6 / 40	Warm	Warm
	Minimum wash	
	Cold rinse. Short spin. Do not wring	

Wool, silk:

	MACHINE	HAND WASH
7 / 40	Warm	Warm
	Minimum wash	Do not rub
	Spin. Do not hand wring	

Non-colour-fast silk, acetate:

	MACHINE	HAND WASH
8 / 30	Cool	Cool
	Minimum wash	
	Cold rinse. Short spin. Do not wring	

Drip-dry cottons, which may be boiled:

	MACHINE	HAND WASH
9 / 95	Very hot to boil	Hand-hot or boil
	Maximum wash	
	Drip-dry	

Non-machine washables:

	HAND-WASH
	See garment label

Labels show

(a) Washing temperatures:
   100°C: boiling — cotton and linen only.
   95°C: very hot — near boiling.
   60°C: hotter than hands can bear.
   50°C: barely hand hot.
   40°C:warm.
   30°C: cool.

(b) Length of wash — this depends on how strong the fabric is:— long (maximum); medium or short (minimum). Some garments must not be washed. They will carry this label.

(c) Rinsing instructions *e.g.* cold rinse.

(d) Drying instructions:- spin, wring, drip dry or tumble dry. Some labels show these symbols:

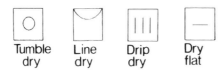

| Tumble dry | Line dry | Drip dry | Dry flat |

(e) Whether you can use chlorine bleach, *e.g. Parazone.*

Chlorine bleach may be used

Do not bleach

(f) Ironing instructions:-

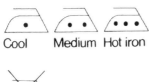

Cool   Medium Hot iron

Do not iron

(g) Dry cleaning instructions:–

May be dry cleaned   Do not
(letters are to help the dry cleaner)   dry clean

The letter in the circle tells the dry cleaner which cleaning solvent to use.

Preparing Clothes for Washing or Dry Cleaning

1. Empty pockets and shake well.
2. Mend tears, darn holes (they might get bigger in the wash).
3. Close zips, buttons, *etc.* and loosly tie apron strings, tapes, *etc.,* to prevent tangling.
4. Remove any belts, trimmings, *etc.* which might be damaged by washing.
5. Examine for stains and remove if necessary, *p. 315/6.*
6. Sort clothes for washing into groups, according to the wash care labels. Take care to separate non-fast items and delicates, for handwashing.

Washing Requirements

1. Water

Water is necessary when washing, to remove dirt from clothes. Hard water (*p. 261*) wastes detergent and soap. It can be softened by adding washing soda before washing.

Rinsing: Plenty of clean water is necessary to rinse the dirt and soap away. If clothes are not rinsed properly they can be damaged and discoloured.

Steeping: Many stains on fabrics can be removed, or at least softened, by steeping the fabric for a few hours before washing. When you steep clothes in detergent, particularly biological detergent, a gentle wash is usually sufficient to get them clean.

2. Detergents

A detergent is a substance which cleans — soap and water are detergents, as well as the washing powders which we generally call detergents.

> *Note:* All washing powders should be dissolved completely before adding the fabric. Undissolved powder will not work as well and may damage the fabric.

(a) **Soap and soap powders:** These are made from fats and alkalis. They remove dirt but tend to form a scum, particularly in hard water areas. Soap powders are gentle on fabrics, as they do not contain harsh bleaches, like other detergents. They are not suitable for automatic machines. Soap flakes and liquid are ideal for delicate fabrics.

(b) **Synthetic detergents,** *e.g. Surf, Daz:* These are made from chemicals. They clean clothes well but are a bit harsh on some fabrics (particularly if not fully dissolved) and on the hands. They do not form a scum, even in hard water areas. They are not suitable for automatic machines, as they create too much lather.

(c) **Low lather detergents** *e.g. Bold, Persil automatic:* These are specially made for front loading automatic machines. They wash well without producing too much lather.

(d) **Enzyme powders:** These are synthetic detergents, with enzymes (chemicals) added, which break down protein stains, *e.g.* blood, egg, which are usually difficult to remove. Stained articles should be soaked or prewashed in warm water containing enzyme powder (very hot water destroys the enzymes). They are then washed in hot water in the usual way.

> *Note:* Some fabric finishes, *e.g.* flame resistant fabrics, should not be steeped in biological detergent.

3. Bleach

This helps keep white cottons and linens white. It also removes stains and sterilises clothes. It is not so important nowadays, as hot machine washing in synthetic detergents keeps clothes sufficiently white:

(a) Avoid using household (chlorine) bleach unneccessarily — it is very strong.
(b) Never use it undiluted on fabrics.
(c) Never use on:
   (i) coloured fabrics — they fade;
   (ii) synthetic or drip dry fabrics — they go yellow;
   (iii) wool or silk.
(d) Rinse, very thoroughly, at least 2 or 3 times after use.
(e) Dilute according to directions. Too strong a solution, or too frequent use, will yellow and rot fabric.
(f) Wear rubber gloves when using bleach — otherwise rinse the skin well after use.
(g) Never use domestic bleach for babies napkins — it is too harsh. Use a gentle bleach specially formulated for nappies, *e.g. Napisan.*

4. Fabric conditioners

These, *e.g. Comfort, Lenor,* soften fabrics which may have been hardened by frequent washing *e.g.* towels. They also help reduce static electricity, which makes nylon and synthetic garments, *e.g.* slips, cling to the skin. They are added to the final rinsing water. First make sure that all traces of detergent have been removed or otherwise conditioner will not work.

5. Starch

This gives a crisp finish to cottons and linens. It also helps keep them clean for longer. You can buy starch (a) powdered (b) liquid (c) spray. Follow directions exactly:

(a) Starch is usually dissolved in hot water,

then diluted with cold water, according to stiffness required.

(b) Dilute with water, then add wet clothes; wring well and dry. Damp down starched items before ironing.

(c) Spray starches are sprayed directly onto fabrics, then ironed at once. These are very useful for collars, cuffs and other small areas which need stiffening. Hold can upright and lift garment when spraying.

6. Disinfectants

These are used to kill bacteria in clothes and bed linen, *e.g.* during illness. They have no cleaning or stain-removing affect. As most washing programmes are hot enough to kill bacteria, they are not really necessary.

Make up solution to correct strength, according to directions, using hot or cold water. Leave clothes soaking for at least 15 minutes to sterilise.

Doing the Family Wash

1. Empty pockets, mend or darn holes, sew on loose buttons.
2. Check stains — steep first in cold water, then in warm water containing enzyme powder. If this does not work, use a stain remover, *p. 314/5/6.*
3. Sort washing into groups, according to wash care labels. Separate any garments which might run and keep delicates for handwashing.
4. Machine wash:
   (a) Wait until you have a full load of a particular type — it is extravagant to wash a few items unless there is an economy half-load programme on the machine.
   (b) Put in washing and detergent (take care not to overload).
   (c) Set dial to correct wash programme. If you have to wash a mixture

of fabrics, *e.g.* white cottons and synthetics, use the cooler programme. It is safer to have the temperature too cool than too hot.

5. Twin tub wash:
   (a) Fill and bring to high temperature; wash white cottons and linens.
   (b) Rinse and spin these while washing synthetic whites in a cooler wash.
   (c) Rinse and spin these while washing coloureds. Continue washing in this way until all clothes are washed (turn the temperature down a little with each wash).
   (d) After final rinse, drain machine, wipe inside and out and return to its place.

6. Hand washing:
   (a) Sort washing into groups — according to wash care labels.
   (b) Dissolve detergent thoroughly in hot water. Add sufficient cold water to make it hand hot.
   (c) Start with white cotton/linen: then fast, pale coloured cotton/linen/rayon; then white nylon/polyester/cotton mixtures; then coloured synthetics; then darker coloureds.
   (d) Change water and, using cooler soapy water, wash acrylics and wool mixtures; then wool and silk; then non-fast silks and synthetics; then delicate fabrics requiring special treatment.
   (e) Clothes should be squeezed gently in the water.
   (f) Rub stains gently — pay particular attention to collars, cuffs, hems and areas likely to be more soiled.
   (g) Wring out — or squeeze synthetics, except drip-drys.
   (h) Rinse well in warm water, and then in cold. Squeeze or wring.
   (i) Hang to dry. To drip-dry clothes:— shake off excess water and then hang on plastic coated hangers to drip-dry.

Special points

1. *Synthetics:* Never allow to become too soiled. Wash often, using fabric conditioner in final rinse to reduce static electricity.
2. *Underwear:* Should be washed frequently, as it is worn against the skin. Many items of underwear contain elastic which is damaged by too much heat. Wash in cooler machine wash or hand hot water. Rinse in warm water, then cold.
3. *Sportswear:* Soak in a mild solution of vinegar to remove perspiration.
4. *Muddy clothes:* Allow to dry, then brush off as much dirt as possible. Wash in very hot soapy water, according to fabric type.

Woollens

'Woolmark'

1. Use gentle soap powder. Dissolve it thoroughly in hot water before adding cold to bring it to luke warm temperature. Too high temperatures causes wool to shrink and felt.
2. Wash by squeezing gently in soapy water — avoid rubbing, this causes it to matt and pill (form into little fluffy beads).
3. Rinse 3 or 4 times in luke warm water. Squeeze excess water out each time. *N.B.* handle with care when wet.
4. Arrange garment on a towel, pull carefully into shape. Roll up, to remove extra moisture.
5. Dry flat — away from direct heat. Press with a cool iron.

PURE VIRGIN WOOL

Superwash Wool
Machine Washable
Machine Dryable

Note: Only 'super wash' wool or woollens labelled machine washable may be washed in a machine.

To Test Fabrics for Colour Fastness

Wash an inconspicuous part of the garment in the usual way. Rinse and iron while damp between two pieces of white fabric. If any colour comes out, wash separately in warm — not hot — water. Rinse in warm water and then in cold water containing a little vinegar.

Drying

Excess water can be removed from rinsed clothes by:
   (i) wringing by hand or machine
   (ii) rolling in a towel
   (iii) spin drying
   (iv) drip drying.

Spin dryers extract most of the water from clothes. They may be part of a twin tub or a separate piece of equipment. Automatic machines also spin dry clothes.

Clothes may be completely dried by:
1. *Hanging outside on a clothes line.* This keeps clothes soft and smelling fresh. It costs nothing and prevents condensation (dampness) in the house.

Sunlight helps keep white clothes white. Dry woollens away from direct sunlight.

2. *Indoor pulley or clothes horse* in a warm kitchen. Rails are also available which clip over radiators. These are handy during wet weather but cause condensation. Make sure the room is well ventilated.

3. *Tumble dryer:-* this tumbles clothes in a current of warm air. Moisture is removed through a duct to the open air. Length of drying time can be controlled — clothes may be damp dried or completely dried.

   (a) Always remove as much moisture as possible before tumble drying, *i.e.* use the spin dryer.

   (b) Never overload the machine — this results in uneven drying.

   (c) Never tumble-dry light and dark colours together — each gives off fluff which soils the other.

   (d) Avoid tumbling woollens (unless care label directs it).

Advantages

1. Clothes, *e.g.* towels, nappies stay soft and fluffy.
2. Clothes have fewer wrinkles, may need no further ironing.

Disadvantages

1. Expensive to run.

Ironing

Modern irons are either (a) dry irons or (b) steam irons. Both have controls which can be set at different temperatures, to suit various fabrics, and a thermostat which keeps them at the set temperatures. Dry irons are efficient and cheaper. Steam irons can be used dry, or with steam, for pressing and ironing dry garments.

Care of Irons

1. Stand iron on its heel when not ironing.
2. Use correct temperature for fabric being ironed — too high temperatures will melt most synthetics, scorch woollens and damage iron.

Don't forget!

Cool   Medium   Hot iron

3. Never wind flex around hot iron.
4. Fill steam iron before switching on — then turn switch to steam setting.
5. Use distilled water only in the steam iron (unless instructions say otherwise), as vents will become clogged with mineral deposits.
6. Unplug after use and empty out water.

Ironing surfaces:

The surface on which you iron should be smooth and clean.

Ironing boards: good for ironing clothes, skirts, *etc.* It is shaped so that garments can be slipped easily over it. Height can be adjusted and you can sit down to iron if you wish. It can be put away after use.

Ironing tables: a table, well covered with blankets and a clean cloth, is more suitable for large items such as sheets, towels, curtains or garments *e.g.* trousers which need heavy pressing.

Sleeveboard: like a small ironing board, this is a handy aid for dressmaking and pressing small items, such as sleeves.

General Rules for Ironing

1. Use a medium weight dry or steam iron and make sure it is clean.
2. Most garments iron best when very slightly damp. Completely dry fabrics should be damped down with water, rolled in a towel and left for 30 minutes before ironing.
3. Always use iron at correct temperature for fabric (check care-label). If in doubt, begin with a cool iron.
4. Sort ironing into fabrics which require cool, medium and hot temperatures.
5. Switch on iron and allow a few minutes for it to heat. Begin with fabrics requiring a cool iron, then increase heat for those in the medium range. Finish with garments which need a hot iron, *i.e.* cottons and linens. Test doubtful fabrics on an inconspicuous part first.
6. Most garments are best ironed on the reverse side, unless a shiny finish is wanted *e.g.* starched articles.
   Ironing on the reverse side:
   (a) Prevents shining — especially on dark fabrics.
   (b) Prevents flattening pile of corduroy, *etc.*
   (c) Prevents marking and soiling raised seams.
   (d) Prevents melting iron-cn transfers, plastics, *etc.*
   (e) Shows off quilting, embroidery, crochet and lace to advantage — these finishes should be ironed on reverse side over a folded flannel pad or towel.
7. Iron double parts first, on the wrong side, *e.g.* hems, seams.
8. Iron all garments until completely dry — touch up on the right side when necessary.
9. Take care to avoid creasing by arranging ironing carefully, squaring up corners. Iron with smooth movements.
10. Pleats, gathers and trouser creases need special care to get a well pressed finish.
11. Garments such as shirts should be ironed in the following order: yolk; one side of front; back; other side of front; collar; sleeves and cuffs.
12. Allow to air, then fold as follows: fasten buttons; put garment facing downwards; fold each side of back towards centre; fold sleeves; then fold from the bottom in 2 or 3 folds.
13. Place folded ironing in the hot-press to air.
14. Do not waste time ironing items which don't need ironing, *i.e.* towels, nappies, underwear, socks, candlewick and drip dry fabrics. Give them a good shake, fold neatly and put in hot press to air. Never iron plastic type fabrics.
15. Ironing temperatures:

cool	*acrylics* *rayon* *nylon* *polyester*
mediun	*polyester mixtures* *wool* *silk*
hot	*cotton* *linen*

N.B. Iron acrylics dry, with a cool iron.

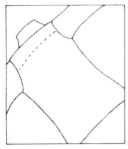 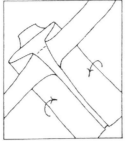 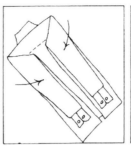 

| Fasten buttons, lay face down, smooth out creases, check collar | Fold two sides parallel to each other | Fold sleeves back on themselves | Fold garment once or twice |

Folding shirt or blouse

Stain Removal

(required also for Intermediate Certificate)

Stain Removing Agents

1. **Synthetic detergents,** *e.g. Tide,* remove grease and general soil, *e.g.* tea, coffee, fruit juice, alcohol.

2. **Enzyme detergents** are good for removing protein stains, *e.g.* blood, gravy. Do not have water too hot or the enzymes will not work.

3. **Acids,** *e.g.* lemon juice or salts of lemon, remove iron mould. Vinegar helps remove perspiration stains.

4. **Alkalis,** *e.g.* washing soda, remove grease stains, *e.g.* oil, and they also soften water.

5. **Bleaches** are only suitable for removing stains from cotton and linen. Never use undiluted. Always follow instructions.

6. **Solvents** such as turpentine, carbon tetrachloride, benzine, are usually used on non-washable fabrics.

7. **Other agents,** *e.g.* acetone, remove specific stains.

Rules for Removing Stains

1. Blot off excess and remove stain at once — before it has had time to set.
2. Use the least harmful method first, *e.g.* steep in cold water.
3. Remove stains before washing.
4. Keep all stain-removing agents out of the reach of children.
5. When using a solvents, place a pad of clean white cotton under stain, rub on solvent with a piece of white fabric working from the outside in.
6. Never use solvents in an unventilated room — many give off dangerous fumes. Air well after use.
7. Many are highly inflammable — never use near a naked flame.
8. If in doubt about a stain-removing agent, test it first on an inconspicuous part of the fabric.

Note: Treatment depends on (a) type of stain, (b) type of fabric.

Table 42.1

	Stain	Treatment	Precautions
1.	Blood, egg, meat and other protein stains.	Soak in cold water, then in a warm solution of biological detergent. Rinse well, then wash as usual.	Hot water sets these stains. Enzymes will not work if water is too hot or too cold.
2.	Grease, *e.g.* oil, butter, make-up or crayon.	Soak in hot soapy water. Wash, rinse and dry. If not washable use a solvent, *e.g.* benzine or carbon tetrachloride.	Use solvents near an open window — many give off dangerous fumes. Air well after use.
3.	Tea/coffe (black) with milk	Soak in hot soapy water. Wash in very hot water containing detergent. Soak in warm biological detergent solution *(see 1 above)*.	*(See 1 above)*
4.	Grass	Rub gently with methylated spirit. Rinse. Wash according to fabric *or* soak in biological detergent, *(see 1 above)*.	Methylated spirit is highly inflammable. Air well.
5.	Ballpoint pen	Rub with methlated spirit. Rinse and wash according to fabric.	*(See above)*
6.	Felt tipped pen	Soak and wash in biological detergent, *(see 1 above)*.	
7.	Prespiration	Soak and wash in biological detergent.	
8.	Urine	Steep in cold water. Wash in hot soapy water according to fabric.	Avoid using biological detergent or bleach on nappies.
9.	Chewing gum	Use ice cube to harden, then pull off gently. Soften remainder by rubbing with butter. Then remove grease stain with a grease solvent *(see 2 above)*.	
10.	Tar	Scrape off as much as possible. Soften by rubbing with butter, wipe off with a tissue. Use a solvent or wash in hot soapy water to remove grease stain.	

Table 42.1 (continued)

	Stain	Treatment	Precautions
11.	Beer	Wash in hot soapy water. If stain persists, rub with solution of vinegar or surgical spirit and water.	
12.	Paint (oil based)	Use turpentine or white spirit. Rinse well and wash according to fabric.	Remove immediately.
	Emulsion	Wash at once in cold water or use methylated spirits.	*See 2 above*
13.	Nailpolish	Use nail polish remover or acetone. Then wash according to fabric.	Acetone is inflammable. Never use these solvents on Tricel or acetate fabrics (test first on a hem to check it will not damage fabric).
14.	Shoe polish	Use carbon tetrachloride. Then wash according to fabric.	Air well after use.
15.	Mildew and difficult fruit stains.	Soak white fabrics *only* in a solution of hypochlorite bleach, *e.g.* Parazone. Rinse well and wash according to fabric. Use hydrogen peroxide on coloureds.	Do not use hypochlorite bleach on wool or silk.
16.	Iron mould, ink	Rub in salt and then lemon juice, or use commercial iron mould remover. Rinse well and wash according to fabric.	Iron mould remover is highly poisonous.
17.	Unidentified stains	Rinse first in cold water. Soak in biological detergent. White cottons and linens may be bleached. If this does not work, bring to a professional dry cleaner.	

4

Needlework

43 *All About Sewing Equipment*

Learning to sew is a useful skill — knowing how to sew helps us to keep our clothes neat and tidy, to repair damage and to make a wide selection of clothes. We can also make and repair household items, such as cushions, curtains and bed linen.

Advantages of Making your own Clothes

1. Saves money — in most cases it is far cheaper to make clothes than to buy them.
2. You can have a greater selection of styles and fabrics than is available in a shop.
3. It allows greater scope for having your own individual style.
4. Those with difficult figure types, who may not be able to buy clothes in their size, can make cothes to fit themselves.

Sewing Box

Keep all your sewing needs in one place. You might use a special sewing basket with spaces for spools, *etc,* but a medium sized cardboard box or biscuit tin would do just as well.

Sewing equipment

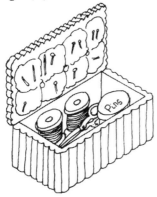

Basic Sewing Needs

Needles: Use good quality fine needles.
Sharps — long general purpose needles.
Betweens — shorter general purpose needles.
Crewel — these have a large eye for embroidery.
Darning — large needle with large eye.

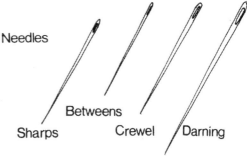

Needles

Betweens

Sharps   Crewel   Darning

Sizes: range from 1 – 12. The higher the number, the finer the needle. Number 7 or 8 is a useful size for general hand sewing.

Thread: Sewing thread should match the fabric being sewn, in colour and type. Use:

(a) **Cotton thread** — for natural fibres.

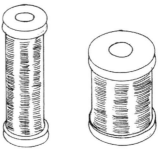

(b) **Polyester thread** — for man-made fibres.

No. 40 or 50 thread is a general all purpose thread, suitable for hand sewing or sewing by machine.

Cheap spools may be available which are suitable for tacking. When tacking, or tailor tacking, choose a colour which contrasts with the fabric. You can economise by using up ends of old spools for tacking. Thick strong thread is available for sewing in buttons and for decorative use.

Thimble: A thimble is useful for pushing a needle through fabric, particularly if it is hard or thick, *e.g.* poplin or corduroy. Wear a thimble on your middle finger.

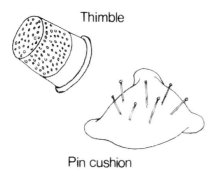

Thimble

Pin cushion

Pins: Fine stainless steel pins are best. Store them in a paper lined box to prevent rusting. Never use blunt or rusting pins.

Cutting out

Scissors: (a) Sharp cutting out shears.
(b) A small, sharp scissors for trimming.

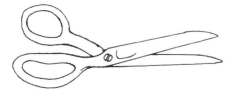

Only use dressmaking scissors for cutting fabrics — cutting paper will blunt them. Keep scissors dry and clean and sharpen them occasionally (if necessary).

Measuring

Buy a good quality tape measure in non-stretch fibreglass.
A metre stick is useful — if not, a transparent ruler may be used.
A hem gauge — to measure the depth of hem.
Tailors chalk — for making alterations, *etc.*

Pressing

Iron: A steam iron is useful for pressing thick fabrics — otherwise use a dry iron with a damp cloth.
An **ironing board** or table is needed for pressing.
A **sleeveboard,** *i.e.* a small ironing board, is handy for small awkward areas, *e.g.* sleeves, cuffs.

Sleeveboard

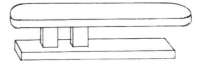

Pressing cloths: White sheeting will be needed if you are using heavy fabrics which need to be damp pressed.

The Sewing Machine

The most expensive piece of equipment you will need for dressmaking is a sewing machine. Place your sewing machine at a suitable height, in a good light. You will need an electric socket nearby, if the machine is electric, and plenty of space on which to lay pieces of sewing before and after you stitch them.

Sewing machines can be worked (a) by hand, (b) by foot pedal or (c) by electricity.

Electric sewing machines are quick to use and leave both hands free for guiding the fabric.

The basic sewing machine sews forwards and backwards. Many modern machines can sew a variety of embroidery stitches and also:

Zig-zag stitch — useful for neatening seams.

Buttonholes and buttons.

Stretch stitch — for jersey fabric.

Blind hem stitch — for turning up hems.

Overlocking — a neatening stitch.

Attachments

(a) **Zipper or cording foot** — a one-sided presser foot which is useful for putting in zips and sewing piping cord onto cushions.

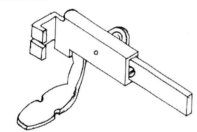

(b) **Quilting foot or hem guide** — to help you sew lines of machining exactly parallel.

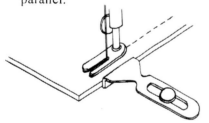

Care of a Sewing Machine

1. Follow instruction book — for threading, adjusting and general use.
2. Keep machine covered, when not in use.
3. Clean machine regularly *i.e.* unplug, remove bobbin, needle, bobbin plate and face plate. Dust with a fine soft brush, to remove fluff and dust.
4. Oil once every couple of months — using special machine oil:
   (a) Place one drop of oil in each oiling point (see instruction book).
   (b) Wipe over with a clean rag, then run machine without thread.
   (c) Thread up and sew a few rows of machining on an old piece of fabric in order to soak up any excess oil.
5. Now and then wipe over the body of the machine with a damp cloth.
6. Keep presser foot raised when not in use.
7. Have machine serviced occasionally by a qualified sewing machine mechanic.

How a Machine Stitches

The main difference between hand sewing and sewing by machine is that with hand sewing, only *one* thread is used, while in machining, each stitch is formed by *two* threads which interlock — one from the needle and spool, the other coming up from the bobbin.

Tension: Both upper and lower threads must be equally tight. In order to control the tension or tightness of a stitch there is an adjustable *tension screw* which tightens or loosens the thread passing from spool to needle. Tension which is too tight causes puckering.

A. If it looks like this, the top thread is too loose — you must tighten the tension screw.

Top tension too loose

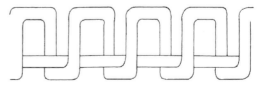

B. If it looks like this, the top thread is too tight — loosen the tension screw.

Top tension too tight

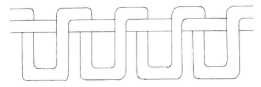

C. A normal stitch looks like this.

Correct tension

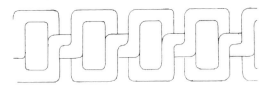

Threading

Follow the instruction book exactly. Most machines are threaded in this order:

1. Raise presser food and have needle at its highest position.
2. Place spool on spool pin on top right hand corner. Hold.
3. Bring thread across machine to first guide.
4. Bring it down around tension discs, catching it in tension spring.
5. Thread into take-up lever, then down towards the needle, through two or three guides.
6. It passes into the needle from the direction of the last guide, *i.e.* if the final guide is on the left, thread the needle from the left.

Sewing machine

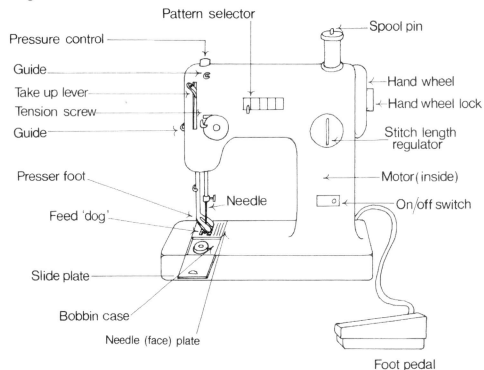

Pattern selector
Pressure control
Guide
Take up lever
Tension screw
Guide
Presser foot
Feed 'dog'
Slide plate
Bobbin case
Needle (face) plate
Spool pin
Hand wheel
Hand wheel lock
Stitch length regulator
Motor (inside)
On/off switch
Needle
Foot pedal

Bobbin

1. Wind bobbin evenly, using the bobbin winder.
2. Place the bobbin in position, according to directions on instruction book, making sure that thread passes through bobbin tension (in bobbin case).

Raising the Bobbin Thread

1. Hold needle thread loosely with left hand.
2. Turn machine wheel towards you, with right hand, so that the needle lowers into hole underneath it and then returns to its highest position.
3. Pull needle thread — this should bring up a loop of bobbin thread.
4. Pull out loop and pass both threads between 'toes' of presser foot.

Machine Needles

These should be sharp — blunt needles cause snagging of work. The needle must be correctly inserted, *i.e.* with the flat side facing the direction indicated in instruction book, then tighten the needle screw. Machine needles are available in sizes:

80 (11) for thin fabrics
90 (14) average fabrics
100 (16) thick fabrics.

Stitch Length: The length of stitch can be adjusted by a lever or dial to the right of the machine.

Using a Machine

1. Follow instruction book.
2. Use suitable needle and thread; bobbin and thread should match fabric.
3. Thread needle and bobbin correctly; close bobbin case.
4. Adjust tension and stitch length to suit fabric.
5. Test stitch first, on a doubled scrap of fabric.

6. Remove all pins before sewing.
7. When sewing, keep the bulk of the fabric to the left of machine.
8. *Always* turn machine wheel *towards* you — *never away* from you.
9. Start and stop with needle and take up lever at their highest point.
10. At the end of a line of stitching, raise presser foot and pass threads under presser foot. Pull fabric towards the back and cut thread — leaving about 8 cm of thread for finishing off.

Special Points for Beginners

* Never run threaded machine without material — knots will form.
* Guide fabric gently into machine — *do not push* fabric under the needle or pull it out — the feed controls the length of stitch and guides the fabric evenly into the machine.

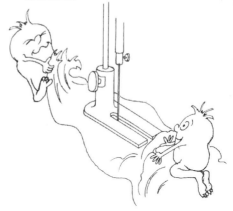

* Never let anyone press the pedal or turn the handle for you — this leaves you completely out of control.
* Press pedal lightly if you want to go slowly; strongly if you want to go fast.
* If you need to stop in the middle of a line, leave needle in fabric.
* Check stitching after every line.

Starting the Machine

1. Raise needle to its highest point.
2. Raise presser foot — make sure threads lie towards the back.
3. Insert from the front, lower needle gently onto fabric.
4. Lower presser foot.
5. Begin stitching — holding threads at the back for 2–3 stitches.

For the Expert Touch

1. Wind a bobbin full of thread that matches your fabric when your are starting something new.

2. Do not sew one seam at a time — prepare lots of stitching for machining together.
3. When you get more experienced, try machine tacking — using the longest machine stitch.
4. Use the numbered guidelines on the needle plate or the edge of the presser foot to help you sew straight.
5. To turn a corner: sew up to the corner, lower needle into fabric, raise presser foot and swivel fabric on needle. Lower presser foot and continue sewing.
6. When sewing jersey and stretch fabrics, use a slight zig-zag stitch for 'give'.

Table 43.1

Machine Faults	Possible Reasons
Uneven stitches	1. Pulling or pushing fabric into machine.
	2. Feed dog – faulty, dirty or worn.
	3. Stitch length adjuster faulty.
	4. Needle in wrong way round.
	5. Needle and/or thread size incorrect.
	6. Incorrect pressure, or presser foot not lowered.
Skipped stitches	1. Blunt or bent needle.
	2. Needle set too high, or too low.
	3. Needle wrong size or in wrong way round.
	4. Machine (especially needle) incorrectly threaded.
	5. Top and lower threads of different quality.
	6. Pulling or pushing fabric into machine.
Bobbin thread breaking	1. Lower tension too tight.
	2. Bad quality thread.
	3. Bobbin case incorrectly threaded.
	4. Bobbin unevenly wound, or wound too full.
	5. Dirt or fluff in bobbin case.

ctd. ⟶

Needle thread breaking	1. Top tension too tight. 2. Thread too fine, or bad quality. 3. Incorrect threading. 4. Needle bent or blunt. 5. Needle too fine, or wrong way round.
Looped stitches	1. Needle not threaded correctly, especially through tension. 2. Upper tension too loose. 3. Bobbin not threaded correctly.
Puckered seams	1. Either tension too tight. 2. Top and lower threads of different quality. 3. Blunt needle. 4. Stitch too long especially on fine fabrics. 5. Pressure too tight.
Needle breaking	1. Upper tension too tight. 2. Needle incorrectly inserted. 3. Needle not at highest point when pulling fabric from machine. 4. Fabric pulled towards front. 5. Fabric pulled roughly during sewing. 6. Loose presser foot. 7. Needle too fine.
Jammed machine	1. Thread caught up in bobbin case. 2. Thread twisted around spool pin. 3. Machine handle not unlocked after threading bobbin.
Noisy machine	1. Lack of oil. 2. Dirt trapped inside. 3. Loose parts *e.g.* bobbin holder.

44   *All About Fibres and Fabrics*

If you look carefully at most fabrics, you will see that they are made up of thousands and thousands of tiny threads. If you pull out one of these threads and examine it, you will probably find that there are several fibres in each thread. Most fabrics are made by spinning fibres into thread or yarn. This is then either knitted or woven on a loom, to produce cloth.

Cloths

Woven Cloth

Woven cloth is made up of two sets of threads:
1. The lengthwise threads (also called the *selvage* or *warp* threads).
2. The crosswise threads (also called the *weft* threads).

When weaving on a loom, the strongest (selvage) threads are stretched lengthwise on rollers and the weft are woven in and out through them.

The Selvage

To strengthen the lengthwise edges of the fabric when weaving and to prevent fraying, the threads at the edge are packed tightly together. This closely woven edge is known as the selvage.

Straight Grain

In clothes, the lengthwise threads should run down the garment, *e.g.* from shoulder to hem, rather than across. This is because they are stronger and less likely to stretch.

When you are cutting out a pattern, make sure that the pieces are laid accurately, so that the lengthwise threads or *straight grain* runs down the garment. If not, it may hang badly and quickly lose its shape.

On areas where there is strain, *e.g.* belts/cuffs/waistbands, the lengthwise grain runs across the garment.

Woven fabric

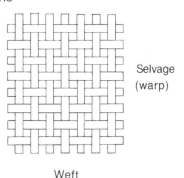

Selvage (warp)

Weft

Knitted fabrics

These are formed from loops of thread which are linked into one another by hand or on a knitting machine, *e.g.* jersey, crimpelene, sweaters.

Knitted fabric

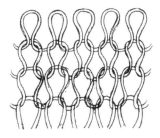

Types of Fibres

Fabrics are made from a wide range of fibres which may be grouped under two key headings:

Table 44.1

Natural fibres	
Animal	*Vegetable*
wool; silk	cotton; linen
Man-made fibres	
Regenerated	*Synthetic*
rayon; acetate	nylon; polyester

A good clothing fabric should be:
1. Absorbant.
2. Comfortable to wear.
3. Easy to wash.
4. Crease resistant.
5. Hardwearing.
6. Non-inflammable.
7. In cold weather, a bad conductor of heat — keeping body heat in.
8. In warm weather, a good conductor of heat — letting body heat out.

Natural Fibres

Sources of fabric

Wool

Silk

Cotton

Linen

Wool

Wool is obtained mainly from sheep. The largest producers of wool are Australia, New Zealand, the USSR and Argentina.

The fleece is sheared from the sheep, graded and cleaned. It is then teased (carded) and combed into long strands which are spun, *i.e.* twisted, to make yarn. Long strands of wool are called *worsted* and made into fine woollen fabrics *e.g.* serge, gabardine, suiting. Short wool fibres are spun into softer woollen yarn. This is woven into soft wool cloth, *e.g.* blankets, or used for knitting.

Wool as a Clothing Fabric

Advantages
1. Soft and comfortable.
2. It absorbs perspiration.
3. Wears well.
4. Good insulator — keeps body warm.
5. Very elastic — sheds creases easily.
6. Doesn't burn easily — it smoulders rather than bursts into flames.

Disadvantages
1. Easily damaged by careless washing.
2. It shrinks and felts.
3. Damaged by moths.
4. Expensive.
5. Hairy — to those with sensitive skins.
6. Scorches easily.

Care of Wool (Use wash code 7), *p. 307*
1. Air and brush often.
2. Protect from moths and perspiration.
3. Handwash woollens in warm (not hot) soapy water. Rinse well.
4. Handle gently — do not rub or wring. Dry flat.
5. Press on wrong side using a damp pressing cloth.
6. If in doubt — dry clean.

Important

Wool fibres are covered with rough scales. These catch in one another and help to trap air, so that it insulates the body and keeps it warm. *But* it is these scales which cause shrinking and felting. If wool is roughly handled during washing, or washed at high temperatures, the scales become tangled in one another and cannot untangle, so that the woollen shrinks and becomes felted.

Wool fibre(scaly)

Wool Fabrics

1. Tweed   5. Gaberdine
2. Flannel   6. Serge
3. Crêpe   7. Velour
4. Jersey   8. Bouclé

Silk

Silk is an animal fibre, obtained from the silkworm. The worm spins a cocoon of silk around itself, which, when unravelled, produces a long filament (fine thread) of silk. These threads are wound off and spun into yarn, from which cloth is woven.

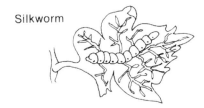
Silkworm

Silk as a Clothing Fabric

Advantages
1. Lightweight, soft and comfortable.
2. It has a smooth attractive sheen.
3. It is absorbent.
4. Slightly elastic and crease resistant.
5. It drapes well — good for evening dresses.
6. Non inflammable — it doesn't burst into flames.

Disadvantages
1. Expensive.
2. Damaged by perspiration, moths and sunshine.
3. Silk is easily damaged by careless handling — it should be washed carefully or dry cleaned.
4. Easily damaged by chemicals; use gentle detergents and cleaning agents.

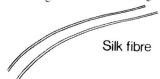
Silk fibre

Care of Silk

1. Protect garments against perspiration stains by wearing dress shields or a good anti-perspirant.
2. Wash carefully by hand (wash code 7).
3. Use warm (never hot) water and a detergent designed for delicate fabrics, *e.g. Dreft.*
4. Handle gently, do not rub or wring.
5. Rinse and roll in a towel before hanging to dry.
6. Iron slightly damp on the wrong side, using a moderate iron.
7. If in doubt — dry clean.

Cotton

Cotton plants grow in warm sunny climates, particularly the U.S.A., India, China and Egypt.

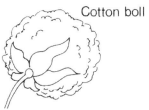
Cotton boll

A pod or 'boll' grows on the plant and bursts on ripening, releasing a mass of fluffy white fibres. The fibres are cleaned, teased or carded, then combed and spun into cotton threads which are woven to produce cloth. Cotton may be subjected to various treatments *e.g.*

Mercerising — which makes it smooth and glossy.
Flame proofing.
Drip-dry treatment.

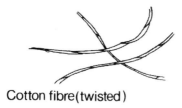

Cotton fibre(twisted)

Cotton Fabrics

1. Lawn	6. Flannellette
2. Muslin	7. Denim
3. Gingham	8. Towelling
4. Poplin	9. Corduroy.
5. Seersucker	

Cotton as a Clothing Fabric

Advantages
1. Fairly cheap.
2. Easy to sew.
3. Soft and smooth.
4. Dyes and bleaches easily.
5. Strong, especially when wet.
6. Lightweight.
7. Absorbs moisture easily.
8. Cool to wear in hot weather.
9. Easy to wash and iron.

Disadvantages
1. Creases easily.
2. Little elasticity.
3. Shrinks easily.
4. Burns rapidly.
5. Easily damaged by mildew.
6. Cheap cottons contain stiffening, which comes out in the first wash, leaving the fabric limp.

Care (Use wash code 1, 2, 5 or 9)

1. Cotton can withstand high temperatures, even boiling.
2. It can be washed by hand or machine.
3. Iron damp, on the wrong side, using a hot iron.
4. Treated cottons, *e.g.* drip-dry cottons, need little or no ironing.

Linen

Linen is a vegetable fibre made from the tough inner fibres of the flax plant. Flax grows in a cool damp climate — Ireland is an ideal climate and Irish linen is famous world wide.

Flax stems are soaked in water to rot the outer bark, then crushed and combed before spinning and weaving into fabric. It is then bleached — either in the sun, or by chemicals.

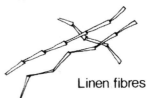

Linen fibres

Linen as a Clothing Fabric

Advantages
1. Strong — wears well.
2. Dirt resistant.
3. Very absorbant.
4. Cool to wear.
5. Washes well. Can be boiled.
6. Chemicals have little effect.

Disadvantages
1. Expensive.
2. Difficult to dye.
3. Creases easily.
4. Affected by mildew.
5. Shrinks considerably.
6. Burns easily.

Care (Use wash code 1, 2 or 5)

1. Can be washed by hand or machine and boiled if necessary.
2. Can be starched, if wished.
3. Iron damp on the wrong side for a dull finish, or on the right side for a shiny finish. Use a hot iron.

Uses for Linen

1. Handerchiefs.
2. Underwear
3. Outerwear
4. House furnishings
5. Table cloths
6. Sheets
7. Tea towels

Damask is a special weave, using a dull and gloss finish. Damask is used for table linen.

Man-made Fibres

Some man-made fibres are made from natural products, *e.g.* wood, cotton waste, seaweed, peanuts. These are known as regenerated fibres. Others are made completely from chemicals, such as oil and coal. These are known as synthetic fibres.

Man-made fibres

Table 44.2

Regenerated	Synthetic
Rayon (viscose)	Nylon
Rayon (acetate)	Polyester
Triacetate (Tricel)	Acrylic
Fibrolane	Plastic
(a protein fibre)	(*e.g.* P.V.C.)

Rayons (Viscose/Acetate/Triacetate)

Viscose rayon: is made from wood pulp; **acetate** from cotton linters. Both are treated with chemicals to form a thick pulpy liquid, which is forced through tiny holes in a machine called a spinneret. The liquid filaments are hardened to produce threads which are twisted into yarn, then knitted or woven into fabric.

Viscose rayon usually looks like silk — many satins, taffetas and brocades are made from viscose. Underwear, nightwear, ties, evening wear, rainwear and swimwear are often made from one of these fibres.

Care of Rayon-type Fibres (Use wash code 6)

1. Most are weakened by water — handle gently when wet.
2. Use warm soapy water, squeeze but do not rub; rinse and iron while still damp.
3. Some types should be drip dried — check care label.

Advantages
1. Absorbant.
2. Attractive sheen.
3. Acetate — non flammable.
4. Can be made into a wide variety of fabrics.

Disadvantages
1. Weak when wet.
2. Damaged by heat.
3. Viscose is inflammable.

Nylon and Polyester

Nylon is made from chemicals obtained from coal tar. It is melted and forced into filaments in the same way as rayon. It can be made into sheer fabrics, such as satin, as well as thicker fluffier brushed nylon.

Made in a similar way to nylon but from chemicals obtained from petroleum, polyester can be made into such different fabrics as curtain net, men's suitings, jersey (Crimpelene), linen, flannel, *etc.*

Nylon and Polyester as Clothing Fabrics

Advantages
1. Strong and durable.
2. Do not stain easily.
3. Crease resistant.
4. Easy to wash.
5. Elastic and resilient.
7. Do not shrink or stretch.

Disadvantages
1. Non-absorbant.
2. Melt at high temperatures.
3. Can be damaged by washing or ironing at very high temperatures.
4. Clammy in hot weather.
5. Weaken if continually exposed to light and air.
6. Build up of static electricity which attracts dirt.

Acrylics

Brand names: *Orlon, Acrilan, Courtelle.*

These are usually made into soft knitted garments which, like woollens, may pill, *i.e.* form little balls. They are easy to wash and quick to dry. They should only be ironed when dry.

Care of Synthetic Fabrics (Use wash code 3, 4 or 6)

1. Do not allow them to get too dirty.

2. Wash in warm, soapy water, rinse well in warm water. Avoid rubbing and wringing.
3. Nylon is usually drip dried, other fabrics may be rolled in a towel to absorb excess moisture before line drying.
4. Most are ironed dry, using a cool iron — a hot iron will melt synthetics.
5. Use of a fabric conditioner in the rinsing water will help prevent the building-up of static electricity which is common in man-made fibres.

Mixtures and Blends

Sometimes two fibres are mixed, *e.g.* cotton/linen; wool/polyester. Blends of man-made and natural fibres produce fabrics which have the advantages of both — they are easy to wash, absorbant and comfortable to wear. Each fibre retains its own characteristic and mixtures should always be laundered carefully, *e.g.* a blend of cotton/wool must be laundered as for wool.

Finishes

The finished look of a fabric depends on:
1. The fibre used, *e.g.* cotton or nylon.
2. The type of weave or knit.
3. The finish, *e.g.* dying, printing, pleating, *etc.*

Types of Weave or Knit

Finishes with a woollen look

Twill — a diagonal weave.
Tweed — a rough woven finish.
Gabardine — a fine, diagonal weave.
Bouclé — a looped fabric.
Flannel — has a felt-like appearance.
Jersey — stretchy knitted fabric.
Worsted — a plain weave, made from fine twisted wool — used for suits.

Finishes with a silky look

Satin — a very smooth, shiny finish.
Brocade — a satin type fabric with a rich patterned design, often in glitter threads.
Chiffon — a sheer lightweight fabric.
Taffeta — a slippy fabric which feels crisp.
Velvet — has a raised pile *i.e.* vertical cut threads.

Linen-type finishes

Cambric — a plain weave in a lightweight fabric (one side is shiny).
Damask — a glossy patterned weave, used in tablelinen.
Rep — a ribbed weave.

Cotton-type finishes

Lawn — a plain fine weave.
Gingham — an even check on a white background.
Denim — a strong fabric with a twill weave.
Seersucker — has a wrinkled appearance.
Flannellettes — a soft 'brushed' cotton.
Corduroy — a velvety ribbed fabric.

Some finishes which improve a fabric

1. **Shrink resistant finish (brand name —** *Sanforized).*

2. Drip dry or crease resistant (brand names — *Tebilized, Calpreta).*

3. Mothproof finish — useful for woollens.

4. Flameproofing — important for childrens nightwear (brand name — *Timorax).* Do not use bleach or enzyme detergent.

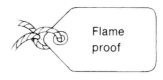

5. Waterproofing (brand name — *Scotchgard).* Many plastics are naturally waterproof.

6. Permanent pleating (brand names — *Evaprest; Koratron).*

7. Napped fabrics are brushed to give extra warmth and softness.

Over to you . . .

1. What fabric would you consider best for: (a) a beginner at dressmaking; (b) a sports outfit; (c) casual clothes — for rough wear; (d) underwear; (e) nightwear.

2. Compare wool and terylene as fibres for men's suiting. Describe how a pair of terylene trousers should be washed and pressed.

3. **Project**
Pick one of the fibres/fabrics mentioned in this chapter and write a project on it **or** collect samples of as may fabrics as possible and stick them into your project, with a brief description of each.

45   *All About Stitches*

Although most clothes made today are sewn by machine, there are still many occasions when it will be necessary to hand sew part of a garment, *e.g.* the hem, particularly when you do not want the stitches to show through on the right side.

Tips for Successful Stitching

* Use a single thread — not too long, or it will twist and knot.
* Most stitches are worked from right to left (left handed people may find it easier to work from left to right).
* Pin and tack seams, hems, *etc.* in place, before stitching.
* Make a secure stitch to start off.
* Keep stitches even and do not pull too tightly.
* Stitches should not be too large.
* Cut thread at an angle — this makes it easier to pass it through the eye of a needle.
* Finish off securely or stitches will unravel.
* Use a thimble for tough fabrics (*e.g.* corduroy).
* Last — but not least — remember: Practice makes Perfect!

Tacking (Basting)

Tacking is a temporary stitch. It is used:
1. To hold a garment together for fitting.
2. To hold two pieces of material in position while the permanent stitching is being done.
3. It also acts as a guide for machining.

Straight Tacking

1. Pin fabric in position — usually with edges together.
2. Start with a knot and a small double (back) stitch, *i.e.* take a straight stitch and go back into same stitch again.
3. Work from right to left, making even stitches 10 mm in size, as shown. Stitches and spaces should be equal.
4. Finish off by making two or three back stitches.

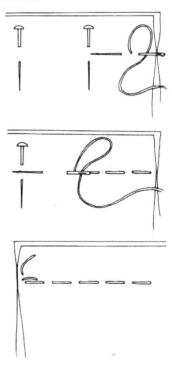

Tacking Tips

* Use a single thread in a contrasting colour so that it shows up easily.
* Do not pull tacking too tightly or it will pucker.

* For extra strength, when tacking a garment for fitting, make a back stitch every few stitches.
* Large tacking stitches do not save time — they simply allow the fabric to slip out of place.
* Don't try to hurry things up by skipping the tacking — it helps give a professional finish to your dressmaking.

Machine Tacking

On straight seams, pin carefully together, with pins at right angles to seam, then, using the longest stitch, in a contrasting thread, machine stitch down the length of seam.

Tailor Tacking

This is used to transfer important pattern markings from pattern to doubled fabric. Make a tailor's tack on each balance mark, on corners and on any other important places.

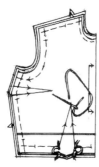

1. Use a long double thread without a knot.
2. Take a small stitch through the pattern and both fabric layers, leaving a thread 25 mm long.
3. Take a second stitch back over the first, leaving a 25 mm loop. Cut thread 25 mm from stitch.
4. When all balance marks have been tailor tacked, remove pins.
5. You may or may not cut the loop. By **not** cutting the loop, the stitch is more secure, but you will make a small tear in the pattern. By cutting the loop, the

tailor tacks are more likely to fall out, particularly if the fabric is slippy.

6. Remove pattern carefully, pinching the pattern over the tack as you pull, to avoid tearing a large hole.
7. Pull fabric layers carefully apart and cut threads between them — a tuft of thread remains on each piece.

Threadmarking

Used to mark centre lines of garment, curved seams and difficult details, such as collars. Thread marking is useful for beginners who may find it hard to sew straight. All you have to do is sew along the thread-marked lines.

1. Use a long double thread, without a knot.
2. Work a line of tacking along pattern fitting lines, leaving 25 mm loops between each stitch.
3. Cut loops and carefully remove pattern.
4. Separate layers of fabric and cut threads between.

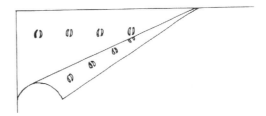

Running

Running is a small straight stitch. It is used instead of machining for sewing tucks and seams where there is little strain on the material. It is also used for gathering.

1. Running is worked from right to left.
2. Begin and end stitching with a small back stitch.
3. It is worked like tacking, but stitches are much smaller — about 1 – 2 mm.

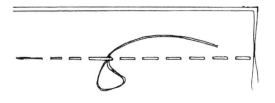

Gathering

Gathering is used to ease in material and control fullness, *i.e.* make a wide piece of material fit into a narrower one. Gathers add interest and shape to a garment.

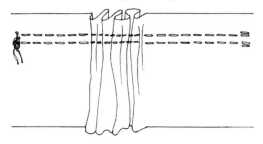

1. Gathers are made by working two parallel rows of running.
2. They are worked from right to left, within the seam allowance, *i.e.* about 12 mm and 14 mm from the edge of fabric.
3. Begin with a knot or a backstitch and leave the threads free at the end.
4. To pull, hold both threads and gently slide the fabric along the threads until it gathers to the required width.

5. To prevent gathers unravelling, insert a pin at the end of the gathering and wind the ends of thread in a figure of eight around the pin.

> *Note:* Gathering may also be done by machine; make two rows using a medium length stitch and a fairly loose tension.

Backstitching

This is a secure straight stitch, used to join seams together in place of machining. Backstitching looks like machining at the front but, at the back, it looks like stem stitch.

1. To start, make a small double stitch, bringing the needle out 2–3 mm beyond the first stitch.
2. Put the needle back into the end of the last stitch and bring it out 2–3 mm beyond, as shown.
3. Continue in this way and finish with a double stitch. Pass the needle out through fabric and cut.

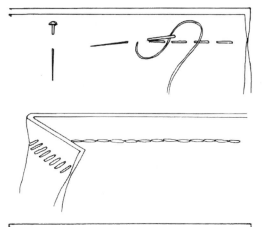

> *Note:* Slant the needle very slightly downwards, so that the stitches at the back are all overlapping in the same direction.

The following stitches hold folded edges in place:

Top-sewing or Oversewing

This is a small secure stitch, worked on the right side of the fabric. It is used to join finished edges together, *e.g.* lace onto a hem; tapes onto a teatowel.

1. To begin, insert needle through the **single fold** nearest the worker — the needle should point straight towards you.

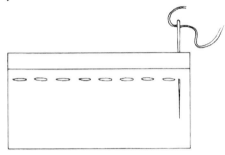

2. Pull through, leaving 1 cm of thread lying along the top edge.

3. Working very close to the edge, insert needle through the top of **both folds** and, working from right to left, sew a row of stitches very close together.

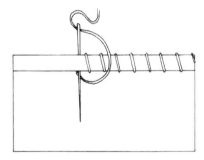

4. Stitches should be small, slanted and evenly spaced.

5. Finish by working three stitches from left to right, so that they form three crosses.

6. Slip needle through the fold and cut thread.

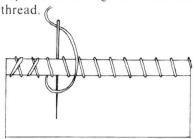

Hemming

Hemming is a small slanted stitch used to hold down small hems, such as facings, bindings, tapes and the turnings of waistbands, collars and cuffs. As this stitch is visible from the right side, it is not generally used on the hems of clothes.

1. Hold hem over the outstretched fingers of the left hand.
2. To begin, run the needle through the fold, from **left to right,** leaving a 'tail' of thread in the fold.

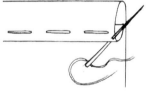

3. Sew small slanting stitches from right to left, picking up two or three threads of the single material and two or three threads of the folded edge. The needle should slant to the left, at an angle of 45°.

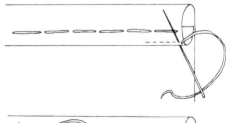

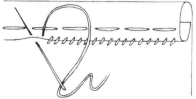

4. Make the stitches small, even and not too tight.
5. To finish, sew back into the last stitch twice, making a V shape. Pass needle through the fold and cut.
6. To join a new thread, unpick half a stitch, then bring the needle out through the hole left by the ripped stitch; tuck both threads under the fold and continue stitching.

Slip Hemming

This is an almost invisable way of sewing a folded hem. It is used on the hems of garments such as skirts, dresses and trousers. It is not as secure as hemming but can be strengthened by sewing a back stitch now and then along the fold.

1. Slip hemming can be worked with the hem facing towards or away from you. Work from right to left.
2. To begin, pass the needle through the fold from left to right and secure with a small back stitch.
3. Take a tiny stitch on the single fabric, picking up only one or two threads.
4. Slip needle through the fold for about 5–15 mm, depending on type of fabric and depth of hem.
5. Continue in the same way, leaving stitches quite loose.
6. Finish by making a back stitch on the fold.

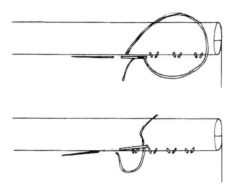

Blind Hemming or Tailor's Hemming

On hems where the edge is neatened without a fold (*e.g.* by overlocking, zig-zag machining or seam binding), fold back hem and take a small stitch inside the hem, instead of passing it through the fold.

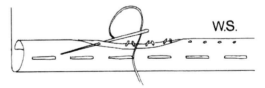

W.S.

The following stitches prevent fabrics from fraying (neatening stitches):

Blanket Stitch

This is used:
1. To neaten the raw edges of seams.
2. As a decorative stitch, *e.g.* for appliqué or scalloping.
3. To make thread loops, *e.g.* for holding buttons or belts.

Stiches are widely spaced for neatening edges and worked close together for scallops and other embroidery. Blanket stitch is one of the few stitches worked from left to right.

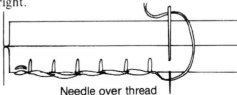

Needle over thread

1. To begin, take a tiny backstitch at the edge of the left side of the fabric.
2. With the raw edge of the fabric towards you, put the needle into the single fabric as shown.
3. Hold the thread from each previous stitch under the left thumb and pass the needle over the thread.
4. This forms a loop at the edge, which helps prevent fraying.
5. Keep stitches straight and evenly spaced and do not pull too tightly.

Overcasting

This is a quick way of neatening the raw edge of heavy fabrics by hand. It is worked from left to right.

1. Hold work parallel with forefinger, as shown.
2. Begin with a double stitch and, working from left to right, insert needle, from back to front, making a slanting stitch about 5 mm deep.
3. Needle should slant slightly to the left. Keep stitches evenly spaced and do not pull too tightly.
4. Finish with a secure double stitch.

Herringbone Stitch

This is used to turn up hems on heavy fabrics such as flannel, which do not fray too much. It both hems and neatens the edge at the same time. Herringboning may also be used as a decorative stitch. Work from left to right with needle pointing to the left.

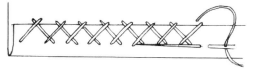

1. Secure with a double stitch on fold, about 4 mm from the edge.
2. Pick up a stitch of the single material just above the raw edge, a little to the right.
3. Work a stitch on the folded fabric.
4. *N.B.:* The crosses formed on the double fabric should be exactly opposite the spaces on the single fabric.
5. Secure with a double stitch.

Embroidery Stitches

1. Embroidery thread is sold in skeins. Each thread is made up of six strands. Unless you are embroidering very thick fabrics, it is necessary to divide the embroidery thread, so that you have three strands in each.

2. Use a crewel (embroidery) needle — it has a large eye to make it easier to thread the embroidery thread through it.

3. Start embroidery by making a few running stitches along the line to be stitched. These are then covered with embroidery stitches as you work.

4. Finish off embroidery by weaving the end of the thread through the wrong side of the stitches. Then cut.

5. Embroidery can be worked by hand or by using a 'swing needle' sewing machine.

Stem Stitch

This is used for outlines, stems, *etc.*

1. Begin with a backstitch.

2. Work from left to right as shown, taking even, slightly slanted stitches along the line of the design. The thread always emerges on the top left of the previous stitch.

Satin Stitch

This is used to fill in shapes, such as petals and leaves.

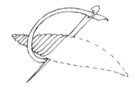

1. The needle passes in through one side of the design and out through the other.

2. Keep stitches close together — they may be straight or slanted.

3. To give extra thickness, a running stitch may be used to pad out the work.

4. Do not make stitches too long or they will drag the fabric. A long and short stitch is more suitable if space to be stitched is too wide.

Long and Short Stitch

This is used to fill in designs which are too large to be filled by satin stitch alone. It is also used to give an attractive shaded effect on designs such as petals and feathers, making them look very real.

1. In the first row, the stitches are worked alternatively long and short.

2. In the next row, the long and short stitches should fit neatly into the previous stitches.

Chain Stitches

Used as an outline stitch or to fill in a design.

1. Start with a back stitch at the top of the outline.

2. Work downwards, holding the thread with the left thumb, to form a loop.

3. Insert needle *inside* loop, beside where thread came out, as shown.

4. To finish, bring needle through to back of work and weave through last few stitches. Cut thread.

Lazy Daisy Stitch

This is a type of chain stitch which is worked in a circle to produce a simple daisy design.

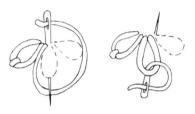

1. Work as for chain stitch, inserting needle *outside* loop before continuing to next stitch.

French Knots

Used in centre of a small flower design, or close together, to provide a textured finish. They may also be used to create a spotted effect.

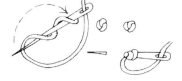

1. Bring thread through from the back, hold the thread down with the left thumb and wind the needle around the thread twice or three times.

2. Still holding the thread, bring the needle back to the starting point and insert it close to where thread first emerged.

3. Secure thread or pass on to next stitch.

Cross Stitch

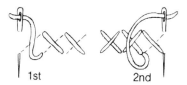

1. Begin with a small back stitch.
2. *1st line:* Right to left. Bring needle through on lower right hand corner of cross. Insert needle towards worker as shown, making a slanted stitch.
3. *2nd Line:* Left to right. Bring needle out at bottom left hand corner of work and insert needle as shown to form crosses.
4. Secure with back stitch on reverse side.

Other stitches used in embroidery include:
 (a) Running
 (b) Backstitching
 (c) Blanketstitching
 (d) Herringboning.

Over to you . . .

1. Name two temporary and two permanent stitches. In the case of *one* of each, describe: (a) where it is used in dressmaking; (b) how it is worked; (c) how to start and finish the stitch.

2. Name *two* methods of holding a folded edge in place. Describe, with the aid of diagrams, how to sew *one* of these stitches.

3. Name *three* stitches used to finish off edges. Show, with the help of a diagram, how to work *one*. On a practice piece of fabric, work this stitch, then stick it into your copybook.

4. Make a list of the embroidery stitches you have learned. Draw a design of an embroidered decoration for a cushion or for an apron pocket and show which stitches could be used in the design. Describe how to sew *one*.

46 All About Seams

Seams

Seams are used to join pieces of material together.

A Plain or Flat Seam

This is the seam most often used on clothes, as it can be easily altered by taking it in or letting it out. Flat seams are usually sewn 1.5 cm from the raw edge.

1. Pin the two pieces of material together, right sides facing and match any notches or balance marks (tailor tacks).

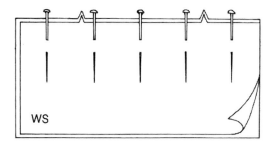

2. Tack about 2 mm outside fitting line. Remove pins.

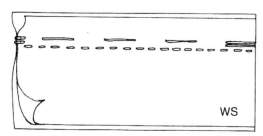

3. Machine on fitting line from the edge of the fabric at the top of the seam to the end. (Do not leave a space at the top or bottom of seam.)

4. Remove tacking and press seam open.

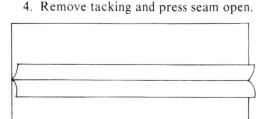

5. Neaten raw edges, according to fabric type.

Methods of Neatening

1. **Pinking** — used mainly on non-fraying fabrics. If wished, the whole pattern can be cut out using a pinking shears. A row of machining can be worked on the turnings, before pinking, if wished.

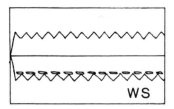

2. **Overcasting** — suitable for medium weight fabrics which do not fray too much. Work from left to right, bringing needle over turnings. Keep stitches fairly loose. A line of machining may be worked 3–4 mm from edge, to strengthen edge and act as a guide for overcasting.

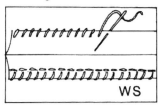

3. **Blanket stitching** — used on fabrics which fray easily but are too thick to turn a hem under. It is also used to neaten double turnings, *e.g.* around sleeves and pockets.

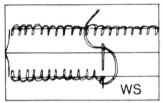

4. **Zig-zag machining** — worked on each turning separately or, in some cases, together. Set machine to a suitable zig-zag stitch and test on a scrap of the garment fabric. Stitch 2–3 mm from edge and trim off edges or trim seam turnings evenly, then zig-zag along the edge.

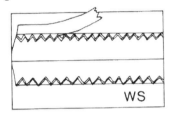

5. **Edge machining** — used on fine and medium weight fabrics. Turn under a narrow fold on the raw edges of seam allowance. Tack and machine about 2 mm from the edge.

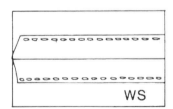

6. **Bias binding:**
   (a) Open fold of one side of bias binding.
   (b) Place right side of bias binding to right side of turnings, with raw edges together.

   (c) Pin, tack and machine on crease line.
   (d) Remove tacking, turn binding to wrong side and pin, tack and hem to machining.

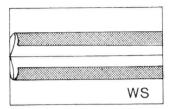

Trimming Seams

Certain seams must be carefully trimmed after machining if they are to lie flat.

1. **Curved Seams:**
   (a) First trim turnings in layers, *e.g.* one 5 mm, the other 10 mm.
   (b) On outward curves, cut V-shaped notches in turnings.
   (c) On inward curves, snip turnings with point of scissors every 5 mm.

2. **Corners and Points:**
   (a) Trim turnings in layers.
   (b) Outward corners — trim fabric close to corner as shown.
   (c) Inward corners — reinforce corner with a row of stitching inside seam allowance. Then clip right into stitching line, as shown.

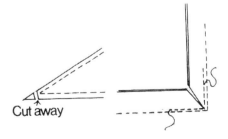

Cut away

3. Crossing Seams:

(a) Make two seams in the usual way, press open.

(b) With right sides together, pin seams, matching exactly at crossing point.

(c) Pin, tack and machine. Remove tacking, trim and press open.

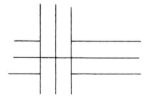

French Seams

These are used on fine fabrics, *e.g.* when making underwear, nightwear and blouses. As the raw edges are enclosed within the seam there is no need to neaten them.

(a) Pin both pieces of material together, *wrong sides facing*, matching notches and balance marks.

(b) Tack along fitting line. Remove pins.

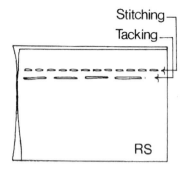

(c) Machine 5 mm outside fitting line or according to width of finished seam.

(d) Remove tacking and trim close to stitching. Press seam open.

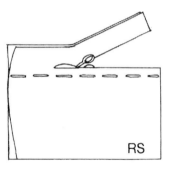

(e) Turn seam so that right sides are together and the seam lies along the top of work. Press.

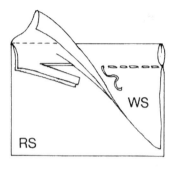

(f) Pin, tack and machine on fitting line, so that raw edges are enclosed.

(g) Remove tackings and press seam towards back of garment.

> *Note:* A French seam may also be sewn by hand. Use a small running or back stitch instead of machining.

A Machine Fell Seam

This seam is sewn on the outside of the garment so that the lines of machining are visible on the right side. It is frequently used on shirts, trousers and denim clothes.

(a) Pin both pieces of material wrong sides together, matching notches and balance marks.

(b) Tack along fitting line. Remove pins.

(c) Machine on fitting line, remove tacking.

(d) Trim one seam allowance to 5 mm, the other to 10 mm.

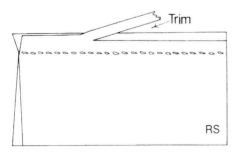

(e) Open out material and press seam flat.

(f) Turn under raw edge of top seam allowance (above 4 mm).

(g) Pin and tack in position on fabric and machine close to the folded edge.

(h) Remove tacking and press.

Run and Fell Seam

This is worked in the same way but use running in place of the first row of machining and hemming in place of the second row of machining. Work on wrong side of garment.

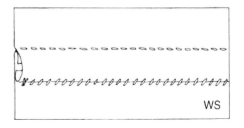

The name 'run and fell' comes from the two stitches used in this seam — running and 'felling', an old-fashioned word for hemming.

Hems

A good hem lies flat and even all round. The stitches should not show through on to the right side, yet the hem must be securely sewn.

Preparing the Hem

Hem lengths are determined by fashion, but should also suit the style of the garment and the wearer. The length of hem is vitally important to the appearance and proportion of the garment.

1. Allow garment to hang for 24 hours before making the hem.

2. Marking the hem length is best done by another person — unless a chalk hem marker is available.

3. Try on garment, wearing the shoes you will be wearing with garment; fasten belt, zip, buttons, *etc.* Stand erect — don't be tempted to look down as this will make hem uneven. Stand on a table, so that hem will be at the eyelevel of person marking it.

4. Mark position of hem with pins.
5. Remove garment and lay flat on a table, wrong side out.
6. Seams must be pressed open and turnings within hem trimmed to reduce bulk, especially in heavy fabrics.
7. Turn up hem on fitting line, matching seams, press lightly (on edge only) and tack 1 cm from fold.
8. Trim away excess fabric (see 'Tips' for depth of hems).

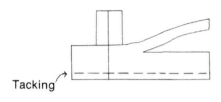

Tacking

9. Neaten or fold in hem edge and stitch loosely in position. Remove tacking.
10. Press lightly on fold of hem — avoid pressing over stitching.

Tips on Hems

* Depth of hem depends on type of material and type of garment.
   (a) Cottons and fine fabrics: — a medium hem about 2–3 cm.
   (b) Blouses/Shirts: — 1.5 cm.
   (c) Dresses: — 3.5 cm, depending on fabric thickness.
   (d) Flared garment: — 1.5 – 2 cm.
   (e) Sheer fabric: — 3 – 5 mm.
   (f) Children's clothes: — 8 – 10 cm, to allow for growth.

* Hem stitches should be invisible from right side — only pick up 1 or 2 threads of garment.
* Hems on pleated garments should be completed before pressing in pleats.

Hem Finishes

Fine Fabrics — *use one of these methods:*

1. Turn under raw edge and slip hem.
2. Edge machine and slip hem.

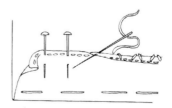

3. Zig-zag on machine and use tailors hemming.

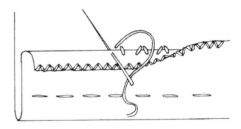

4. Blind hem by machine.

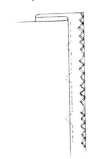

5. Sew a narrow machined hem.

Heavy Fabrics — *use one of these methods:*

1. Herringbone — thick fabrics.

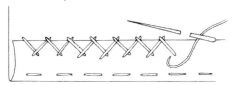

2. Overcast and catch stitch.
3. Biasbinding and slip stitch (A and B).

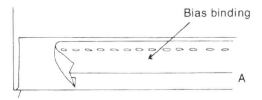

Bias binding

A

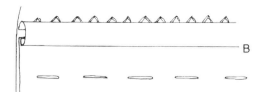

B

4. A bonded hem — using fusible tape (test before use on scrap of fabric).

* Avoid deep hems on very flared garments — they will be difficult to turn up.

* Narrow machined hems (6 mm) are good for garments which get hard wear — jeans, childrens' clothes, aprons, *etc*.

* When skirt is bias cut or flared, it will first be necessary to adjust or reduce fullness of hem before turning up. This may be done by:
(a) Taking tiny pleats here and there on the hem.

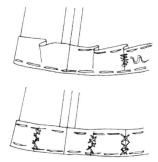

(b) Running a line of gathering thread through hem and pulling slightly.

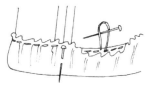

(c) Using a false hem, *i.e.* applying bias binding as a facing to right side of hem, then pressing under and slip stitching in place.

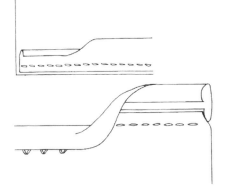

47 *All About Using Patterns*

Before you go out to buy a pattern you must know:
- (a) Your figure type;
- (b) Your exact measurements.

Figuretype

You have only to look around you to see that figures vary a lot — both a very tall person and a very small person could be a standard size 12. For this reason patterns are grouped into figure types. Figure types are based on height and body proportions. Study your shape in the mirror to find out what figure type you are.

Female Figure Types

Male Type Figures
Boys': For the boy who has outgrown children's sizes.
Teen/Boys': Between boys' and men's sizes.
Men's: Average build. Height: 1.77 m.

Children's Figure Types
Toddlers': Range from size ½ - 4.
Children's: Range from sizes 1 - 6, with a longer body than a toddler.
Girls'/Boys': From size 7 - 14, for growing children.

N.B. Children's patterns are sold by height rather than age. Check children's measurements each time you buy a pattern — they grow very quickly.

Young Junior Teen

Young slight figure.
Teenage style fashions.
Height: 1.55 – 1.60 m.

Junior Petite

Short well developed figure
with a short waist.
Height: 1.51 – 1.55 m.
Height: 1.51 – 1.55 m.

Miss Petite

Between Junior Petite and
Miss.
Shorter figure than average.
Height: 1.57 – 1.63 m.

Miss

Well proportioned average
figure.
Height: 1.65 – 1.68 m.

Half Size

Short well-developed mature
figure.
Height: 1.57 – 1.60 m.

Woman's

Larger more mature figure.
Very large sizes available.
Height: 1.65 – 1.68 m.

Pattern Sizes

These are based on measurements around the body *i.e.* bust, waist and hip measurements.

Taking Measurements

1. It is better to have another person take your measurements.

2. Wear normal underclothes or a close fitting garment.

3. Stand straight.

4. Tie a tape or ribbon around the waist to find your true waist.

5. Measure snugly, but not too tightly.

6. Check measurements now and then — as figures change — especially those of children and teenagers.

Females

Bust: Taken from behind. Pass tape over fullest part of bust, with the tape measure slightly higher at the back.

Waist: Measure snugly around natural waistline.

Hips: Place tape around fullest part of hips — usually about 22 cm below waist.

Back waist length: From bone at nape, straight down the back to the waist line.

Cross Chest: Above bust from shoulder to shoulder.

Cross Back: Across back — from armhole to armhole.

Shoulder: From neck to edge of shoulder.

Sleeve length: Bend arm slightly and measure over the bend, from the edge of the shoulder to the wrist.

Full length: From nape of neck, in at the waist, to required length, *e.g.* hem of dress.

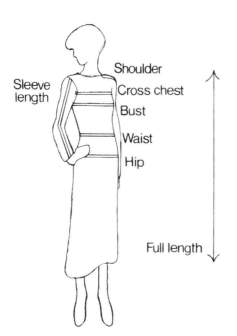

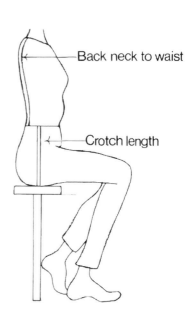

Males

Height: Without shoes.

Neck: Measure around the neck, adding 13 mm for ease.

Chest: Measure around fullest part of chest.

Waist: Around natural waistline.

Hips: Around fullest part.

Outside leg (trouser length): From waist down side of leg to required length (usually base of ankle bone).

Inside leg: From crotch to required length.

Sleeve length: From edge of shoulder, over bent elbow, to wrist.

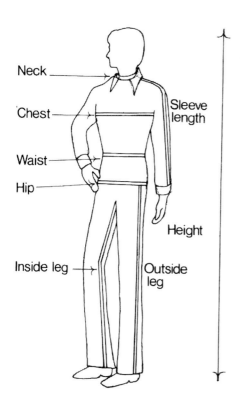

Buying a Pattern

1. Know your figure type and exact measurements.
2. Consider your figure — and pick a style to suit it.
3. Buy a pattern in your correct size. If it is not available, or your measurements fall between two sizes, choose the next largest size.
4. Beginners should choose a simple design with few seams and as little detail as possible. Certain patterns are specially designed for beginners, *e.g.* *Easy to sew* or *Jiffy* patterns.
5. Choose a reliable pattern make, which has good, well-fitting designs and clear instructions.
6. Patterns for clothes worn on the upper half of the body, *e.g.* shirts, jackets, dresses, are sold by the bust/chest measurement; trousers and skirts by the waist measurement.

Buying Fabric

1. A good dressmaking fabric will be:
   (a) Shrink resistant;
   (b) Washable (ask sales assistant for instructions);
   (c) Without flaws;
   (d) Not too stretchy or too loosely woven; } especially for beginners
   (e) Without nap or one way design.
2. Fabrics are sold in the following widths: 90 cm/115 cm/120 cm/140 cm/150 cm. The wider the fabric, the less you require.
3. Choose a fabric suitable for the style you are making. Check pattern envelope for suggested fabrics:
   (a) Stiff fabrics, *e.g.* linen, gaberdine, give a sharp tailored look.

(b) Soft fabrics, *e.g.* silk, brushed nylon or rayon, are more suitable for soft flowing designs.

(c) Beginners should choose a light to medium weight fabric, *e.g.* printed cotton or a polyester and cotton mixture, which are easy to sew.

4. Study the chart on the back of the pattern to find out how much fabric to buy.

5. Check pattern for advice. It may warn against unsuitable fabrics, *e.g.* plaids or one way designs, or may specify a fabric which *must* be used, *e.g.* a knit fabric.

6. Check for crease resistance by crushing fabric in your hand.

7. Nap[1] or one-way fabrics[2] require extra fabric.

8. Buy thread, zips, *etc.* at the same time, so that you can match colours, *etc.* A list of sewing requirements is given on the pattern envelope.

---

[1] **Nap:** A napped fabric has hairs or threads on its surface, which, if brushed one way are smooth; the other way are rough. Velvet and mohair are 'nap' fabrics. When you use a fabric with a nap, all the pieces must be laid in the same direction — usually with the hair or 'pile' running *up*, in velvet and corduroy, and *down* in mohair, brushed fabrics and fur fabric.

[2] **One way designs:** A fabric with a one-way design, *e.g.* with pictures on it or an uneven plaid, must also be laid with the pattern pieces all facing the same direction. Every effort must be made to match checks or any other design when laying out. To do this, position pattern pieces so that corresponding notches lie on the same colour stripe/check.

Using a Pattern

A good sewing pattern has a lot of helpful information — read envelope and instructions carefully, before starting.

A. The Envelope Front: shows a sketch or photograph of the garment, which usually has more than one version or 'view'.

B. The Envelope back:
(a) Shows the back view of the garment;
(b) Gives a description of the garment;
(c) Gives standard body measurements — check them against your own;
(d) Lists suggested fabrics;
(e) Lists sewing requirements (notions) to complete garment;
(f) Gives a chart to help you calculate the amount of fabric, interfacing, *etc.* you require.

C. The instruction sheet gives:
(a) General hints on using the pattern;
(b) Clear instructions on how to lay out the pattern on fabric of different widths;
(c) Alteration instructions;
(e) A list of pattern pieces required for each view;
(e) Step by step instructions on how to make up the garment.

D. The tissue pattern pieces: These are clearly marked with lines and symbols which make it easy to cut out and make up garment.

1715

12 PIECES GIVEN

CHILD'S NIGHTDRESS IN TWO LENGTHS AND DRESSING GOWN: Nightdress softly gathered onto yoke has front slit opening and sleeves gathered into armholes have elasticized lower edge forming frill. View 1 has collar, long sleeves, ribbon bow and trim. View 2 has self fabric bound neckline with ties and short sleeves. Dressing gown with collar has front button fastening, long raglan sleeves, pockets and purchased motif.

METRIC MEASUREMENTS SHOWN IN BLACK

Extra fabric is needed to match plaids, stripes and one-way designs.

STANDARD BODY MEASURE-MENTS	Breast		53		56	58	61	64	cm
	Waist		51		52	53	55	56	,,
	Hip		—		—	61	64	66	,,
	Back — neck to waist		22		23	24	25.5	27	,,
Fabric required		Size	2		3	④	5	6	
View 1 Nightdress									
90cm	without nap		1.90		2.10	2.20	2.50	2.70	m
115cm	,, ,,		1.50		1.60	1.80	2.00	2.10	,,
1cm wide trim			3.00		3.10	3.20	3.40	3.50	,,
View 2 Nightdress									
90cm	without nap		1.50		1.50	1.60	1.80	1.90	,,
115cm	,, ,,		1.10		1.10	1.20	1.40	1.50	,,
Dressing gown									
90cm	without nap		2.10		2.30	2.50	2.70	2.90	,,
140cm	,, ,,		1.30		1.40	1.50	1.60	1.60	,,
165cm	,, ,,		1.10		1.20	1.30	1.40	1.60	,,

Finished back length of View 1 from 71 to 92cm   ; **View 2 from 52 to 68cm**
Dressing gown from 73 to 93cm
Width at lower edge of View 1 from 146 to 177cm   ; **View 2 from 126 to 150cm**
Dressing gown from 116 to 142cm

To complete garment — Thread. View 1 and 2: Bias binding, 6mm wide elastic. View 1: 0.70m of 1cm wide ribbon. Dressing gown: Five 2.2cm buttons, purchased motif.

Suggested fabrics — Soft cotton, lawn, rayon, wool/cotton blends, man-made silk, lingerie jersey, winceyette and synthetics. Dressing gown also in fine wool, jersey, knitted fleece and double sided quilted fabric.

Pattern Markings

These vary slightly between one pattern and another. Check instruction leaflet.

1. **Straight grain of fabric:** This line must be placed exactly on the lengthwise grain.

2. **Place to fold:** A bracketed grainline — the thin line at the edge of this symbol should be placed to the fold of fabric, parallel with the selvage.

3. **Cutting line:** The heavy outline of the pattern.

> *N.B.* remember certain patterns, *e.g. Burda,* have no seam allowance, so they must be cut at least 1.5 cm. *outside* the pattern outline.

4. **Notches:** Diamond shaped symbols on the cutting line which show where to match different pattern pieces. They are numbered in the order in which seams are joined.

5. **Stitching line (or fitting line):** Shown by a broken line, usually 1.5 cm from cutting line. **Arrows** on line indicate direction of sewing.

6. **Balance Marks (usually dots):** These indicate important construction points and must be placed together when making up garment.

7. **Darts:** Shown by broken lines and dots.

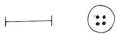

8. **Buttonholes and buttons.**

9. **Centre front or back line.**

10. **Construction markings:** *e.g.* pockets, pleats, are shown by solid and/or broken lines. These are clearly marked.

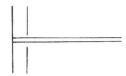

11. **Alteration lines:** Lengthen or shorten pattern on these lines.

Preparing for Cutting

(a) Fabric:

1. Straighten cut ends of fabric by drawing a thread and cutting on this line.
2. If fabric appears to be off grain, pull on bias to straighten it.
3. Examine for flaws.
4. If creased, press with a warm iron.
5. Lay fabric on a large table or on a clean floor.
6. Fold as instructed on layout instructions — right sides together:
7. If selvages are to be placed together (see next page) pin to hold them in place.

Fabric may be laid out in several ways

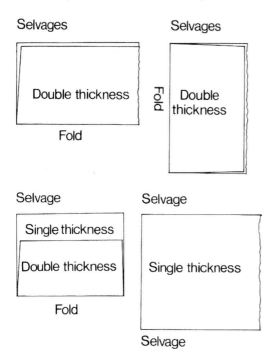

Selvages   Selvages

Double thickness   Fold   Double thickness

Fold

Selvage   Selvage

Single thickness

Double thickness   Single thickness

Fold

Selvage

(b) Preparing Pattern:

1. Check instruction sheet for a list of pieces required for the view you choose.
2. Mark lay-out for your view, size and fabric width.
3. Pick out pattern pieces required and replace extra pieces in envelope.
4. Separate pattern pieces if necessary, leaving a tissue margin outside cutting line.
5. Press pattern pieces with a cool iron.
6. Check measurements against those of pattern pieces and adjust if necessary.

Adjusting a Pattern

1. Use alteration lines on pattern to alter pattern length.
2. Small adjustments can be made on seamlines — adding or taking away a little.

3. **To lengthen** — cut pattern in two on alteration line. Insert backing paper, allowing required amount. Cellotape in position.

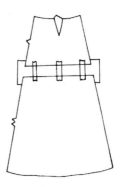

4. **To shorten** — make a fold on alteration line, half the depth required and pin in position.

5. **To adjust width** — take a vertical pleat in pattern, or insert strip as in no. 3.

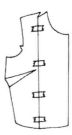

6. A major alteration should be distributed between two or three areas rather than all in one place, *e.g.* the hem, which would make it out of proportion.

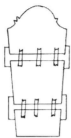

7. Remember if you alter one pattern piece, the adjoining pieces must also be altered or they will not match.
8. If an alteration crosses a design feature, *e.g.* dart or pocket, this must be redrawn or altered to correspond. Buttonholes, *etc.*, may have to be respaced.

Laying out a Pattern

Each pattern is marked with a name, number and size. Most pattern pieces are cut on the double — any pieces to be laid on the single will indicate this.

1. Circle correct cutting layout and lay out pattern pieces as instructed — remember to check whether fabric is folded lengthwise or crosswise.
2. Place large pieces on first, then fit in smaller pieces. Those cut on the single are left to the end.

3. Place pattern pieces with straight grain running parallel with selvage. Check with tape measure, then pin in position.
4. Pattern pieces marked 'place on fold' should lie directly on fold.
5. Check *all* pieces fit on fabric before pinning or cutting out.
6. Fix pins securely about 10–15 cm apart, placing pins within seam allowance.
7. If a piece has to be laid on twice, lay on, mark outline of pattern with chalk or pins, then remove and lay on a second time.
8. Remember 'one-way' fabrics, such as velvet, corduroy and certain prints, must have all pattern pieces laid in one direction — this requires more fabric.

Cutting Out

1. Using a sharp scissors, cut out with long smooth strokes.
2. Hold fabric flat on table with left hand (with right if left handed).
3. Never lift fabric.
4. Cut exactly on thick cutting line.
5. Cut notches *outwards* to avoid reducing seam allowance.
6. For patterns without a seam allowance, allow 1.5 cm around seams and more on hems. Mark clearly with pins or chalk and cut along marked line.

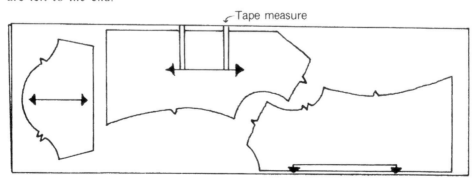

Tape measure

Marking

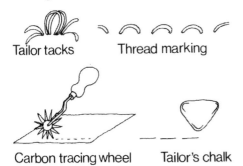

Tailor tacks   Thread marking

Carbon tracing wheel   Tailor's chalk

Before removing pattern pieces, all important markings must be transferred from pattern to fabric. Work on a hard surface when marking fabric. This may be done by:

(a) **Tailor tacks** *(p. 334):* This is the best method as they can be used on any fabric to transfer dots, darts, buttonholes and other design features.

(b) **Threadmarking** *(p. 334):* This is used to transfer seam lines, foldlines, pleats, *etc.* Use different coloured thread for tailor tacks and threadmarking.

(c) **Dressmakers carbon and tracing wheel:** This is useful on smooth fabrics. Fabric must be folded right side out so that markings show on wrong side.

(d) **Tailors chalk:** Unless you are going to stitch immediately, this is not a good method, as chalk rubs off easily.

Over to you . . .

1. Find out which figure type *you* are. Working with a friend, take one another's measurements and jot them down like this:

	Now	In 3 months	In 6 months	In 1 year
Bust				
Waist				
X Chest				
X Back				
Length to waist				
Sleeve length				
Shoulder				
Neck				
Outside leg				

2. Sketch and describe a simple outfit you would make for yourself for casual summer wear. Visit a pattern shop (or look at a pattern book at school) and find the pattern as close as possible to the outfit you had in mind. Find out (a) the cost of patterns; (b) the amount of fabric required; (c) the extras required, *e.g.* zip, interfacing; (d) the type of fabric suitable.

3. List eight well known pattern markings. Draw a sketch of each and describe what it is used for.

4. List *four* basic points to remember when preparing fabric for dressmaking. State how you would prepare the pattern, lay it on the fabric and cut it out.

5. Name *four* methods of marking pattern symbols onto fabric. In the case of *one* describe, with diagrams, how to mark with it.

48   *All About Pattern Layouts*

> *Note:* **Fabrics required** refers to *sizes 10/12/14.*

A Gathered Apron

Fabric required: 90 cm wide: 0.80 metre.
Suitable fabrics: Crisp cotton; gingham; cotton/polyester mixture.

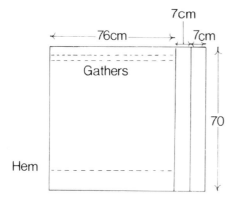

Order of Work

1. Cut out apron according to diagram.
2. Turn in a narrow double hem at each side of apron skirt, tack and edge machine.
3. Make two rows of gathering on upper edge of apron skirt.
4. Make band and ties: Cut one waistband pieces 70 cm × 7 cm and divide it in two — making two pieces 35 cm × 7 cm. Attach one piece to each side of remaining waistband piece by machining.

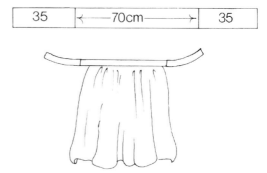

5. Attach apron to waistband *(p. 383)* matching centre fronts.
6. Machine 'ties', right sides together, turn inside out and press.
7. Hem back of waistband.
8. Turn up apron hem and slipstitch in place.

Nightdress

Measurements
    required: Bust, length to hem.
Fabric required: 90 cm wide: 3 metres.
                115 cm wide: 2.5 metres.
Suitable fabrics: Fine cottons; polyester; gingham; seersucker; brushed nylon.

Order of work

1. Lay out pattern on fabric, having first made necessary alterations.
2. Pin and cut out, mark with tailor tacks or tracing wheel.
3. Remove pattern and cut tailor tacks.
4. Tack and machine side and shoulder seams.
5. Remove tacking, press and neaten.

6. Apply lace and/or bias binding to neck and armhole edges.
7. Using bias binding, make a casing above waistline for elastic.
8. Fit and turn up hem. Slip stitch or attach lace and machine in place.

A Nightdress front
B Nightdress back
C Drawstring
D Bias strips for facing

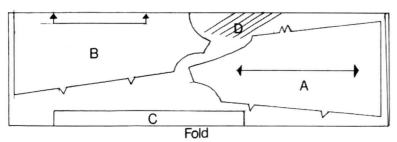

Fold

Gathered (drindl) Skirt

Measurements
required: Waist, length of waist to hem.
Fabric required: Double waist to hem length plus 10 cm for turning and hem (approx. 1.70–2 metres).
Suitable fabrics: Crisp cottons; rayon; lightweight wool; brushed fabrics.

Order of work

1. Fold fabric as shown on diagram — a pattern is not required. (Cut waistband on single thickness — 10 cm deep and length of waist plus 4 cm).
2. Cut out skirt pieces.
3. Tack up side seams of skirt — leaving opening for zip.
4. Press and neaten seams. Insert zip.
5. Run a double line of gathering at top of skirt.
6. Make up waistband, adding interfacing if necessary.
7. Attach waistband to skirt, adjusting gathers to fit.
8. Fit and turn up hem — slip stitch in place.
9. Press completed skirt.

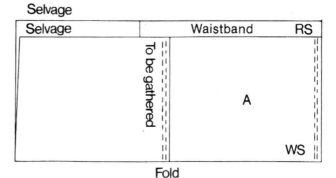

Selvage
Selvage | Waistband | RS
To be gathered
A
WS
Fold

Flared Skirt

Measurements
required: Waist, hip, length of waist to
hem.
Fabric required: 90 cm wide: approx. 1.50 m.
115 cm wide: approx. 1.20 m.
140 cm. wide: approx. .8 m.
Suggested
fabrics: Glazed cotton; denim; corduroy; lightweight wool; rayon.

Order of work

1. Lay out pattern as shown on diagram.
2. Cut out and tailor tack. Remove pattern and cut tailor tacks.
3. Tack darts and seams. Fit and adjust if
necessary. Attach pocket.
4. Machine and press darts and seams.
Neaten seams.
5. Insert zip.
6. Prepare and apply waistband.
7. Sew waistband fastening, *e.g.* button,
hooks & eyes.
8. Fit and turn up hem. Stitch in place.
9. Press completed skirt.

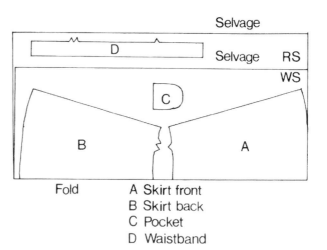

A Skirt front
B Skirt back
C Pocket
D Waistband

Shirt

Measurements
required: Bust (chest), waist, hip, finished length (neck to hem),
length of sleeve.
Fabric required: 90 cm wide; approx. 2 m.
115 cm wide: approx. 1.80 m.
Suggested
fabrics: Cottons, *e.g.* lawn/gingham/
cheesecloth; silk; rayon;
polyester; soft 'brushed'
fabrics.

Order of work

1. Check measurements and alter if
necessary.
2. Lay out pattern as shown; pin; cut
and tailor tack.
3. Remove pattern, cut tailor tacks.
4. Edge machine facings.
5. Tack darts, shoulders and sideseams.
Fit and alter if necessary.
6. Machine darts and seams, press.
Neaten seams.

7. Prepare (interface if necessary) and attach collar.
8. Make up and attach sleeves and neaten armhole.
9. Make up (interface if necessary) and attach cuffs.
10. Make buttonholes and sew on buttons.
11. Turn up hem and stitch.
12. Press completed shirt.

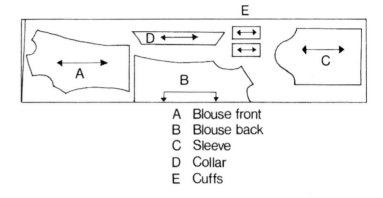

A   Blouse front
B   Blouse back
C   Sleeve
D   Collar
E   Cuffs

Dress

**Measurements
   required:** Bust, waist, hip length from neck to hem.
Fabric required: 90 cm wide: approx. 3 m.
   115 cm wide: approx. 2.5 m.
Suitable fabrics: Cotton; rayon; polyester; linen.

Order of work

1. Check measurements; alter, if necessary.
2. Lay out pattern; pin, cut and tailor tack.
3. Remove pattern, cut tailor tacks.
4. Tack darts, shoulders and side seams.
5. Fit and alter if necessary.
6. Machine darts and seams; press. Neaten seams.
7. Insert zip.
8. Make up and attach collar.
9. Make up and attach sleeves. Hem sleeves.
10. Turn up hem and stitch. Press completed dress.

A   Dress front
B   Dress back
C   Sleeve
D   Collar
E   Back neck facing
F   Front neck facing

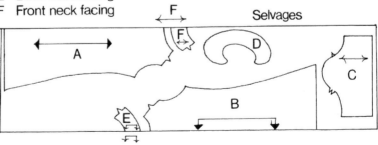

Trousers/Shorts/Pyjamas

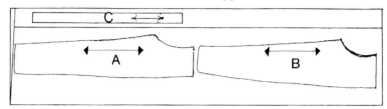

Trousers

Measurements: Waist, hip, crotch length, length of trousers.

Fabric required: 90 cm: 2.4 m. approx.
115 cm: 2.20 m. approx.

Suitable fabrics: Heavyweight cottons, *e.g.* denim/poplin; linen, light-weight wool; corduroy.

Shorts

Measurements: as above.

Fabric required: 90 cm: 1.00 m.
115 cm: 0.70 m.

Suitable fabrics: Heavyweight cottons *e.g.* poplin/sailcloth/denim; linen; polyester; blends.

Order of Work: as for Trousers.

Pyjamas

Use layout and order of work for (a) shirt, (b) trousers.

Order of work

1. Check measurements and alter if necessary.
2. Lay out pattern as shown; pin, cut and tailor tack.
3. Remove pattern; cut tailor tacks.
4. Tack darts and seams. Fit and adjust if necessary.
5. Machine darts and leg seams. Press. Neaten seams.
6. Machine crotch seam. Press and neaten.
7. Insert zip.
8. Prepare and attach waistband. Press. Sew on fastenings.
9. Fit and turn up hems. Stitch in place.
10. Press completed trousers — taking care to press trouser creases down centre leg.

Fitting

When making up a garment, the main pieces must be tacked up and tried on *before* machining, so that any alterations can be made. It is more accurate to have a second person at hand to help you fit the garment.

5. Mark any alterations with pins or chalk.

6. Remove garment and re-tack along new fitting lines.

7. Try garment on again — several times if necessary, until you are satisfied that it fits correctly.

Preparing for First Fitting

1. Pin pieces of garment together, matching notches, tailor tacks and fitting lines. Leave out collar and sleeves — these should be fitted later.

2. Tack darts and seams securely in position and try on, right side out.

3. Make sure centre of garment lies on the centre of the body. Close opening with pins and tie belt around waist (if the garment is belted).

4. Stand in front of a mirror and examine the garment. Ask yourself:
   (a) Does it hang correctly, without dragging or wrinkling?
   (b) Is it too tight or too loose? It should be comfortable.
   (c) Are darts in the correct position? Are they the right length?
   (d) Is the waistline exactly on the waist?
   (e) Do the shoulder seams lie along the line of your shoulder?
   (f) Are front, back and side seams straight (exactly vertical)?
   (g) Does the neckline/armhole fit snugly against your neck/shoulder or does it hang loose?
   (h) Sleeves should be fitted at a later stage. They should hang straight without wrinkling.

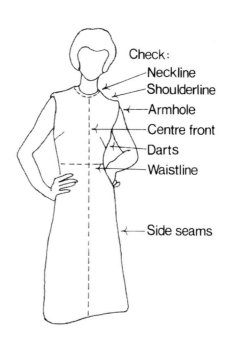

Check:
Neckline
Shoulderline
Armhole
Centre front
Darts
Waistline

Side seams

Press As You Go!

Pressing is a very important part of dressmaking. Every stage must be pressed before proceeding to the next stage — this makes it easier to see what you are doing and helps give the garment a well made 'professional' look. A garment that looks 'homemade' is often so due to insufficient pressing during construction.

Rules for Pressing

1. Pressing is *not* a sliding movement, like ironing. When pressing, the iron is lifted and placed down on the fabric.
2. Press with the grain, using enough pressure to flatten fabric.
3. Press on the wrong side of fabric. If you must press on the right side, use a pressing cloth.
4. Use correct temperature for fabric — test if necessary on a scrap of the fabric.
5. Moisture may be necessary for woollens and heavy fabrics. Pressing cloth should be damp — not wet. Be sure to press fabric until dry, and hang up to air afterwards.
6. Remove pins and tacking before pressing.
7. Press every dart and seam after it has been stitched — before joining it to another section.
8. Press each stage (*e.g.* collar) after it has been completed — before attaching to garment.
9. Arrange fabric carefully before pressing, to avoid creasing or stretching.
10. Give a thorough final pressing when garment is complete.

Pressing Hints

Seams: Press stitching flat, then press open, or to one side.

Curved seams: Arrange carefully on a rounded surface, *e.g.* a tailors 'ham' or cushion and press with point of iron.

Darts: Press to one side. Horizontal darts are pressed down, vertical darts towards the centre. Do not press beyond point of dart.

Gathers: Avoid pressing over gathers — press into gathers with point of iron, holding gathers with left hand.

Pressing seams and hems: Place a strip of brown paper beneath turnings to avoid making a ridge on the right side.

Over to you . . .

1. Pick the pattern layout for (a) shirt; (b) trousers and copy it into your copybook. Which pieces would you leave out if you were making a sleeveless shirt?

2. Describe the order of work to be followed when making up a summer dress with collar, long sleeves and cuffs.

3. Write a note on the importance of fitting in dressmaking — what flaws should you look out for when fitting a garment for the first time?

4. List the five points you consider most important in pressing — state the reason for choosing each one.

49   *All About Trimmings*

Attaching Lace

Lace is a quick and attractive way of decorating underwear, nightwear, blouses and evening wear.

Top Sewing Lace

1. Turn under a narrow hem onto wrong side of garment and hold in place with hemming or machining.
2. Place wrong side of lace to wrong side of garment, with edges together and pin in position.
3. Tack and topstitch neatly in place.
4. Remove tacking, open out lace and press on wrong side.

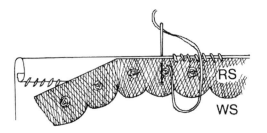

Machining Lace

(a) Straight stitch

1. Turn a narrow hem onto right side of garment.
2. Tack in position.
3. Place edge of lace to fold of hem and tack in position.

4. Machine close to edge of lace, catching in garment hem at the same time.
5. Remove tacking and press on the wrong side.

Straight machining

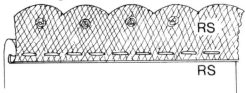

(b) Zig-Zag Machining

1. Turn hem onto wrong side of garment and tack in position.
2. Place lace to tacking line on right side, pin and tack.
3. Machine, using a zig-zag stitch, so that it stitches half onto lace and half onto garment. Remove tacking.

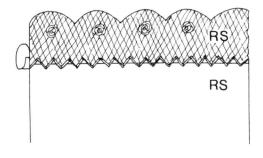

Bias Facing

Some forms of lace, *e.g.* Broderie Anglaise, have a raw edge. Use bias binding to attach this type of lace, so that the raw edge is enclosed.

1. Cut bias strips approximately 25 mm deep, or use ready made bias binding.
2. Place raw edge of lace to raw edge of hem, right sides together.
3. Lay bias facing on top of lace, right side down, with raw edges together.
4. Tack and machine 5 mm from edge.
5. Remove tacking and press.
6. Turn bias to wrong side, turning in a 4 mm turning; hem in place, enclosing raw edges.

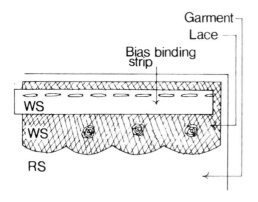

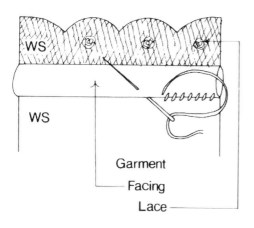

Frilled Lace

1. Run a gathering thread through the top of lace and pull up.
2. Pin in position on garment, right sides together, raw edges even. Adjust gathers to fit.
3. Apply bias facing and finish as above.

Appliqué

Appliqué is a quick way of decorating garments, aprons, bags, *etc.* It involves cutting out simple shapes and designs in contrasting fabrics and applying them to a garment: (a) by hand, using closely worked blanket stitch; (b) by machine, using a close zig-zag stitch. It is particularly suitable for childrens clothes.

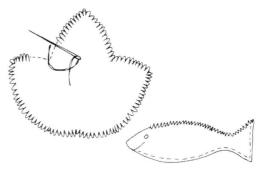

1. Choose a simple design with few details.
2. Trace onto fabric and cut out.
3. Pin and tack in position on right side of garment.
4. Make a line of running stitches around outline, then machine or blanket stitch in place, using matching or contrasting thread.
5. Details may be filled-in using embroidery.

> *Note:* To prevent fraying, iron on fusible interlining to wrong side of appliqué.

Bias Binding

We have already learned that woven fabric has a strong **lengthwise** grain and a **crosswise** grain. Neither has much 'give'.

If you fold a piece of fabric at **right angles,** so that the lengthwise threads lie directly on top of the crosswise threads, you will get a diagonal fold which is called the **true bias.**

As this is very stretchy, strips cut on the bias are very useful for neatening curves, such as necklines, as they stretch around the curve, and lie flat when finished. Bias binding is used:

1. **As a facing:** to finish off a straight or a curved edge, *e.g.* a neckline.
2. **As a binding:** to finish off straight and curved edges.
3. **To neaten raw edges** of seams.
4. **To neaten flared hems.**
5. **As a piping:** with piping cord inside to decorate cushions.
6. **As a rucking,** *e.g.* to slot elastic through waistlines.

Bindings or Facings?

Bindings are visable on right and wrong sides as a narrow border; **facings** are turned completely to the wrong side, so that they cannot be seen from the right side. Both are used to neaten raw edges, particularly curved edges. Bindings often form a decorative feature, particularly if a contrasting colour is used.

1. Ready made bias binding can be bought in several colours and in three or four widths.

2. Bias may be used in matching or contrasting colours.
3. Bias binding should be chosen which can be washed in a similar way to the garment fabric.
4. Bias frays easily — do not handle roughly and avoid too much ripping.
5. Apply bias binding so that joins are as inconspicuous as possible.
6. Allow 5 cm at each end for neatening.
7. On curves, stretch the side of bias being attached to the curve, using a warm iron.

To Cut Bias Strips

1. Fold fabric so that lengthwise threads lie parallel with cross-wise threads — this will give you the **true bias.**

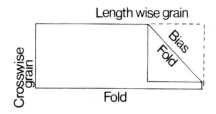

2. Pin fold in position, press lightly, then open out fabric and cut along the fold.
3. Measure strips 3–4 cm wide*, parallel with cut edge, and mark with pins or tailors chalk.

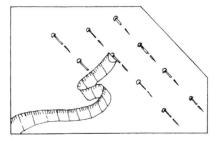

* Width of strips depends on type of fabric and the purpose for which they are being used, *e.g.* 2.5 cm deep for binding; 3 cm wide for facing.

Joining Bias Strips

Straight seams are never used on bias binding. Seams are always sewn on a slant, along the straight grain.

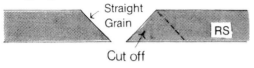

Straight Grain

RS

Cut off

1. Lay strips flat on a table, right sides up.
2. Cut short ends parallel with grain.
3. With right sides facing, place cut raw edges together as shown — corners should project at each end of the little seam.

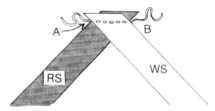

A — RS   B — WS

4. Tack and machine (or backstitch) seam from A to B.
5. Secure threads and remove tacking.
6. Cut off points and press seam open.

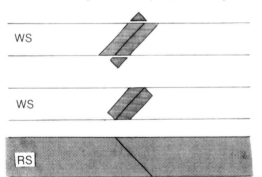

WS

WS

RS

Finished join

Incorrect bias join

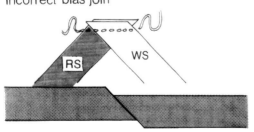

RS   WS

Joining while attaching to garment, *e.g.* to armhole

1. Stop machining about 25 mm from join.

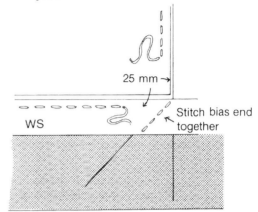

25 mm →

WS   Stitch bias end together

2. Pin bias ends carefully together, remembering to join on straight grain, close to garment.
3. Tack and machine. Remove tackings, trim and press.
4. Finish sewing binding to garment.

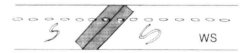

WS

Binding a Curved Edge

1. Trim seam allowance of garment to 6 mm.
2. Stay-stitch edges likely to stretch.
3. Cut, join and stretch enough bias pieces to fit the curve, allowing 4 cm at each end for neatening.
4. Turn under 4 mm turnings on each side, along length of binding.
5. Open one turning and place bias binding on curve right sides together and raw edges even (place stretched edge to outer curve).
6. Pin and tack just above creased edge.
7. Machine on crease line; remove tacking.

8. Turn bias to wrong side of garment; turn under and hem to seamline, picking up machine stitches so that sewing will not be visable on the right side.
9. Press on the wrong side.

Binding a curved edge

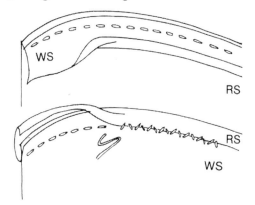

Straight edges, *e.g.* seam turnings, are bound in the same way but without stretching the binding.

Applying Bias as a Facing

This can be worked on straight or curved edges:

1. Cut bias facings 4 cm wide — this allows a 2 cm finished facing plus 2×1 cm turnings.
2. Cut and join enough bias pieces to fit edge to be faced. Stretch one side of bias if it is facing an outward curve.
3. Press in 1 cm turnings on each side along length of binding.
4. Open one turning and place in position, right sides together, with creased line of binding to fitting line of garment.

Binding as a facing

5. Pin, tack and machine on creased line.
6. Remove tacking, trim turnings to 8 mm and clip or notch curve.
7. Press bias upward and turn to wrong side, so that it is not visable from right side.
8. Tack facing to wrong side of garment and slip stitch fold loosely in place.

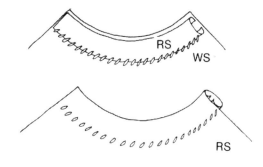

Tapes

Tapes, ribbons and straps are all stitched to garments in a similar way.

Preparation of Tape

1. Turn under 3 mm on raw edge at one end of tape.
2. Crease a diagonal fold as shown, to get a true square. Then crease the lower line of the square as a guide for sewing on tape.

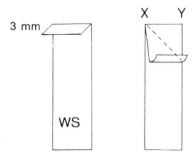

Attaching Tape

1. Pin wrong side of tape in position on wrong side of garment or band — the crease at the end of the square (XY) should lie along the edge of the garment.
2. Fold back tape and top sew from right to left, where edge of tape meets garment.
3. At end of top sewing, turn corner and stitch around three sides of tape using tiny hemming stitches.
4. Secure stitch and slip needle through fold.

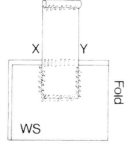

> *Note:* Tape may also be attached by machining around edge of square.

Stitching Loops of Tape

1. Cut a piece of tape 12 cm long. Fold in two.
2. Top sew tapes together, the depth that the finished tape will be attached to fabric.
3. Hem around tape as shown, top sewing where tape touches edge of fabric.

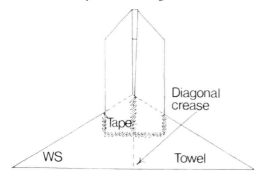

Pockets

Pockets come in many shapes and sizes. The following are two of the simplest.

Patch Pocket (with rounded corners)

1. On top of pocket, turn under 5 mm to wrong side and edge machine.
2. Fold top edge down 2.5 cm to right side. Tack.
3. Machine on fitting line as shown; continue machining around fitting line of pocket, making a double row of stitching at each end, to secure.
4. Trim corners and clip curve.
5. Turn pocket top to right side and press in place. Press turnings under, along stitching line.
6. Pin and tack in position on garment, matching tailor tacks.
7. Edge machine around pocket, strengthening upper corners with a triangle of machining.
8. Finish off threads and press.

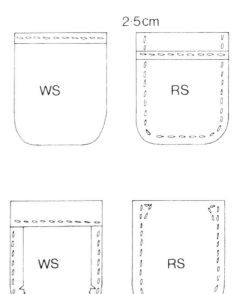

Square pocket: as for patch pocket except press under sides and ends of pocket, mitring corners as shown. Slip stitch mitre in place.

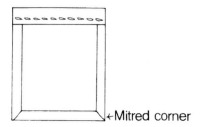

←Mitred corner

Pocket in Side Seam

This may be made from lining if garment fabric is too bulky.

1. Cut out pocket according to pattern directions — 2 pieces are required for each pocket.
2. With right sides together, and matching notches and tailor tacks, tack each pocket piece to side seam turning.

3. Trim seams and press to one side. Neaten by zig-zag machining.
4. With right sides together, pin front and back pieces of garment and pocket together, matching notches and tailor tacks.
5. Stitch side seam from top down, on fitting line, pivoting on corner A, stitch around pocket, then pivot on corner B and machine to hem. Reinforce corners with a second row of machining for 2.5 cm on each side of corner.
6. Neaten side seams.
7. Zig-zag or blanket stitch curve of pocket to neaten.
8. Press.

Pocket in side seam

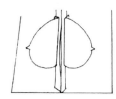 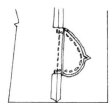

Over to you . . .

1. Name *three* methods of attaching lace to a nightdress hem. In the case of one, describe in detail how it is worked using diagrams.

2. What is the true bias? Describe briefly how to cut and join bias strips and attach them to a neckline as a **binding**. Use diagrams.

3. Name *four* places you might use tapes. Describe how to sew a tape onto the corner of an item in order to hang it.

4. Describe, using diagrams, how to attach a simple pocket to an apron.

50   *All About Disposing of Fullness*

There are several ways of controlling fullness (*i.e.* making a wide piece of fabric fit into a smaller piece), in order to give shape and style to a garment.

A. Darts   C. Tucks
B. Gathers   D. Pleats

Darts

A dart is a wedge-shaped fold of fabric which helps give shape to clothes. Darts are frequently used at the top of skirts and trousers to make them fit neatly at the waist. They are also used on shoulders and under the arms.

Sewing a Dart

1. Transfer pattern markings to fabric, *e.g.* by tailor tacking.
2. With right sides together, pin fitting lines of dart together, tapering towards the point. Tack.

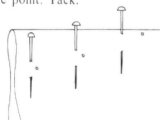

3. Machine in a straight line from the widest part of the dart to the point, tapering to nothing as you come to the point.

4. Secure both ends of dart, by tying a knot or by using remaining thread to sew a double backstitch.

5. Remove tacking.
6. Slash very wide darts, or those on heavy fabrics, to 2 cm from the point. Finish off by overcasting or blanket-stitching.

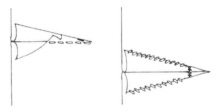

7. Press in one of the following ways:
   (a) *Vertical darts* towards centre front or back;
   (b) *Horizontal darts, e.g.* bust dart, downwards;
   (c) *Slashed darts* are pressed flat.

Double Pointed Darts

These are used in fitted clothes, *e.g.* shirts or dresses which do not have a waist seam.

1. Prepare as for normal darts.
2. Stitch from one end to the other, following the tailor tacks.
3. Secure by knotting or backstitching ends of thread.

4. Clip centre to 5 mm from stitching; overcast raw edges.
5. Press towards centre.

A Dart Tuck

This is an unfinished dart which looks like an unpressed pleat. Dart tucks are used on shoulders and at the waist edge of skirts and trousers.

Gathers

Gathers are used to ease in fullness, so that a wide stretch of fabric is eased along a gathering thread to fit into a narrower section.

Gathers are used:

1. On the yokes of dresses, blouses and smocks;
2. Waists of skirts, trousers;
3. Cuffs of blouses;
4. Sleeveheads;
5. On frills, *e.g.* around the hem of dresses.

Gathering is shown on a pattern by a broken line between two dots or notches. It is normally worked on single fabric, using two parallel rows of stitching. It can be worked by hand, using a running stitch, or by machine.

To Work Machine Gathers

1. Loosen upper tension so that bobbin thread can be pulled easily. Lengthen stitch slightly and test gathering stitch.
2. Machine a row of gathering between gathering points, 2 mm above fitting line and machine a second line 2 mm above first row.
3. Gently pull bobbin threads and slide the fabric along until the correct length is reached. (Threads can be drawn from either end, or from both ends).
4. Secure ends of threads by winding around a pin.
5. Distribute gathers evenly.

> *Note:* If work to be gathered is very long, *e.g.* a gathered skirt, one continuous row will put too much of a strain on the thread. Divide work into sections and sew separate gathering threads for each section.

Attaching Gathers to a Band
(*e.g.* a gathered skirt or apron)

1. Fold band lengthwise in two, right sides together.
2. Tack and machine the short seams at each end, stopping 1 cm from edge.
3. Remove tacking, turn and press. Tack upper edge in position.
4. Mark centre of band and section to be gathered.

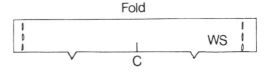

5. Work two rows of gathering at top of fabric and draw it up to fit the band.

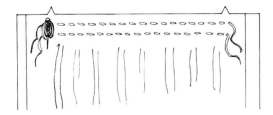

6. Place right side of band to right side of gathers and raw edges together, matching centres notches and fitting lines.
7. Pin single fold of band in position, distributing gathers evenly as you work.
8. Tack and machine on fitting line.

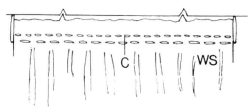

9. Remove tacking and press lightly.
10. Turn under remaining seam allowance and pin, tack and hem back of band to machining.

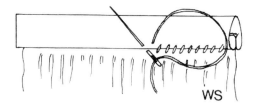

Tucks

Tucks look like small pleats, except that they are usually stitched down their entire length, forming a fold on the right side of the garment. Tucks can vary in width from 2 mm to 2 cm. Tiny tucks are called **pintucks.** They may be stitched by hand (running) or by machine.

Tucks are used as a decoration. They are also useful for shortening childrens clothes so that they can be let down later on.

It is important to be very accurate when measuring and stitching tucks. Crooked or uneven tucks will spoil the appearance of a garment.

Allow 2–3 times extra fabric for tucks, depending on type of tuck.

Tucks

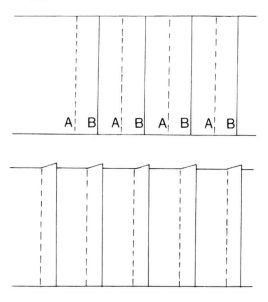

Making Tucks

1. Mark tuck lines accurately onto fabric, using threadmarks or tracing wheel.
2. Working from left to right with wrong sides together, pin tucks straight to a thread placing broken line A, to B.
3. Tack and machine. Remove tacking.
4. Press back of tucks lightly.
5. On front, press tucks in required direction, using a damp cloth.

Pleats

Pleats are decorative folds, used to give extra width to garments. They usually require three times the finished width of fabric. They may be stitched partway down on the inside, on the outside, or left to hang from a band or yoke. Most pleats are pressed carefully to give a sharp edge; some are left unpressed, to give a softer look.

Styles of Pleats

    (a) Knife
    (b) Box
    (c) Inverted.

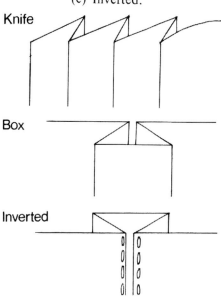

Knife

Box

Inverted

Order of Work

1. Lay fabric flat on table when working with pleats.
2. Transfer pleat lines carefully from pattern to fabric, using threadmarking or tracing wheel.
3. On patterns, pleats are usually marked with a solid and a broken line. Use one colour tack for solid line (fold on this line) and another for the broken lines (bring pleat to this line). Fold in the direction of the arrows.
4. Keeping upper edge even, pin and tack pleats accurately. Press lightly.
5. Tack pleats securely to a piece of tape for fitting.
6. Insert zip.
7. Attach waistband or bodice of dress.
8. Turn up hem, stitch and remove tacking. Press pleats well, both inside and out.

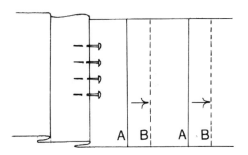

51   *All About Fastenings*

Most garments need fastenings to keep them in position. There is a wide variety of fastenings, many of which also provide decoration or fashion detail.

Points to Remember

1. Most fastenings are sewn on doubled fabric — (a) for strength; (b) to prevent visible stitches on the outside.
2. Fastenings should suit the fabric to which they are attached *i.e.* strong durable fastenings on heavy fabrics, small delicate fastenings on fine fabrics.
3. Fastenings should wash and dry-clean according to the fabric.
4. Fastenings not used as a decoration should be invisible.
5. They should be positioned close enough to keep the garment closed.
6. Remember boys and mens clothes fasten left-over-right, girls and womens right-over-left. Sleeves and cuffs fasten front-over-back.

Buttonholes

Buttonholes should be just large enough for the button to pass through and should be as invisible as possible. They may be horizontal or vertical.

Horizontal buttonholes: are most often used. They usually have a rounded end (nearest the opening) and a straight or barred end.

Vertical buttonholes: are suitable for garments where there is little strain. They may have two round or two barred ends.

Preparing a Buttonhole

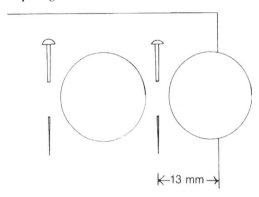

1. Test one or two buttonholes on a scrap of the fabric before attempting to sew one on the garment. Badly sewn buttonholes will spoil a garment.
2. The size of the buttonhole depends on the size of the button. The minimum length is equal to the diameter of the button plus its thickness. If the buttonhole is too tight, it will fray; if it is too large, the garment will not stay closed.
3. Always sew on double fabric, preferably with interfacing for strength.
4. Mark position of buttonholes carefully from the pattern, using tailor tacks and then small tacking stitches.
5. The distance between the outer edge of the buttonhole and the edge of garment should be at least half the width of the button, or 13 mm.
6. Buttonholes should be spaced evenly. If the pattern is altered, remember to re-space buttonholes.
7. Buttonholes should be sewn when garment is completed. *Exception:* bound buttonholes.
8. Always work buttonholes before sewing on buttons.

Working

1. Mark buttonholes, using small tacking stitches.

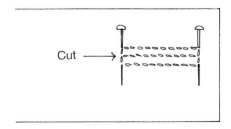

2. Place a pin at either end of buttonhole and slit — using a sharp razor blade or scissors. Remove pins.
3. If fabric frays, overcast edges or apply a thin coat of colourless nailpolish to the edges.
4. Starting at lower left hand corner, insert needle between folds, so that it comes out on the left hand side of slit.

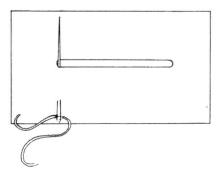

5. Working from left to right, insert needle into back of slit, as shown, bringing it out the required depth of stitch.
6. Wind double thread around point of needle for left to right and pull out, drawing upward to form a knot.

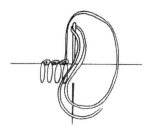

7. Continue in this way, keeping stitches evenly spaced and equal in depth. Do not pull too tightly.
8. **Round end:** Work 5 or 7 overcasting stitches in a fan shape around the outer end of the buttonhole. (An uneven number of stitches ensures that the centre stitch is in line with the slit).

9. **Barred (straight) end:** Take two or three stitches across both sides to draw slit together. Work seven or five buttonhole stitches across end, at right angles to the buttonhole.

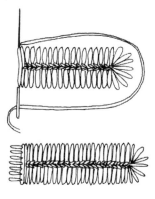

10. Bring needle to back and slip through a few stitches before cutting.

Machined Buttonholes

Most swing-needle sewing machines are capable of stitching buttonholes, by using a very close zig-zag stitch.

1. Follow general rules for preparing and marking buttonholes.

2. The fabric is not slit until after the buttonhole is made.
3. Follow instruction book exactly. This will tell you the length and width of stitch required.

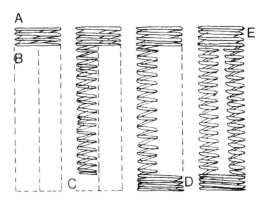

Buttons

Choose buttons which match or contrast well with fabric.

A. Buttons should suit the fabric and garment, *e.g.* tiny shirt buttons would not suit a heavy tweed coat; large heavy buttons would not suit a delicate fabric.
B. Look at the back of the pattern envelope for information about the number and size of buttons required.

Sewing on Buttons — general points

1. Buttons should be sewn on firmly and strongly, yet not so tightly that they cause puckering.
2. A **shank** may be necessary, if there is none on the button, especially on thick fabrics.
3. Use strong thread, doubled if necessary, for extra strength.
4. Work buttonholes before sewing on buttons. Then try on the garment, matching centre fronts, and mark position of buttons with pins.

How to sew on a Button

Underside of button

1. Mark position of button with crossed pins.
2. Make two backstitches over pins to secure thread.
3. Place button over pins, and stitch by stabbing needle up and down through the holes of the button. Do not pull too tightly.
4. Continue until quite secure. Remove pins.
5. Bring needle out between button and fabric and wind thread around stitches to form a shank.
6. Pass needle to back of work and secure by sewing two or three blanket stitches over threads.

A. Buttons with four holes my be sewn like this.

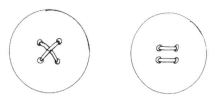

B. Buttons with shanks — stitch through shank, then down into fabric, up and back through shank again.

C. Reinforced buttons — on heavy coats and jackets, reinforce buttons by placing a small flat button directly behind main button, sewing through both. Place shank between outer button and fabric as usual.

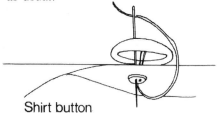

Shirt button

Loops

When an opening meets edge to edge, buttons and loops are a good method of fastening.

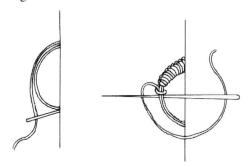

Worked Loop or Bar

This can be used with a button or a hook (see below) and is also useful as a belt carrier. Use strong thread.

1. Loop must be large enough for button to pass through.
2. Secure thread with a back stitch on the edge of fabric; then take a stitch the required distance away (a pencil or similar object will help space the loop).
3. Repeat three or four times, depending on thickness of fabric.
4. Work button-hole or blanket stitch along 'bar-tack', placing stitches closely together.

Hooks and Eyes

These are available in various sizes. Use large, strong hooks for heavy duty fastenings.

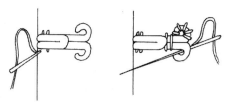

Attaching Hooks

1. Stitch hooks to underside of overlap. The edge of the hook should be in line with the edge of the garment.
2. Attach hook to garment by sewing two stitches under hook.
3. Sew a further two stitches to hold the shaft of the hook in position.
4. Stitch around the two loops of the hook, using blanket stitch, buttonhole stitch or overcasting.
5. Secure with a small backstitch and pass the needle through the fold.

Attaching Eyes or Bars

Eyes are used on garments where edges meet edge to edge and do not overlap. **Bars** are used on garments where edges overlap, *e.g.* waistbands.

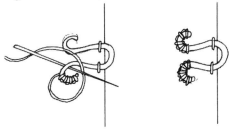

1. Sew eye to *wrong* side of underlap, opposite hook.
2. Position carefully, so that eye is exactly opposite hook, with edge of eye only slightly projecting.

3. Take two stitches at each side of the eye to keep it in position.
4. Stitch loops of eye in position using buttonhole or blanketstitch.
5. Sew bar to *right* side of underlay. Buttonhole or blanket stitch around loops.

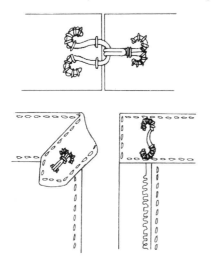

Press Studs or Fasteners

1. Sew the fastner with the 'knob' on first — to wrong side of overlap.
2. To match position of other fastener, pass a pin through the fastener to where it touches underlap when positioned correctly.
3. Sew fastener with hole to right side of underlay.
4. Begin and end stitches with a back stitch and sew fasteners in position, using a buttonhole or overcasting stitch.
5. Sew three or four stitches in each hole.

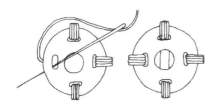

Nylon Fastening Tape
(Velcro)

This consists of two strips of strong nylon tape, both of which are covered with tiny plastic hooks, which cling securely when pressed in position. It is available in a choice of colours and two widths and can be cut to any length as it doesn't fray. It is easy to attach and is useful for children's clothes, outergarments, *e.g.* anoraks, skirt fastenings and soft furnishings, *e.g.* chair covers. It is not suitable for delicate fabrics.

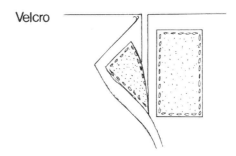

To Apply

1. Cut to size.
2. Pin, tack and machine in position, using a straight or slightly zig-zag stitch.
3. If stitches are not to be seen on the right side, it can be hemmed in place.
4. Finish off threads securely by back stitching.

Zip Fasteners

Zips are a quick, strong and secure method of fastening clothes. They are available in a wide range of colours and lengths — the length of a zip is measured from the top to the end of the teeth, *not* of the tapes. Lengths vary from 10 cm to 75 cm. 18 cm is the usual length for skirts and trousers; 50 cm for dresses.

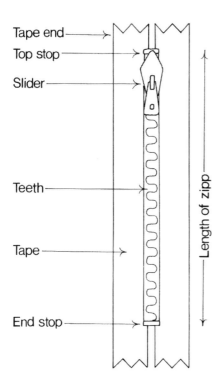

Tape end
Top stop
Slider
Teeth
Tape
End stop
Length of zipp

3. **Invisible:** These give a concealed finish, by drawing the fabric of the opening around them as they are closed.
4. **Open ended:** For using on jackets, *etc.*

General Hints on Sewing in Zips

1. Zips may be sewn in by hand or by machine. If sewing by hand, use a back stitch, for strength.
2. Insert zip before making up garment.
3. Keep zip closed while inserting and stitching.
4. Use a zipper foot, so that zipper teeth do not catch in the machine 'feed'.
5. Never sew too close to the teeth of zip — allow at least 2 mm space for slider to move up and down.
6. Avoid stretching seam when inserting a zip as this will give a bumpy finish.
7. Do not use a hot iron when pressing synthetic zips, they may melt. Use a medium iron and a pressing cloth.
8. Place a hook-and-eye at the top of zip to take the strain.
9. Stitch tapes, lining, *etc.* well out of the way and fasten off all threads to avoid catching them in zip.
10. Never cut away zipper tape — it may fray. Neaten it with blanket stitch or seam binding and include it in waistband or neck facing.

Buying Zips

1. Check pattern envelope for details of length of zip to use.
2. It is a mistake to economise by using a zip which is too short — this will put a strain on the zip which may eventually break it.
3. Choose a zip which matches the colour and fabric thickness of garment.

Types of Zip

1. **Synthetic:** Teeth are made of coils of nylon or polyester. These are ideal for lightweight to medium weight fabrics. They are washable, dry-cleanable and shrink resistant.
2. **Metal:** These may have coloured or plain metal teeth on a cotton tape. They are stronger than synthetic zips — some are extra strong, for jeans, *etc.*

Inserting a Zip

Preparation of Opening

1. Stitch seam to end of zip opening, backstitching for strength. Fasten off threads securely.
2. Press seam flat. Press back turnings of opening.
3. Neaten seam, including edges of zip opening. Then proceed with A or B.

A. Edge to edge (semi-concealed) method
(used on centre front and back seams)

1. Tack opening closed from end of machining along fitting line. Press open.

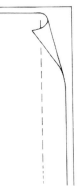

2. Place right side of closed zip onto wrong side of opening, with the teeth centred on the seam. The zip slider should be about 2.5 cm from top of seam; the end stop exactly to end of opening.

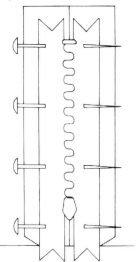

3. Pin at right angles to zip, as shown.
4. From right side, tack in a straight line along each side of zip, checking the tape at the back to make sure stitching is parallel to teeth.
5. From right side, machine zip in place, starting at the top, working down one side, across the end of zip (either straight or pointed) and up the other side.
6. Stitching should be 3–10 mm from centre, depending on width of zip and thickness of fabric.
7. Remove tacking and press.
8. Neaten edges at base of zip using overcasting, blanket-stitching or seam binding.

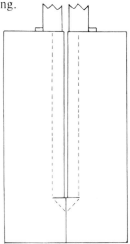

B. Lapped (Concealed) Method *(used for side, front and back openings on skirts, dresses and trousers)*

1. Tack down seam allowances at each side of zip.
2. Working from right side of garment, with zip closed and right side of zip facing wrong side of opening, pin edge of zip teeth to back seam edge.

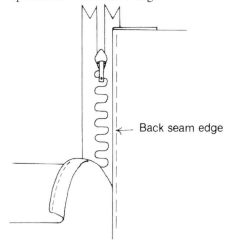

← Back seam edge

3. Tack securely in position.
4. Using a zipper foot, machine about 2 mm from edge. Remove tacking and press lightly.

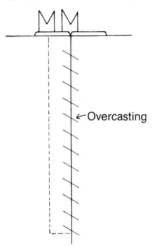

5. Lay front of opening in position over zip, bringing front edge to meet machining, so that zip is completely hidden.
6. Pin in position, overcasting edges to hold them together.

7. Tack from top of zip downwards through all thickness. Tacking should be parallel with zip, 10–13 mm from edge, depending on width of zip and thickness of fabric.
8. Machine across base of zip, pivoting on corner, then up the front of opening. (Pull down slider if necessary when you approach top of zip.)
9. Remove tacking, finish off threads securely then press firmly on wrong side, using a pressing cloth.

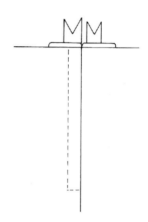

Over to you . . .

1. Describe in detail, using diagrams, how to make one of the following: (a) a hand worked buttonhole; (b) a machined buttonhole.

2. Give the general rules for sewing on buttons. Describe how to sew a button on to a heavy coat.

3. Describe in detail how to apply a set of hooks and eyes **or** fasteners to the waistband closing of a trousers.

4. Name the main parts of a zip. List *five* main rules for applying zips. Describe how to insert a zip in a trousers.

52 *All About Openings*

Openings make it easier to put on and take off clothes. Openings are often necessary at the neck, wrist and waistline of garments.

Faced Slit Opening/Slash Openings
(used on wrists and neckline of garments)

1. Mark position of opening on garment with tailor tacking. Work a row of machine stitches, as shown, to reinforce opening. **Do not cut opening.**

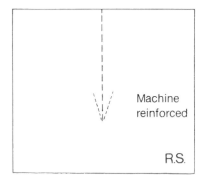

Position of slit

2. Cut facing according to pattern instructions. It should be at least 5 cm wide and 5 cm longer than opening.
3. Turn back raw edges on the three sides of facing as shown.

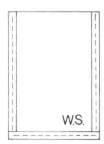

Facing piece with three edges neatened

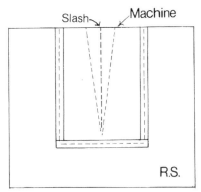

Facing piece tacked in position

4. With right sides together, place centre of facing on tacking line of opening. Pin and tack in position.
5. Mark 7 mm on either side of tacked line and tack a narrow V-shape, as shown.
6. Machine on tacking line, pivoting at point. If necessary, reinforce point with a second row of stitching.
7. Remove tacking.
8. Slash down centre line to within two or three threads of the point.
9. Turn facing to wrong side and press in position.

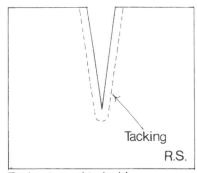

Facing turned to inside

10. Tack around top edge of facing and opening, as shown. Close with loop and button.

Continuous Wrap

(Used for side openings on gathered skirts, py-jamas and wrist openings on shirts and blouses)

1. Mark position of opening. Slash to length required. (If opening is on a seam, press seam open and clip turnings).

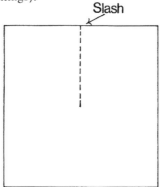

Slash

2. Cut a piece of fabric on the straight grain, 5–6 cm wide and twice the length of the opening.
3. Pin right side of binding to right side of opening, placing raw edges together (the garment will taper in centre) and straighten out opening as you work.

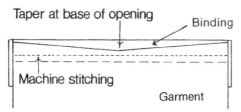

Taper at base of opening

Binding

Machine stitching

Garment

4. Tack and machine 8–10 mm from edge. Remove tacking and press turnings towards binding.
5. Turn under 8–10 mm from outer edge of binding, fold down and tack to machining.

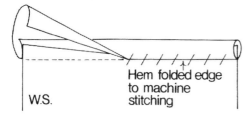

W.S.

Hem folded edge
to machine
stitching

6. Hem folded edge to machine stitches.
7. Remove tacking and press.
8. Fold front of opening over back, keeping edges even and press in position from wrong side.

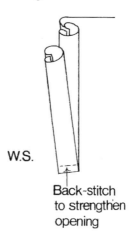

W.S.

Back-stitch
to strengthen
opening

Waistband

A waistband is used to neaten the top of trousers and skirts. A waistband should fit snugly — it should neither be too tight or too loose. Most waistbands are interfaced *(p. 000)* to prevent stretching

1. Stitch and neaten seams. Press. Insert zip or work any waist opening before attaching waistband.
2. Cut and tailor tack waistband.
3. Cut interfacing 1 cm less, all round, than waistband.
4. Iron on, or tack interfacing to wrong side of waistband.
5. With right sides together fold waistband lengthways in two. Pin, tack and machine both ends.

Interfacing

W.S.

6. Trim excess interfacing and cut off corners. Turn to right side and press.
7. Tack along top edge to hold waistband in place.

R.S.

8. With right sides together, pin and tack waistband to waist edge of garment, raw edges together, matching seams, notches and tailor tacks.

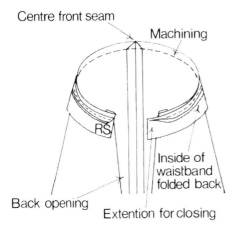

Centre front seam

Machining

RS

Inside of waistband folded back

Back opening

Extention for closing

9. Machine on fitting line. Trim interfacing and turnings in layers to avoid bulk.
10. Press turnings into waistband.
11. Turn under raw edge of waistband and tack on to machined line. Hem folded edge to machine stitches.

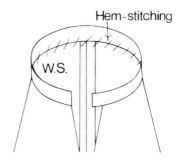

Hem-stitching

W.S.

12. Sew buttons and button holes, or suitable fastenings, on ends of waistband.

Over to you . . .

1.   Name four types of opening you could have on a garment. Describe how to prepare an opening suitable for the wrist of a blouse or shirt — use diagrams where possible.

2.   Describe how to apply a waistband to the top of a trousers or skirt. Name three types of fasteners you could use to "close" a waistband.

53   *All About Facings*

Facings are pieces of fabric shaped to fit the outer edges of clothes. They strengthen the edge and also help to neaten the raw edges.

Facings are cut from the same fabric as the garment and are used to finish off curves and edges, such as necklines, armholes, waistlines and the front edges of jackets and coats.

Most facings are invisible from the outside of a garment. They are attached to the right side of the garment, then turned to the wrong side.

Many facings are stiffened with interfacing (see end of chapter).

Shaped Facings

Neck Facing

1. Stay stitch neck edge 1.3 cm from raw edge.
2. Sew shoulder seams, press and neaten.
3. Cut out front and back facing pieces and tailor tack.
4. Tack and machine seams of facing, remove tacking and press open.
5. Turn under 5 mm on outer edge of facing and edge machine on folded edge.

W.S. of facing

6. With right sides together, pin facing to garment at neck edge, matching centre fronts, shoulder seams and notches. (End of facing will extend 1.5 cm beyond edge of garment at the back).

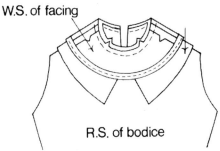

W.S. of facing

R.S. of bodice

7. Tack and machine facing to garment on fitting line — pivoting on corners of squared neckline if necessary.

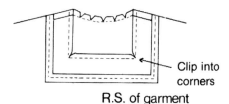

Clip into corners

R.S. of garment

8. Remove tacking, layer seam turnings. Clip curve every 2 cm to help facing lie flat.

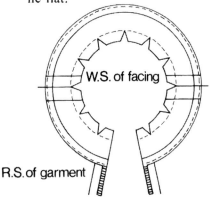

W.S. of facing

R.S. of garment

9. Press facing away from garment, then turn under and press into position, making sure facing is not visible from the right side.
10. Turn under centre back edges and hem to zipper tape or back opening. Hem facing to shoulder seam.

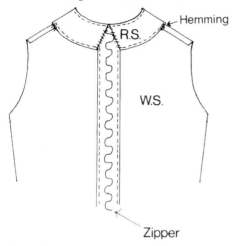

Armhole Facing

(used on sleeveless garments e.g. waistcoats, pinafores, blouses)

1. Stay stitch armhole, if necessary, 1.3 cm from raw edge.
2. Sew and neaten shoulder and side seams of garment.
3. Cut out armhole facing and tailor tack.
4. Turn under 5 mm on outer edge of facing and edge machine.
5. Tack and machine facing seam; remove tacking and press open.

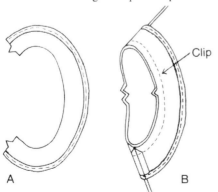

6. With right sides together, pin facing to armhole, matching underarm seams, notches and shoulder seams.
7. Tack and machine facing on fitting line.
8. Remove tacking, trim turnings and clip armhole curve.
9. Press facing outwards, away from garment, then turn under and press into position.
10. Hem facing to seam turnings at shoulder and side seam.

To prevent facings rolling to outside:

1. At *stage 9*, press facing and seam allowances outwards, away from garment.
2. Machine facing and seam allowances through all thicknesses 2 mm from seam.
3. Turn under and press in position; hem to seams in the usual way.

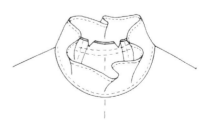

Interfacings

An interfacing is an extra layer of fabric, usually placed between the garment and facing to strengthen and stiffen it. Interfacings are used:

(a) To give crispness and body to areas such as necklines, collars, cuffs, front edges, pockets and belts.
(b) To help a garment keep its shape.
(c) To prevent stretching.
(d) To reinforce areas subjected to strain, *e.g.* waistbands.

There are two types of interfacing:

Woven Interfacings

Like all woven materials, these have warp and weft threads, so they must be cut on the grain like any fabric. Choose an interfacing to suit the type of fabric you are using, *e.g.*

Lightweight fabrics — use lawn/muslin.
Medium weight fabrics — use calico/linen.
Heavy weight fabrics — use canvas.

> *Note:* As many woven interfacings shrink, it is advisable to pre-shrink interfacing with a steam iron or a dry iron and damp cloth.

2. Non-woven Interfacings

These are made from synthetic fibres, which are fused together instead of being woven. This means there is no grain, so pieces can be cut in any direction. Such interfacings can be washed and dry-cleaned and do not shrink or fray. They are available in several thicknesses — lightweight, medium and heavyweight (brandnames: *Vilene* and *Lantor*).

Iron-on or fusible interfacings: are available both woven and non-woven. They are ironed onto the fabric, following instructions for type used. Some may need moisture when ironing on. Test on a small scrap of fabric.

Iron-on interfacings are best used on small areas only, as they may pucker and come away from the fabric after constant use, if used on large areas.

Choosing Interfacing

1. Check pattern envelope for information on the amount and type of interfacing required.
2. Buy interfacing weight to suit the fabric you are using — it should not be heavier than the fabric.
3. Choose washable/dry-cleanable interfacings, if the garment is to be washed or dry cleaned.
4. Use stretch interfacings on stretch fabrics.

Using Interfacing

1. Cut interfacing from pattern as directed on instructions.
2. Seams should be joined by overlapping to reduce bulk.
3. Interfacing is usually attached to the garment on the *wrong* side of collars, cuffs, *etc.* In certain cases, particularly when using bonded non-woven interfacings, it is preferable to attach interfacing to facings rather than garment.
4. Lay fabric to be interfaced wrong side up and place interfacing on top.
5. Interfacing may be (a) tacked in place, then included with machining of seams; (b) catch stitched in place; (c) bonded to the fabric with a warm iron.
6. Trim interfacing turnings to seam level to reduce bulk.

54   *All About Collars and Sleeves*

There is a wide variety of collars and sleeves and many different ways of fitting them into the clothes you make. Follow the pattern directions for the style you choose.

Before you start . . . . .

Try on the garment when seams are sewn and check the fitting lines of the neckline and armhole. If you need to alter them, remember to alter the collar or sleeve as well, or it will not fit.

Collars

Making the Collar

1. Cut out and tailor tack collar, following pattern instructions. Shaped collars have the grain running top to bottom. The grain on straight collars may run horizontally or vertically.
2. Cut out interfacing from collar pattern.
3. Lay undercollar on table, wrong side up and tack or iron on interfacing to wrong side of collar.

Making up shirt collar

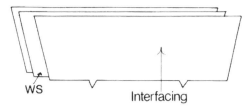

Two thicknesses of collar

WS

Interfacing

4. With right sides together, matching notches and tailor tacks, pin and tack around outside of collar — leaving inner, notched edge unsewn.
5. Machine collar on fitting line, starting at the centre and working outwards (repeat with other half). Remove tacking thread and press lightly.
6. Trim seam allowances in layers, trimming interfacing right down to machining.

Collar layered and corners trimmed

7. Cut corners of straight collars or cut V-shaped notches on the outer edge of curved collars.
8. Turn collar to right side, pushing pointed corners well out. Tack around outer edge, rolling collar slightly to the back.
9. Press carefully from underside.

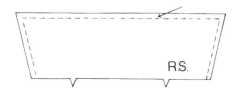

R.S.

Collar turned to right side and pressed

Attaching a Collar

There are many ways of attaching a collar. Here are two:

A Round Collar with a Shaped Facing

1. Stay stitch neckline 1 mm outside fitting line.
2. Make up collar.

Round (peter pan) collar

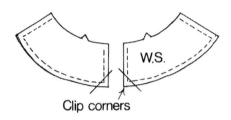

Clip corners

3. Lay collar in position on neckline, under side of collar on right side of neckline and match centre fronts, backs, tailor tacks and notches. (It may be necessary to ease the collar to fit the neckline.) Pin and tack.

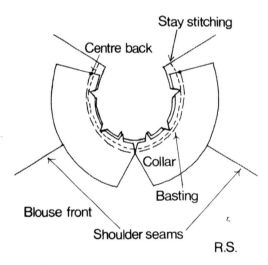

4. Try on. Check that the collar lies flat and that both sides of collar are even.
5. Make up facings: Stitch facing seams and neaten outer edge.
6. Lay facings on top of collar, right side facing collar, matching shoulder seams, notches, *etc.* Pin and tack.

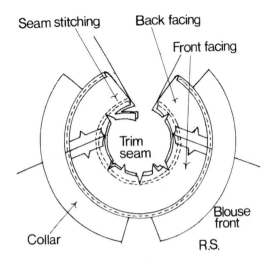

7. Machine on fitting line, remove tacking and trim turnings in layers. Clip curve.
8. Press facings outward. (Stitch to seam allowance if wished, to prevent collar and facings rolling out.)

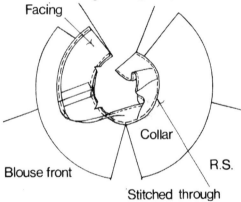

9. Turn facing to inside and press.
10. Hem facing to shoulder seams and centre back opening.

Note: Instead of using a shaped facing, a bias facing may be used to neaten the collar, *see p. 367.* Machine in place as for *No. 7,* trim and clip turnings, then fold under a small hem on binding and slip stitch to garment, under the collar.

Straight (Shirt) Collar

This is a simple shirt collar. More complicated collars may have a 'stand' which must be first sewn to collar before attaching to neckline. See pattern for details.

1. Stay stitch neckline. Make up collar.
2. Pin undercollar to back of neckline, as far as shoulder seams, and tack.
3. Pin both front sections of collar to neckline, matching notches. Bring front collar *exactly* to centre front line.

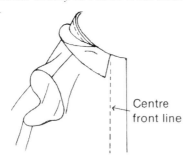

4. Fold front facing to right side, on fold line, and place over collar, matching notches. Pin and tack in position.

5. Clip seam allowances through all thicknesses, at the points where front facings end (A).
6. Machine collar from centreback, outwards to centrefront on each side, leaving the centre part of the upper collar unstitched. Remove tacking, trim and clip turnings.
7. Turn facing to inside, press seam allowances at centre of collar upwards into collar.

8. Turn under 1.5 cm on edge of upper collar. Pin, tack and hem across back of neck.

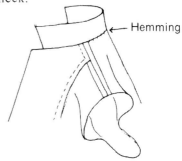

9. Remove tacking and press collar from wrong side.

Sleeves

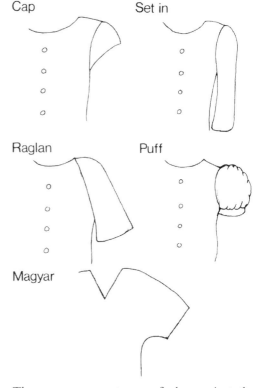

There are many types of sleeve, but the most frequently used is the 'set-in' sleeve. This has a seam all around the armhole.

Preparation

1. Fit on garment, check position and size of armhole and alter, if necessary.
2. Cut out sleeve according to pattern instructions, with straight grain running down the sleeve. Tailor tack.
3. It is very important when you separate sleeves to check that you turn them in the opposite direction, so that you have a right sleeve and a left sleeve (the front of the sleeve has a lower curve than the back, which usually has a double notch). Mistakes are more likely in fabrics which have no right and wrong side.

Turn sleeves in opposite directions

Join underarm Seam (see 6)

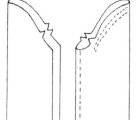

4. Stitch a double row of gathering stitches between notches (or as instructed), keeping stitches just outside fitting line. This will help to ease in sleeve.

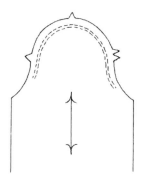

6. Join underarm seam. Press flat and neaten.

Insertion

Work from the inside of garment with sleeve right side out.

1. With right sides together, pin sleeve to armhole, matching underarm(A), shoulder seams (B), notches(C) and tailor tacks.

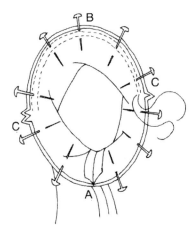

2. Pull gathering threads and divide fullness evenly around sleeve head, avoiding obvious gathers, if possible.
3. Working from the sleeve side, pin sleeve to garment on fitting line. Pins should be inserted at right angles to the stitching. Tack.
4. Fit on garment and check that sleeve hangs correctly, adjust if necessary.
5. Machine on fitting line. Remove tacking.
6. Press seam allowance into sleeve with tip of iron.
7. Trim turnings to 1 – 1.5 cm.
8. Turn garment to right side and press lightly.

To Neaten a Sleeve

1. Machine a second row of stitching 4–5 mm from sleeve seam. Then blanket stitch, overcast or zig-zag edges.
2. Alternately: Apply bias binding to gathered side of turnings; machine, turn over and hem to machining on the wrong side.

Over to you . . .

1. Copying the diagrams in the previous chapter, describe in your own words how to make up and apply a shirt collar.

2. List some methods you would use to decorate a collar and describe one in detail, using diagrams.

3. Describe in detail how to apply a round collar, using bias binding to neaten it.

4. Describe how to prepare and set-in sleeve, into the armhole of a summe jacket.

    Name *three* methods of neatening th sleeve.

55 *Home Sewing and Mending*

Making a Cushion

Cushions can be made from all types of fabric — cotton, linen, velvet, corduroy, silk, tweed and many others. Pick a washable fabric. If the fabric has a large design, make sure to place the design in the centre of the cushion.

> *Note:* Most furnishing fabrics are 122 cm wide.

You will Need

1. 60 cm furnishing fabric, 122 cm wide (cushion 55 cm square).
2. 60 cm fabric, 115 cm wide (cushion 54 cm square).
3. 50 cm dress fabric, 90 cm wide (cushion 40-42 cm square).
4. The same amount of lining fabric (or old sheeting) for cushion pad.
5. 100-800 g. Kapok, or foam pieces, to stuff cushion.
6. 20 cm nylon zip.
7. Matching thread.
8. Bias binding and piping cord (about 2.2 metres), if you want a piped edge.

Cushion Cover

1. Cut out 2 squares.
2. If you wish to embroider or decorate front of cushion, do so before it is sewn up.
3. Place right sides of fabric squares together, making sure that selvedge threads lie parallel.

Cushion

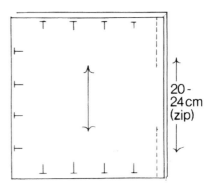

4. Pin, tack and machine one seam, 1.25 cm from edge, leaving a 20–24 cm space for zip. Remove tacking.
5. Press seam flat and neaten seam by blanket-stitching or zig-zag machining.
6. Insert zip using semi-concealed method, *p. 380.*

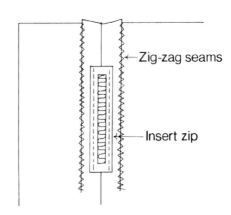

7. Lay right sides of fabric together and pin, tack and machine around remaining three sides of square.

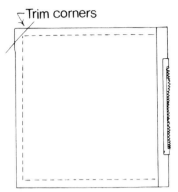

Trim corners

8. Remove tacking and zig-zag seam allowances, to neaten.
9. Turn to right side and press.

Cushion Pad

1. Cut out 2 squares of lining fabric, 1 cm *larger* than the cushion cover.
2. Place right sides together and pin, tack and machine as shown — leaving a 20 cm space for filling.
3. Cut off corners and turn inside out, pushing out corners well.
4. Fill until nice and plump, then top sew opening firmly closed.

Pillow Case 48 cm × 75 cm *approx.*

You will need: 1 m. cotton or linen 90 cm wide.

1. Cut out according to diagram. Cut away a piece 10 cm deep on one piece of fabric.

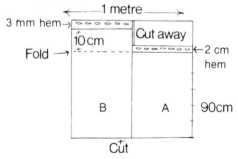

2. On piece (A) at one of the narrow ends, turn under a double hem to wrong side, to make a finished hem 2 cm deep.

3. Repeat on piece (B) making a 3 mm hem.
4. Lay both sides of pillow cases right sides together, matching unsewn end and sides. Pin and tack.
5. Fold extension on (B) back over side (A). Tack.
6. Machine around three sides 1 cm from edge, as shown.
7. Remove tacking threads and zig-zag or blanket stitch edges. Finish off threads and press seams lightly.
8. Turn pillowcase to right side, tucking extension under and give it a final press.

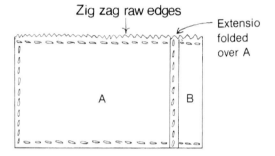

Zig zag raw edges

Note: Decoration, such as embroidery or appliqué, should be worked *before* making up pillowcase.

Mending

Darning

Darning is usually used to repair woollen garments, *e.g.* socks, sweaters and knitted fabrics. Machine darning is worked on woven fabrics.

Up until recently, the practice of mending, patching and darning torn or worn clothes was becoming less common, due to the fact that many clothes were cheap and people discarded them after a season or two. As clothes and fabrics have again become expensive, it makes good sense to learn how to repair them in the neatest possible way. For all mending, make sure you are working in a good light.

Rules for Darning

1. Choose thread which is as near as possible to the garment threads in colour, thickness and composition, *e.g.* wool on wool.
2. Darn thin areas *before* they wear into holes.
3. Darn should be as invisible as possible.
4. Work on wrong side (except for Swiss darning).
5. Darn should not just cover the hole — it should also be worked over the weak area around the hole.
6. Edge of darns should *not* be straight — work round or triangular shapes, to avoid placing a strain on one thread.
7. In case of shrinkage, leave small loops at ends of rows.
8. Pick up every loop at the edge of the hole — if this is not done, it may ladder.
9. Do not pull darning tightly — the use of a darning mushroom helps produce an even darn.
10. Avoid splitting threads when darning.
11. Threads are not secured at beginning or end of work or when joining threads. Leave a short thread hanging and trim when finished.
12. Press lightly, on wrong side, when finished.

Darning Requirements

1. **Darning wool:** Special darning wool is available on cards but colours are limited. A wider range is available in tapestry wools.
2. **Darning needles:** These are available in various sizes.
3. **Darning mushroom.**

Prevention Darn

This is used to strengthen a weak area where threads have worn thin, *before* the threads break and a hole appears.

(a) Woven Fabrics

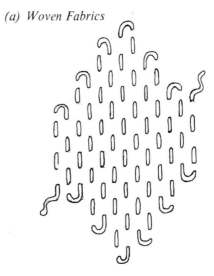

1. Chalk a circle around the area you wish to darn.
2. Work on wrong side of garment, starting with lengthwise threads. Only darn crossways if area is particularly thin.
3. Start darning from strong area, in diamond, circular or hexagonal shape.
4. Weave in and out of fabric, passing over one thread, under the next and so on.
5. Work loosely, leaving slight loops at the end of every row.

(b) Knitted Garments

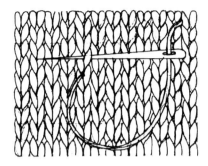

Swiss darning gives a more invisible finish on knitwear:
1. Work vertically up and down loops of knitting, as shown.
2. Needle is inserted horizontally through loops from right to left.
3. Darning threads should lie parallel with knitting threads.

Darning a Hole

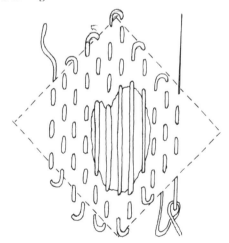

1. Work on wrong side, darning selvage threads first.
2. Weave needle through weak area, over and under threads, then across hole,

catching all loops, and through the weak area on the other side.
3. Work loosely, leaving small loops.
4. Repeat, darning at right angles to first rows, weaving needle over and under threads left by first darning.

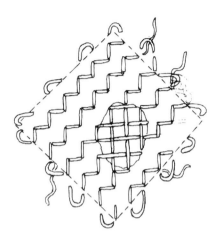

5. Darn rows as close as possible to one another.
6. If necessary, repeat until hole is well filled.
7. Press lightly on wrong side, using a steam iron or a dry iron and damp cloth.

Hedge Tear Darn

This is the method of mending a clean, right angled tear, common in children's clothes.
1. Catch raw edges together, using fish bone or herringbone stitch.

Fishbone stitch

2. Weave in and out of threads at right angles to tear, starting 1 cm outside one side of tear (A) and working across to 1 cm beyond.

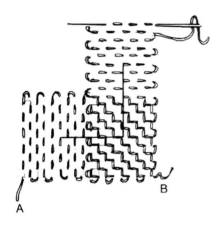

3. Repeat from point (B). Rows of stitches should extend about 1 cm above and below tear.
4. At the corner, both rows overlap, giving strength where it is most needed.
5. Press on wrong side.

Machine Darning

This is a quick method of repairing household items and, in certain cases, repairing garments. It can be done on most sewing machines — follow instructions on booklet. You will need:

1. **Fine machine thread:** which matches fabric in colour and composition, *e.g.* cotton for natural fibres; polyester for synthetics.
2. **Fine machine needle.**
3. **An embroidery hoop** (if possible) — to keep work taut.

Method

1. Tack a piece of fine fabric, *e.g.* lawn, behind darn, for extra strength. It should be slightly larger than the area to be darned. Threads of backing fabric and fabric being darned should run parallel.
2. Stretch area to be darned over embroidery hoop.

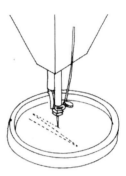

3. Machine tension should be *slightly* looser than normal.
4. Lower feed dog, or use an embroidery plate to cover it.
5. Attach embroidery foot, if necessary, and lower it onto fabric.
6. Machine from right side, working rows of stitching parallel with weave of fabric.
7. Move hoop steadily backwards and forwards, working close rows of stitching 2–3 mm apart. Remember, with the feed down, *you* control the size of stitch. The faster you move the fabric, the longer the stitch.
8. Edges must not be straight to a thread.
9. Darn well into weak area.
10. Stitch at right angles, to complete darn.
11. Trim off backing fabric and press on wrong side.

Note: Darning by machine can also be worked without lowering the feed. Use a small stitch and machine sew backwards and forwards over area to be darned. Small straight tears can be mended by machine using a wide, fairly closely spaced zig-zag stitch.

Patching

Patching is usually used when the hole to be repaired is too big to darn.

Rules for Patching

1. Choose fabric and thread of a similar weight, colour and composition to fabric being patched (for this reason it's a good idea to keep scraps of any clothes you have made). Wash new fabric a few times to shrink and fade it.
2. Cut patch straight to a thread and match selvage of patch to selvage of garment.
3. Patch should be large enough to cover the hole and the weak area around it.
4. Printed fabrics are usually patched on the right side, plain fabrics on the wrong side.
5. When patching an area like a sleeve or trouser leg, it may be necessary to open seam in order to lay fabric flat.
6. Stitches should be small and even; patch as invisibly as possible.
7. Neaten reverse side of patch according to type — to prevent fraying.
8. Press lightly on wrong side.

Print Patch

1. Cut out patch, large enough to cover worn area plus 10 mm turnings on all sides.
2. It should be straight to a thread.
3. Turn under 10 mm, turning evenly, and tack.
4. Pin and tack to right side of garment, matching pattern and selvedge threads.

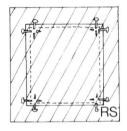 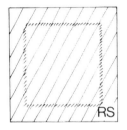

5. Top sew, or machine, edge of patch, starting stitching in the middle of a line. Remove tacking and press.
6. Turn to wrong side and crease patch diagonally from corner to corner.
7. Measure 10 mm diagonally from each corner; mark with pins and cut diagonally from centre hole to pin marks.
8. Crease worn part back and cut away.
9. Blanket stitch raw edges together, taking care not to stitch through onto right side of fabric.

10. On heavy fabrics, instead of blanket stitching both sides together, press turnings open and blanket stitch each side separately. This is called a **dress patch.**

Fancy Patches

Brightly coloured contrasting patches are often used on the knees and elbows of clothes, particularly children' clothes. Attach them by appliqué.

1. Cut patch to required shape — round, oval or diamond.
2. Tack in position over hole or worn area, matching selvages.
3. Work close blanket stitches around the outer edge of patch, or zig-zag by machine.
4. If fabric is inclined to fray, turn under a narrow hem and slip stitch, or machine, the edge of patch to fabric.
5. Trim worn area at back of patch to 6 mm from stitching and blanket stitch closely.

> *Note:* This type of patch is ideal for knit or stretch fabrics — use a knit fabric for the patch.

Quick and Easy Patches

Fusible web, *e.g. Bondina* or *Bondaweb,* has taken a lot of the trouble out of patching. It consists of a sticky substance on a paper backing.

Quick and easy patches

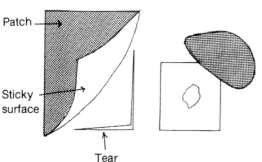

Patch

Sticky surface

Tear

To patch a tear or small hole:

1. Cut patch from matching fabric. It should be larger than the tear.
2. Cut a piece of web the same size as the patch and place in on the right side of the patch, paper side up.
3. Iron on with a warm iron.
4. When cool, remove paper backing and place sticky right side of patch on wrong side of tear, matching selvages.
5. Press with a steam iron (or dry iron and damp cloth) and leave to cool for 10 minutes before handling.

Making New Clothes from Old

(Day Vocational Certificate only)

Fashions change so quickly that we often discard clothes before they have even begun to wear out. Grown up's clothes can often be made down for children. Here are some tips for renovating or remodelling clothes.

1. Wash garment, or have it dry cleaned.
2. Carefully rip seams and press pieces flat.
3. Take note of any faded or worn areas and try to avoid these.
4. Choose a pattern with small pieces in it, *e.g.* a waistcoat, a child's smock or a pair of shorts. ·
5. In certain cases it might be better to use the wrong side of the fabric as the outside.
6. Addition of new trimmings or buttons will brighten up and change the look of the garment considerably.
7. If you are short of fabric, consider using a toning or contrasting fabric for yokes, collars, cuffs and frills. Wash it before use, in case it shrinks.

56   All About Clothes

Clothes help to keep us warm and protect our bodies from the rain, wind and cold. The right clothes can make us feel attractive and self-confident. They are also useful in certain jobs, where they help protect us, or, as in the case of nurses or policemen, make us easy to identify.

At certain times we dress up and try to look our best, for example at a wedding, going for an interview, or to a party. The clothes we wear on these occasions would hardly suit if we wished to play tennis, or clean the house.

It is necessary, therefore, to suit the clothes we wear to the occasion.

Planning Your Wardrobe

Budget your income carefully to allow for clothes. Look through your wardrobe and list all the clothes worth keeping. Alter or give away those which do not suit you or fit you. Make a note of any clothes needed and the colours which would blend in with your existing wardrobe. Have a look through some good fashion magazines — and look around the shops to see what is in fashion and compare costs.

Co-ordinates or separates are a good idea, as they mix and match and several outfits can be built up from them.

Choosing Clothes

1. Clothes should be comfortable — they should fit well, being neither too tight nor too loose.
2. Colours and styles should suit the wearer and his/her figure.
3. Clothes should blend with those already in your wardrobe.
4. Clothes should be well made and well finished off inside.
5. Buy classic clothes which won't date — these can be worn again and again with different accessories. If you feel like buying something 'way out' don't spend too much money on it.
6. Cheap clothes are often badly made and finished, but not always. Shop around for good quality and value, particularly at 'sale time'.
7. Choose washable clothes (check the label). Dry cleaning is very expensive.

Choosing Accessories

1. Buy good quality classic accessories, which will last, without going out of date.
2. Concentrate on neutral colours *e.g.* black, brown, beige and navy — these will go with many colours — purple or pink will not!
3. Accessories should match, tone or contrast with each outfit.

Make the Most of Yourself

Magazines are full of advice about what to chose in order to look your best. Some of these rules hold, but others, like most rules, can sometimes be broken. Here are a few:

1. Dark colours make you look thinner.
2. Neutrals and dull colours are more slimming than bright colours.
3. Sallow skins need warm colours — avoid yellow, green, grey.
4. Brunettes and dark skinned people look well in bright colours.

5. Many traditional rules of colour are often broken — *e.g.* blue and green — traditionally not worn together — are often combined today and look very smart. Some redheads can look great in scarlet or pink — it depends on the shade — and whether you can carry it off.
6. Vertical lines make you look taller and slimmer.
7. Horizontal lines make you look smaller and wider.
8. Straight lines tend to give a severe tailored look.
9. Curved lines and draped fabrics give a soft 'feminine' image.
10. Fitted clothes show off the figure — if yours is far from perfect, camouflage it with semi-fitted clothes and a loose, bloused or smocked look.
11. Consider balance — large patterned fabrics look better on large people. Small prints and designs are better on smaller people.

> **Remember — Suit your clothes to the occasion.**

Clothes for School

These should be comfortable, attractive, neat and tidy, hardwearing, washable and drip dry. A uniform should be worn exactly as it was designed to be. Jewellery and high fashion shoes look out of place with a uniform.

Clothes for Work

These should be comfortable, smart, practical, easy to wash and protective (if necessary). Avoid the latest 'gimmicky' fashions, unless you work in a place where this is expected, *e.g.* a boutique or as a model.

Clothes for Casual wear and Sport

These should be comfortable, absorbent, stretchy if possible, hardwearing, washable and easy to wear.

Clothes for Summer wear

These should be cool, absorbant (*e.g.* cotton); pale colours to reflect sun (dark colours attract it).

Clothes for Winter wear

These should be comfortable and warm. Dark colours need less frequent washing, an important consideration in winter when drying is more difficult.

Clothes for Parties

These should be flattering, attractive to look at and make you feel self-confident. Exciting colours and fabrics can be worn, *e.g.* shiney and glittery fabrics — this is one time when anything goes — almost!

Sponging and Pressing

Sponging removes surface dirt from garments and freshens them up.
1. Shake garment well and brush down thoroughly with clothesbrush.
2. Lay a towel flat on a table, with garment flat on top.
3. Using warm water, containing a solution of 'gentle' detergent *e.g. Dreft,* wipe garment from the top down with a sponge or soft clean cloth.
4. Rub stains gently if necessary.
5. Rinse out sponge/cloth and lightly wipe down again.
6. Repeat on back. Hang up and allow to dry slightly.
7. Press with a hot iron, using a pressing cloth.
8. Air garment thoroughly.

Baggy areas: Shrink by placing a damp cloth over stretched area and move iron lightly over the top — without resting iron on pressing cloth or fabric.

To remove shine: Rub with a solution of vinegar and water (1 tablespoon vinegar + 500 ml water). Wring out cloth with clean water and wipe over again. Press dry, using a slightly damp cloth.

General Rules for Care of Clothes

1. Never let clothes get too dirty — wash or dry clean regularly.
2. Clothes which must be dry cleaned should be sponged down and pressed (see below) between cleaning to keep them fresh looking.
3. Set aside an hour or so each week to check clothes for repairs, stains, and sponging and pressing. Stains are best removed as quickly as possible, *p. 314-6.*
4. Store clothes in a wardrobe to protect them from dust. There should be sufficient room for them to hang loosely and allow circulation of air. If tightly packed, they will become creased and musty.
5. Clean and pack away seasonal clothes at the end of the season, to avoid taking up storage space.
6. Keep all similar items together — sweaters in one drawer, underwear, accessories and so on, together.
7. When you take off your clothes, shake well and hang to air before folding or hanging up and placing in wardrobe. Use good quality hangers and fasten clothes before hanging.
8. Keep underwear fresh and clean. Wash pants and tights/socks every night.

Footwear

Choosing

1. Choose well-made footwear, suitable for the occasion, *i.e.* heavy, comfortable shoes for walking; lighter shoes for indoor wear.
2. Shoes should always be comfortable and fit well. Ill fitting shoes cause corns, blisters, bunions and may lead to more serious problems.
3. Winter footwear should be sound, warm and waterproof.
4. High fashion shoes and sandals are often bad for the feet, giving little support. Many break easily and are not guaranteed.
5. Choose medium heels for everyday wear. Both high heels and very low heels can be tiring.
6. Leather shoes are more comfortable to wear than synthetic materials, which cause the feet to perspire.

Caring for Shoes

1. Clean shoes regularly — it prolongs their life and makes them look well.
2. Have shoes repaired at first signs of wear.
3. Alternate shoes — do not wear the same pair every day or all day.
4. When damp, stuff with paper and leave in a warm place to dry — away from direct heat.
5. Muddy shoes: Wipe off as much mud as possible. Stuff with newspaper and allow to dry. Then brush well with a stiff brush and polish.

Cleaning Shoes

1. Keep shoe cleaning materials together in one box.

2. Protect work surface with newspaper; wear old gloves.

3. **Leather:** Brush over surface with a clean, dry brush. Apply polish with one brush or cloth, rubbing well in. Shine off with another.

4. **Suede:** Use a suede brush to brush up pile. If badly soiled, use a commercial suede cleaner according to directions — rub in, allow to dry, then brush up with suede brush.

5. **Patent leather:** Rub with patent leather cream or *Vaseline*. Do not use shoepolish, it dulls the shine. Rub up with a soft cloth.

6. **Gym shoes:** Brush with a stiff brush. Remove and wash laces. Wash shoes, using a brush and hot soapy water. Rinse, dry with a cloth and leave in a warm place to dry. Then apply commercial white cleaner.

7. **Rubber boots:** Scrape off mud with blunt stick. Wash the outside with cold water. Leave to dry.

Over to you . . .

1. Plan a summer wardrobe for yourself — to include some beachwear and sportswear. Find out the current cost of *three* items in your list.

2. Sketch and describe a school uniform which you would consider suitable for a boy or girl at post-primary school. Refer to: (a) colour; (b) fabric; (c) number of items; (d) footwear; (e) style; (f) price.

3. You have a navy overcoat, black boots and a grey skirt/trousers in your wardrobe. Plan a winter outfit which coordinates with these items — buying up to 5 items — so that you have several mix-and-match outfits.

4. Make a list of accessories which you would like in your wardrobe. Refer to colour; style; quality and cost. List *four* basic rules to remember when buying accessories.

5. Plan an outfit which you would wear for an active sport such as orienteering or jogging. What points should be considered when buying such an outfit?

57   *Sewing Glossary*

Appliqué: A method of decorating fabric by stitching a shaped piece of contrasting fabric to it.

Balance marks: Points in a pattern where two adjoining pieces fit together — the marks are transferred to the fabric by tailor tacking or some other method.

Basting: Tacking.

Bias: A piece of material at an angle to the grain; **true bias** is cut at an angle of 45°, half way between selvage and weft.

Casing: An enclosed channel of fabric, in which elastic or a drawstring is enclosed.

Clip: To cut with the point of a scissors into a corner of fabric, or into a seam allowance, to help it to lie flat.

Crossway strip: Bias binding.

Dart: A pointed, wedge shaped fold of material, used to give shape to a garment.

Ease: To draw in fullness, without actual pleats or gathers.

Edge machine/Edge stitch: To machine very close to the outer fold of a garment. Used to neaten seams, *etc.*

Facing: A piece of fabric, usually shaped, which is used to finish off an edge.

Fitting line (also called the **seam line** or **stitching line**): The lines (marked on pattern by broken lines) on which a garment is sewn together.

Fold: A single turn of fabric.

Gathering: 2 rows of stitching, pulled up to reduce width or fullness.

Grain: The direction in which threads of fabric run.

Hem: A double fold used to finish off an area.

Interfacing: Fabric placed behind garment fabric, to give body and support.

Layering: Trimming double or treble seam allowances in steps of different depth, to reduce bulk.

Layout: A diagram showing how paper pattern should be laid on fabric.

Marking: Transferring important marks from pattern onto fabric.

Mitre: To make a neat pointed corner, without bulk.

Nap: A raised surface, containing fibres which lie in one direction only.

Notch: A triangular symbol on a paper pattern, which is transferred to the fabric when cutting out. It helps to indicate adjoining pieces when constructing garments.

Pivot: A method of leaving the machine needle in the fabric with presser foot raised, when turning a corner.

Raw edge: The unfinished cut edge of the fabric which often tends to ravel or fray.

Right side: The outside of garment when finished.

Rouleau: A tube of fabric used for fastening.

Seam allowance: Width of fabric between raw edge (cutting line) and fitting line — usually 1.5 cm wide.

Selvage: The finished edge of fabric which doesn't fray.

Slash: To cut into a garment with a scissors.

Stay stitching: A row of machining, 1–2 mm outside fitting line, which helps prevent stretching especially on curved edges.

Straight grain: The threads running parallel with the selvage.

Tailor tack: A looped tacking stitch, used to transfer pattern markings onto fabric.

Tension: The pull or tightness of fabric or stitches.

Trim: To cut away excess fabric.

Trimming: A decoration used on garments, *e.g.* braid, lace, *etc.*

Index

Examination Papers

AN   ROINN   OIDEACHAIS   G.318

BRAINSE   NA   SCRÚDUITHE

DAY VOCATIONAL CERTIFICATE EXAMINATIONS, 1982

DOMESTIC SCIENCE

Not more than <u>six</u> questions to be attempted, <u>three</u> of which must be from Section A and <u>three</u> from Section B.

SECTION A

1. List the general rules for making milk puddings.
   Give the ingredients for and the method of preparing, cooking and serving a baked milk pudding <u>or</u> a milk mould of your choice.
   Suggest a suitable accompaniment to serve with the dessert in order to increase its nutritional value.

2. Write a short note on the value of fresh vegetables in the diet.
   What points should be considered when selecting fresh vegetables ?
   Describe how you would prepare, cook and serve <u>one</u> of the following:-

   (a) new potatoes;
   (b) Brussels sprouts;
   (c) swede turnips.

3. Make a list of the internal organs which you have cooked during your course and give the cost of <u>each</u> one.
   Suggest a substantial supper dish which could be made from <u>each</u> organ.
   List the ingredients and give the method of preparing, cooking and serving <u>one</u> of the dishes suggested.

4. Name <u>two</u> appetising fish dishes, each suitable for the main course of a luncheon menu.
   Give detailed instructions for preparing, cooking and serving <u>one</u> of the named dishes, allowing sufficient for four adults.
   What accompaniments would you serve with this dish ?

5. You plan to invite some friends to your home at Christmas time for an evening meal. Set out a menu suitable for the occasion.
   Outline the preparation necessary and the order of work you would follow when preparing and cooking the meal.
   Describe how you would decorate the table to create a festive atmosphere.

SECTION B

6. What directions should be followed when washing and finishing any <u>two</u> of the following:-

   (a) an acrylic hat and scarf set;
   (b) a printed cotton shirt;
   (c) a light coloured easy-care tablecloth;
   (d) a neglected hand towel?

7. Describe in detail how any <u>two</u> of the following should be cleaned:-

   (a) a brass door knocker;
   (b) sports shoes;
   (c) a pressure cooker.

   Name the parts of a pressure cooker using a diagram to illustrate your answer.

8. What are the advantages of a refrigerator in the home ?   State the principal points that should be considered when choosing one for an average sized family.
     Indicate, by labelled sketch, three modern features of a household refrigerator and state the value to the housewife of each one.

9. Give clear directions for the thorough weekly cleaning of a hand-basin and mirror in the bathroom.
     List the items which help to keep the bathroom tidy and hygienic and give the cost of any three items listed.

10. Sketch and describe briefly a garment which you have made for yourself.
     State the type, width, amount and cost of the material you purchased for this garment.
     Give concise instructions for the method of using a paper pattern in home dressmaking.

AN   ROINN   OIDEACHAIS   G.318

BRAINSE   NA   SCRÚDUITHE

DAY VOCATIONAL CERTIFICATE EXAMINATIONS, 1981

DOMESTIC SCIENCE

Not more than six questions to be attempted, three of which must be from Section A and three from section B.

SECTION A

1. Name four fruits available in summer. What points should be considered when selecting fresh fruit ?
     Using fruit in season, give the ingredients together with instructions for making and serving an attractive dessert allowing sufficient for four adults.

2. Classify the types of soup and name one soup in each class.
     Describe how you would prepare, cook and serve a soup made from fresh ingredients.
     Cost the finished soup.

3. Using uncooked minced meat complete the ingredients and give the method for preparing cooking and serving a hot appetising dish suitable for the main course of a family lunch.
     Name three cuts of beef and suggest a suitable method of cooking for each cut named.

4. State the composition of eggs and write a concise note on the value of eggs in the diet.
     Name two varieties of egg custard which you have made.
     Outline the general rules that should be followed when (a) preparing and (b) cooking egg custards.

5. Plan and set out a menu for a three course typical Irish meal that you would serve to four foreign students staying in your home.
     Assuming that you wish to serve the meal at 7 p.m. set out a time plan, showing the order of work you would follow when preparing and cooking the meal.
     State how you would prepare and serve an attractive cold drink suitable for serving with the main course of the above meal.

SECTION B

6. Describe fully the correct method of cleaning each of any two of the following:-

    (a) a polythene refuse bin;
    (b) a tarnished silver-plated dinner fork;
    (c) a carpet sweeper.

    What general care should be given to a kitchen refuse bin ?

7. Give clear directions for the method of washing and finishing any two of the following:-

    (a) a woollen cardigan;
    (b) a pair of white nylon knee socks;
    (c) a polyester-cotton pillow case;
    (d) a cotton dress.

8. List the personal toilet requirements essential for a teenager and state the cost of each item.
    Give detailed directions for the daily care and cleaning of the teeth.
    What points should be considered when selecting and buying a tooth brush ?

9. Write a note on 'Safety in the Home' with special reference to children and old people.
    Suggest some precautions which should be taken to avoid accidental fires in the home.
    What action would you take if a deep fat fryer you were using caught fire ?

10. State the amount, width, type and cost of the material you would select for one of the following:-

    (a) a sleeveless nightdress for yourself.
    (b) a hostess apron for your mother.

    Give clear instructions for making up one of the garments.

_____

AN   ROINN   OIDEACHAIS   G.318

BRAINSE   NA   SCRÚDUITHE
─────────────────────

DAY VOCATIONAL CERTIFICATE EXAMINATIONS, 1980
─────────────────────

DOMESTIC SCIENCE
─────────────────────

Not more than six questions to be attempted, three of which must be from Section A and three from Section B.
─────────────────────

SECTION A

1. Using mutton or bacon suggest two appetising dishes each suitable for the main course of a luncheon menu.
    Describe fully how you would prepare, cook and serve one of the dishes suggested. Provide sufficient for two adults and two teenagers.
    Write a concise note on the nutritive value of the finished dish.

2. Name two cake mixtures with which you are familiar and mention two examples to illustrate the use of each.
    Give the ingredients together with directions for making, baking and serving any one cake mentioned above.
    Comment on the use of packet cake mixes for home cooking.

3. What do you understand by the preservation of food ?
Using a different process in each case, recommend a suitable method of home preservation for each of the following:

(a) tomatoes; (b) fillets of plaice; (c) strawberries.

Give detailed instructions for preserving <u>one</u> of these foods by the method mentioned above.

4. Plan and set out a menu suitable for a buffet party to celebrate your own birthday. Include (i) a hot savoury dish; (ii) a cold sweet.
Assuming that you have invited ten school friends, give the quantities and the total cost of ingredients required for (i) <u>or</u> (ii) above.
What are the advantages of buffet meals for home entertaining ?

5. Write an account of milk under each of any <u>three</u> of the following headings:

(a) average composition; (b) value in the diet; (c) uses in cookery;
(d) storage in the home.

Describe the method of making and serving a nourishing and palatable milk drink for a child.

SECTION B

6. Give clear directions for the method of washing and finishing any <u>two</u> of the following:

(a) corduroy jeans;

(b) a printed cotton quilted waistcoat;

(c) a flannelette cot sheet.

7. Describe fully the correct method of cleaning each of any <u>two</u> of the following:

(a) a varnished wooden salad bowl;

(b) a stainless steel bread bin;

(c) a set of personal brushes.

Name <u>three</u> cleaning agents suitable for use in the home and give the approximate cost of each.

8. Suggest <u>two</u> small electrical appliances which would minimise work in the kitchen, giving reasons for your choice.
Select <u>one</u> of the suggested appliances and state how it should be cared for and cleaned in order to keep it in good working condition.
List <u>three</u> safety rules which should be observed in relation to the use of electrical equipment in the kitchen.

9. Your mother will be away from home and you are asked to manage the household for <u>one</u> day. Make out a time-plan of work which you would follow giving consideration to (i) routine tasks; (ii) cooking and serving of meals; (iii) leisure time.
Describe how you would prepare a simple table decoration for the living-room.

10. State the amount, width and cost of material required for <u>one</u> of the following:

(a) a household article of your choice;

(b) a denim skirt for a fourteen year old girl.

Give clear directions, with the aid of diagrams, for:

(i) applying a decorative trim to the household article;

<u>or</u>

(ii) preparing the waistband and applying it to the skirt.

AN   ROINN   OIDEACHAIS   M.71

INTERMEDIATE   CERTIFICATE   EXAMINATION,   1982

HOME ECONOMICS

(360 marks)

Six questions to be answered, of which at least two must be from Section A, at least one
from Section B and at least one from Section C.
All questions carry equal marks.

SECTION A

1. Write a note on the nutritive value of meat.
   Name two substantial dishes which you have made using the cheaper cuts of meat.
List the ingredients and give the method of preparing, cooking and serving one of the
named dishes.
   State the effects of cooking on meat.

2. Classify carbohydrates and list (a) their sources and (b) their functions in the body.
   Using fresh ingredients in correct proportions, give the method of preparing, baking
and serving soda bread or tea scones.
   Explain the action of the raising agent used.

3. List the rules that should be followed when shopping for food for the household.
   What important points should guide you when choosing each of any three of the following:-

   (a) a head of lettuce;
   (b) fillets of fish;
   (c) fresh fruit;
   (d) a small quantity of potatoes ?

   Give directions for the method of storing vegetables at home.

4. Plan a menu for a three-course luncheon suitable for four of your school friends.
   Set out a time plan for the order of work which should be followed when preparing
and cooking the meal in order to serve it at 1.00 p.m.
   Give full directions for the method of preparing and serving the dessert which you
have chosen.

SECTION B

5. Set out full details for the method of cleaning each of any two of the following:-

   (a) an aluminium kettle with brown 'fur' on the inside;

   (b) an earthenware teapot that is stained with tannin;

   (c) a meat mincer.

   List the basic cleaning agents necessary in order to keep kitchen equipment in good
condition and give the cost of each.

6. Describe the structure of the heart.   Use a well-labelled diagram to illustrate
your answer.
   State the functions of the blood in the body.
   Explain how the blood is purified in the lungs.

7. Enumerate the points that should guide you when selecting a gas cooker for your own
home.
   In relation to the selected cooker, state (i) how it should be cared for in order to
keep it in good working condition and (ii) the safety precautions which should be taken
when using it.
   Give some suggestions for the economical use of fuel when cooking family meals.

SECTION C

8. Design and sketch a practical two-piece outfit suitable as a school uniform for yourself.
    State (i) the type, (ii) the colour, (iii) the amount and (iv) the cost of the fabric you would select for one of the garments.
    Outline the order of work that should be followed when sponging and pressing a skirt or trousers.

9. Show, by clearly labelled diagram, the correct method of top threading a sewing machine.
    Set out a list of points that should be observed when using the machine in order to obtain good results.
    Mention any two common faults that may occur when machining and state the possible cause in each case.

10. Give clear and detailed instructions for the method of working each of any two of the following seam finishes:-

    (a) edge-machining; (b) overcasting; (c) binding; (d) zig-zag stitching.

Use well-labelled diagrams to illustrate your answer.
    What is the purpose of neatening seams on garments ?

AN   ROINN   OIDEACHAIS   M.71

INTERMEDIATE   CERTIFICATE   EXAMINATION,   1981

HOME ECONOMICS

(360 marks)

Six questions to be answered, of which at least two must be from Section A, at least one from Section B and at least one from Section C.
All questions carry equal marks.

SECTION A

1. Name the chief constituent present in each of the following foods:

    (a) liver;
    (b) brown bread;
    (c) cheese.

    State the function of any one constituent named.
    Suggest some points to guide you when: (i) using cheese for cooking; and (ii) storing a small quantity of cheese.

2. Explain clearly the changes that occur as fruit ripens and decays.
    List some of the advantages of home preservation.
    Using a small quantity of fruit, give the recipe together with the directions for making, potting and storing a jam of your choice.
    Describe in detail any one method of testing the jam for setting point.

3. Give the ingredients in correct proportions for each of the following:

    (a) brown stewing sauce;
    (b) white coating sauce.

    Outline the method of making, cooking and serving (b) above.
    Mention some important rules relating to sauce-making.

4. Write an informative note on:

(a)   shallow frying;
(b)   deep frying.

Give clear instructions for preparing,cooking and serving bacon, egg and tomato for breakfast for three adults.
Plan a breakfast menu to include bacon, egg and tomato in the main course.
Show by diagram the table setting for one person.

SECTION B

5. Plan a systematic weekly cleaning routine which could be followed in order to keep a kitchen clean and hygienic.
Outline the daily care and the weekly care which should be given to kitchen cloths.
Write an informative note on the use of modern household detergents and include the safety precautions which should be taken when using them.

6. Sketch and name the main organs of the digestive system.
Name the enzymes present in (a) the mouth and (b) the stomach and give an account of the changes in foods brought about by these enzymes.
Write a brief note on the large intestine and state its function in the process of digestion.

7. List the guidelines you would follow in order to keep the body fit and healthy.
State the importance of personal hygiene. Describe in detail the care and cleansing routine a young girl should follow when caring for (a) her hair; and (b) her hands.

SECTION C

8. Show the layout of a simple shirt blouse pattern on material of suitable width.
Outline the order of work which should be followed when making up the blouse.
Show the correct method of making and finishing the bust dart.
Use diagrams to illustrate your answer.

9. Give detailed directions for the correct method of working any two of the following processes:
(i)   the preparation and the application of a waistband to a gathered skirt;
(ii) the preparation and the insertion of a sleeve into the armhole of a summer dress;
(iii) the preparation and the application of a neckfacing to a collarless garment.

10. List the garments you would consider necessary in the average teenagers' wardrobe.
What guidelines would you offer on each of the following:

(a)   general care of clothes;
(b)   preparing clothes for drycleaning;
(c)   care of footwear;
(d)   choosing accessories ?